NATURE ON THE RAMPAGE

Nature
on the Rampage

A NATURAL HISTORY OF THE ELEMENTS

By Ann and Myron Sutton

J. B. LIPPINCOTT COMPANY

PHILADELPHIA AND NEW YORK

To Agnes M. Allen

CONTENTS

INTRODUCTION

BEGINNING with the Greek philosopher Empedocles, in the fifth century B.C., the universe was long presumed to consist of four essential elements: fire, water, earth, and air. All natural phenomena originated from these four elements, and by any standard the most exciting were manifestations of violence, such as volcanoes from fire, storms from air, and floods from water.

Because these natural forces strongly influence life, liberty, and the pursuit of happiness, they have been widely pondered by philosophers and scientists since time immemorial. Our purpose is to set information about the rampageous elements in modern perspective—past, present, and future—describe them, and compare them, to debunk some myths, destroy some fears, correct some impressions, and inspire new faith in the indomitable human spirit.

Such a collection of diverse and often disputed information can never be wholly accurate, for man's knowledge of these things is still primitive. While a considerable bulk of reference material has been examined, and every statement checked and rechecked as far as the literature allows, records change, and new discoveries alter prevailing opinions. Some phenomena are indeed so wild that no living soul has the final word. The highest waves at sea, they say, were seen by men who went down with their ships. Few people have explored the muzzle end of catastrophe and lived; fewer still have brought back careful scientific accounts.

9

Nature on the Rampage

For various reasons, some characters in this book have been disguised. Some characters are composites. All the portraits are drawn from life, however, and nothing fictitious is incorporated. The events are real.

ACKNOWLEDGMENTS

To SPECIALISTS and organizations in the fields concerned we extend, with deepest appreciation, our thanks for help and examinations of many portions of the manuscript. These specialists deleted major and marginal misconceptions and any remaining discrepancies are ours.

Many thanks are due Dr. Agnes M. Allen, Arizona State College at Flagstaff; Dr. Edward Weyer and the staff of the American Museum of Natural History; Lemuel A. Garrison, Superintendent, and the Park Naturalist staff, of Yellowstone National Park, Wyoming; Dr. F. W. Reichelderfer, Chief of the United States Weather Bureau; D. Harper Simms, Soil Conservation Service, United States Department of Agriculture; Dr. Dean S. Carder, Chief Seismologist, Coast and Geodetic Survey, United States Department of Commerce; Drs. Fred L. Whipple and Richard E. McCrosky, Astrophysical Observatory, Smithsonian Institution; Professor Leonard B. Loeb, Department of Physics, University of California; Dr. Don Tocher, Seismographic Stations, University of California; and William E. Benson, National Science Foundation.

We are grateful also to the United States Geological Survey; Department of the Navy; Corps of Engineers, United States Army; Federal Power Commission; National Academy of Sciences; Bureau of Reclamation; Bureau of Public Roads; Wave Research Laboratory, University of California; highway departments of the states of California, Colorado, Virginia, and Washington; American Hoist and Derrick Company; Bethlehem Steel Company; Armco Drainage and Metal

Introduction and Acknowledgments

Products, Inc.; General Electric Company; and Bell Telephone Laboratories.

Additional gratitude must go to the patient and helpful staffs of the Library of Congress and the libraries of the Department of Interior, Department of Agriculture, Weather Bureau, Geological Survey, and city and county of San Francisco; to Ben A. Bernard, Mayor of the city of Santa Monica, California; to Jennie M. Livesay for help and encouragement; to Douglas and Elizabeth Rigby for inspiration and optimism; to Charles and Joyce Warren for varied assistance; to Marjorie Hackett for seeing the typescript through; and to George Stevens and Tay Hohoff, of J. B. Lippincott Company, for wisdom and counsel throughout.

We thank the editors of *Popular Science Monthly*, *Natural History*, *Science Digest*, and *The American Mercury* for permission to reprint portions of this book which appeared in their pages, and the following publishers and authors for permission to quote selected passages from the publications cited:

Alfred A. Knopf, Inc., New York, and D. C. Benson & Campbell Thomson, Ltd., London, *The Cruel Sea*, by Nicholas Monsarrat.

The Macmillan Company, New York, *Home Is Upriver*, by Brian Harwin.

Random House, Inc., New York, *Candide and Other Writings*, by Voltaire, ed. by Haskell M. Block.

Eyre & Spottiswoode, Ltd., London, *The Mountains of Youth*, by Arnold Lunn.

D. Van Nostrand Company, Inc., Princeton, New Jersey, *The Survival Book*, by Paul H. Nesbitt, Alonzo W. Pond, and William H. Allen. Copyright 1959 by D. Van Nostrand Company, Inc.

Duke University Press, Durham, North Carolina, *Handbook of Renaissance Meteorology*, by S. K. Heninger.

Oxford University Press, Inc., New York, *Meteorology*, by Aristotle, as translated under the editorship of W. D. Ross.

E. P. Dutton and Company, Inc., New York, and J. M. Dent and Sons, Ltd., London, *History of Herodotus*, translated by George Rawlinson (Everyman's Library).

Dodd, Mead and Company, New York, *The Hurricane Hunters*, by Ivan Ray Tannehill. Copyright © 1955 by Ivan Ray Tannehill.

W. H. Freeman and Company, San Francisco, *Elementary Seismology*, by Charles F. Richter, 1958.

Encyclopædia Britannica, Chicago, *Great Books of the Western World*, Vols. 12 and 24, *Gargantua and Pantagruel*, by Rabelais, translated by Thomas Urquhart and Peter Motteux; *On the Nature of Things*, by Lucretius, translated by H. A. J. Munro.

Nature on the Rampage

American Geographical Society, New York, *Bering's Voyages*, Vol. II, "Steller's Journal," by F. A. Golder.

Thompson, Quarrell & Megaw, London, *South*, by Sir Ernest Shackleton.

Harvard University Press, Cambridge, Massachusetts, *A Source Book in Geology*, by Kirtley F. Mather and Shirley L. Mason.

Harper and Brothers, New York, *The Rains Came*, by Louis Bromfield.

Alfred A. Knopf, Inc., New York, *Avalanche!*, by Joseph Wechsberg.

Irving Shepard, Glen Ellen, California, *Cruise of the Snark*, by Jack London.

J. M. Dent and Sons, Ltd., London, *Typhoon* and *Mirror of the Sea*, by Joseph Conrad.

Dodd, Mead and Company, New York, and John Murray (Publishers), Ltd., London, *Scott's Last Expedition*, by Robert Falcon Scott. Copyright 1913 by Dodd, Mead & Company, Inc.

Farrar, Straus, and Cudahy, New York, and Weidenfeld & Nicolson, Ltd., London, *Rivers in the Desert*, by Nelson Glueck.

John Lear, Science Editor of the *Saturday Review*, Science and Humanity Section.

The St. Louis *Post-Dispatch*, R. L. Crowley, Managing Editor; excerpts.

The Chicago *Tribune*, Dan Maxwell, Editor, excerpts.

The Cleveland *Plain Dealer*, E. Deretrick; excerpts.

The Associated Press, New York, excerpts.

The Austin *American*, Austin, Texas, Dick Brown, Acting Managing Editor, "Lampasas Record Down But Not Out," by Anita Brewer.

National Academy of Sciences, National Research Council, Washington, *Convergence Behavior in Disasters*, Disaster Study Number 9, Publication 476, by Charles E. Fritz and J. H. Mathewson.

Ann and Myron Sutton

Yosemite National Park, California

1

MAN AND THE ELEMENTS

The only argument available with an
East wind is to put on your overcoat.
 . . . JAMES RUSSELL LOWELL

Ever SINCE Neolithic men crawled from their caves and looked about, man has been assaulted by the elements around him, and by the earth or sea beneath him. From time immemorial, man and planet have been repeatedly sacked and ransacked by nature on the rampage—storms, floods, earthquakes, volcanoes, and all the rest.

"If we had a million sandbags," said the farmer, "we couldn't do it. You can't tame the old Mississippi—I don't give a damn how you levee it."

"Oh wretched man," cried the poet, "earth fated to be cursed; abyss of plagues, and miseries the worst!"

"And fires and flames have consumed the earth," said the ancient philosopher, "gushing forth and breathing . . . as when the craters of Etna burst and flowed like a torrent over the earth."

Even before the coming of man, so violent and relentless have been these natural forces that the earth's destiny has been radically altered and shifted. We read in the rocks how swamps dried up and turned into searing deserts; how floods scoured ancient canyons; how glaciers gouged through solid rock; how volcanoes flared and shriveled the primeval countryside; and how the land shook, and mountains were built, and whole races of animals were wiped off the face of the earth. The record is there. The clues are engraved in stone.

When man arrived, the wonders of earth and sky became the subject of vigorous religious and scientific comment. The wise men of Greece speculated vividly on the origin of the universe and on the violent things that happened in it. So also did literature take fire. Goethe wrote earthquakes and storms into *Faust*. Gibbon told how critical was weather in the blossom and burst of the Roman Empire. Shakespeare repeatedly livened his plays with references to sudden disaster.

But more than awe and more than fear were struck into the hearts of men by weather and earthquakes and volcanoes. Men were curious about such things, too, curious to the point of doing something about them. At first, however, the only recourse was to try to avoid them. Early Mediterranean mariners hied themselves to safe sea lanes away from presters and other mighty winds that swooped down from the mountains. Sea routes zigged and zagged from island to island for safety, and nearly every island had a settlement bound to its neighbors by trade.

At the beginning of Magellan's voyage the crew was grumbling and ready to return until in a storm they saw a display of St. Elmo's fire, the seaman's good omen.

Stormy seas and treacherous winds kept Australia secret for decades, until finally the Dutchman Hartog sailed a southerly route and so reached the western coast. And how many vessels, like that of Sir George Somers in 1609, drifted off course and landed not at their destination—Virginia in his case—but on some new and unknown land, like Bermuda?

Natural violence has repeatedly shaped and modified human history. Tropical storms since Columbus have altered the course of events in the Atlantic and Caribbean. Historians tell us that in 1773 there would have been a New York "Tea Party" like the one in Boston, had not fresh winds kept tea-bearing ships from entering the harbor. In the winter of 1777 General Washington relied on extremes of cold at Princeton to freeze the muddy roads so that he could bring artillery within range of Cornwallis.

What if the winter *hadn't* been so cold? What if Magellan *hadn't* sailed on?

From the time human life appeared on earth, natural forces have

14

been man's malefactor and benefactor, and will continue to be until he disappears from it. But the elements could be used—and were. This is of epic significance in itself. How could men harness such elusive entities as flashing currents of twenty thousand amperes, whirling winds of five hundred miles per hour, and deluges the like of which had never before been seen? The battle was joined—with stirring successes—but would not be readily won. As one author has said: "Merely because a few clever men in particular places under favorable circumstances have caused clouds to drop rain, we talk glibly of tailoring weather to suit our fashion. What we really know about weather-making is, scientifically speaking, little better than witches' brew."

Nonetheless, what Franklin did with lightning, and Slocum with the sea, and Heilprin with volcanoes, makes dramatic reading.

From men like these we have gained a new and encouraging view of this topsy-turvy world and of the forces that change its face. Our fears are slowly crumbling. If once upon a time a tornado spelled black terror and our only action was to flee immediately, anywhere, now we know differently. We know that there is a right place and a wrong place to go, and it gives us comfort to realize the difference. During lightning we stay *in* our automobile. In a tornado we get *out* of it. At last we can defend ourselves. Perhaps in our relative calmness we can offer a helping hand to less fortunate neighbors.

And there are less fortunate neighbors. History records the time and the damage and the sum of casualties, but other things it can never record. It does not see the face of a fisherman lost in a cold and angry sea. It does not know whose bones lie bleaching in the desert sun, or why the frozen men had failed those last few steps of Arctic snow to warmth and food.

Time forgets the face of the seaman's wife who reads a hurricane casualty list; forgets the letter fallen from trembling hands miles from the tornado's path; forgets the silent prayer beside the church-yard. These the inexorable march of man and progress pass on by, but they are deep and real, and a part of the tragic consequence where raging elements meet human life.

Yet there is some measure of humor, excitement, and inspiration in any study of the natural laws of the universe. If we sift and sort the facts as they have become known, we shall see how human knowledge has advanced. We may also project ourselves into the future and predict the progress of man's dramatic battle with the elements.

It is a stirring battle, fought on many fronts, against tremendous odds. And we have just begun to fight.

2

WINDS

Many can brook the weather that love
not the wind.

. . . SHAKESPEARE

PETE RAMSAY was an Air Force pilot, fighting headwinds
at ten thousand feet altitude in the days of medium-speed, propeller-
driven aircraft. The day was clear, the weather good. There were a
few clouds in sight, but these lay dreamily far away on the distant horizon. Visibility: unlimited. Two hundred miles ahead on flight course
lay X-Mountain, barely discernible on the skyline.

The air was unsteady, though Pete expected that. He had encountered
rough air in the lower layers early this morning, but it was not too
severe. "Watch for dips and troughs," the weather officer had said. "It's
going to be rough."

Pete spotted a low band of cirrus clouds hugging the horizon ahead.
Routine, he thought. At X-Mountain minus a hundred miles he saw
these clouds more clearly, but he gave them little thought. On days of
scattered cloudiness like this you paid little attention to lines of cirrus.
They were fair-weather clouds.

As the turbulence continued and the miles jerked by, Pete kept his
eye on X-Mountain as it drew closer. Soon he could see that it was
capped by a thin skin of cloud. And other clouds seemed to hang
lazily around the summits along the edge of the entire range. "Harmless," Pete said to himself. "Nothing there. Cloudbank is stationary."

17

With the miles and minutes passing, he made out more details. The clouds now appeared less white than they had; in fact, he watched for a moment some dense dark patches in the cloudbank, and began to wonder how high the clouds were. Nor would he even call them cirrus any more. They looked more like cumulus.

At fifty miles from X-Mountain Pete took the ship into a slow, steady climb. "Ought to pass that cap cloud on the summit easily," he said, half aloud. He checked his instruments. Nothing seemed amiss.

Still the cap clouds looked harmless. Pete figured there would be no trouble getting over.

He was almost on them. As he looked on either side he could see that the clouds were spread out in long lines athwart his path. He would have to cross several of them before clearing the crest. The plane was climbing steadily, and if everything went as expected, he should pass well above the first line.

Then he noticed something strange, something he had not seen before.

Staring at the approaching clouds, Pete's breath caught for an instant: some of the clouds were rolling strongly, around and around, over and over, without moving anywhere, like surf foaming on the beach.

And then, before he knew it, he was flying directly into the first cloudbank.

Instantly everything was cockeyed. As if the world had been up-ended and some calamitous force had wrenched the ship out of the sky, the plane banked sharply without warning and Pete was thrown with a thump against the side of the cockpit.

The ship climbed and descended dizzily, pitching like a skiff on a stormy sea. His breath half knocked from him, Pete fought to keep position and hold on to some vestige of equilibrium. The wind was slamming the plane into one plunging air mass after another. Pete was stunned, caught by complete surprise.

The strange aerial dance raged for two minutes. Then, as abruptly as the whole thing began, the air became smooth again and the ship settled into a good rate of climb. Pete looked back. He had passed the first roll cloud.

The air was smooth now and all traces of turbulence had vanished. Pete saw that his rate of climb continued unusually good, and he quickly calculated that there ought to be plenty of height to clear the next roll cloud. The air was so smooth, he figured. He must be out of trouble. Glancing far below to the valley floor he saw what appeared to be jetlike streaks of dust sweeping the countryside. That meant strong surface winds.

"Well, I never felt such turbulence before," he conceded. "Certainly not in clear weather, and never here—over X-Mountain—or over any other range on this course. An accident, I guess. A bad pocket. Some strange draft you don't hear about."

Now the upper winds had become stronger. The aircraft slowed. Pete looked down on the next boiling roll cloud. He was glad it was below him this time. The cap cloud over X-Mountain shone brilliantly ahead, snow white in the sun. It, too, had a rhythmic motion like the roll cloud. It seemed to pour down the rocky ledges like a cloud waterfall.

Then suddenly, crazily, everything began to go wrong. The turbulent roll cloud Pete thought he was going to pass over so easily started to rise ominously toward him. A patch of cloud drifted by, barely under the plane. If the cloud bands kept rising that way, he was not sure he could make it.

Pete looked at his instruments again and froze. He was not climbing at all. On the contrary, the rate-of-climb indicator showed that the plane was falling at over two thousand feet per minute in smooth air.

He nosed down and roared into full power. The clouds seemed to shoot by beneath the plane, but still, in relation to the ground, he noticed little change in movement. The plane was moving very slowly now. Except downward. The rate of sudden descent was increasing to 2,500 feet per minute.

Pete had done all he could. Now he watched helplessly as a giant cumulus turret built up ahead and engulfed the plane within seconds. Just as if he had plunged in a canoe over a roaring, seething cataract, the plane fell into the roll cloud again.

What followed was no longer controlled flight. Even the instruments spun wildly, and Pete, losing his balance almost completely, could make little sense from them. It was a fearful sensation. The speed dropped, then rushed ahead. The rpm's changed quickly. The engine howled.

Around and around he whirled, hanging in his seat belt without the slightest idea of which way was up or which way was down. In all his years in the air he had never encountered anything like this before.

All at once the ship dropped out of the cloud base. Still dizzy, Pete looked around. Everything had changed. X-Mountain now rose above him as a forbidding rock barrier. Clouds were sweeping down its jagged cliffs and dissipating directly before his eyes.

Hardly had he studied the scene and gotten his bearings when the wind began to quicken again. Pete's first instinct was to turn back, but then he saw that the plane was being lifted with tremendous power at two thousand feet per minute. Up . . . up . . . up he went.

Desperately he pushed the nose down to avoid being pulled back into the roll cloud. At that moment the rising gusts died out. The air became as smooth as glass. The plane leveled off. It was an eerie feeling; it had all happened without a single direction from Pete.

As soon as the updrafts had tapered off, Pete opened the throttle to keep altitude, but it was no use. The plane started falling again.

Once more came that jetlike headwind and the smooth downdraft, and he felt the plane slipping uncontrollably once more. He looked down and saw the cloud waterfall directly beneath. A yawning pit formed in the bottom of his stomach.

The cap cloud hugging X-Mountain built up fast. The air was smooth, but Pete saw with stunned disbelief that the ship was falling at three thousand feet per minute. Through the cap cloud he could see the summit coming closer and closer, and could make out rocky crags on the crest. They were getting larger.

With all the power the ship could command, he banked into a steep left turn. The air became hazy. The rate of descent increased to almost four thousand feet per minute.

Then he plunged into the lower end of the cloud waterfall. A tremendous gust pulled the plane into a steep right turn toward the sheer cliffs. Pete saw the rocks and the trees and the ravines coming rapidly nearer. In a moment he would slam head-on into them.

At the last possible instant he pulled desperately away, banking up and back and finally out from the stone wall. The plane lurched and was caught by powerful tail gusts that catapulted it 1,500 feet out over the valley floor.

In a matter of minutes he had passed under the roll clouds and the nightmare was over.

What kind of a nightmare? What in thunderation had happened? Similar reports had been coming in for years, reports that described experiences far more disastrous than Pete's, and every bit as mysterious. High-flying aircraft had no reason to ram into mountainsides in broad daylight over familiar terrain. The crews were well trained. The planes were in top condition. What was wrong?

There was an official report on a DC-3 named *Saint Kevin* over Wales's Mount Snowdon, January 10, 1952: "The *Saint Kevin* left Northold at 1725 GMT for Dublin and after flying along the Airway to Daventry, turned into 60 knot headwinds on course for Dublin. The course should have carried it some 15 miles south of Snowdon to reach the coast at the Nevin radio beacon but, owing to unexplained errors in navigation, the aircraft followed a track which took it directly towards Snowdon. An error in estimated ground speed was also made with the result that the Captain thought he was progressing faster than he was. . . .

"At 1854, when a reconstruction of the flight suggests that he had just reached the first Welsh hills west of Oswestry, he sought and received permission to climb from . . . 4500 feet to . . . 6500 feet. No reason was given, but the fact that the request came on his arrival over the first hills suggests that rough air was the cause. After flying at 6500 feet for about ten minutes the captain reported, erroneously, that he had reached the sea and requested a descent clearance. . . .

"The last message indicated that the captain began to let down from 6500 feet in the belief that he was over the Irish Sea. In fact, he was ten miles downwind of Snowdon in meteorological conditions favouring the setting up of powerful lee waves. . . . The pilots, thinking that they were now over the sea would not be expecting violent turbulence; and it appears that they lost control of the aircraft which then shed part of a wing just before diving into the ground 1200 feet above sea level. . . .

"The report of the public inquiry into the causes has been published, and the findings give the probable cause of the crash as 'the encountering of a powerful down current of air on the lee side of Snowdon which forced the aircraft down into an area of very great turbulence.' "

Pilot error, then. But was it? Pilots don't miscalculate mountain peaks. Something had to be done.

By the time the *Saint Kevin* went down and there had been numerous other crashes in the United States, it was clear that some strange force grasped a plane and flung it against a cliff.

A "Mountain Wave Project" was set up under the sponsorship of the Geophysics Research Directorate of the Air Force Cambridge Research Center and the Office of Naval Research. The study was carried out by the University of California in cooperation with the Southern California Soaring Association, the United States Weather Bureau, the Air Weather Service and other agencies.

In 1951-52, field tests were conducted in the Sierra Nevada mountains, where downwinds are known to reach exceptional proportions. It was a vigorous and concentrated attack. Up went specially instrumented sailplanes to trace lines of air flow and temperature and pressure gradients. Tracked by radar and other means, these planes went as high as 44,500 feet.

Motion picture cameras, filming in time-lapse techniques to speed up the action of the clouds, recorded the exact visible conditions in the sky while the instrument-laden sailplanes were rising. Further, meteorological stations were established up to an elevation of nine thousand feet.

The result was a technical report called *Flight Aspects of the Mountain Wave*, from which Pete Ramsay's story was adapted—a "typical occurrence." For the first time, man had discovered the "mountain wave," a deadly layer of treacherous air hovering at times over mountain ranges, stirring up air currents, creating downdrafts, and putting aircraft altimeters out of kilter.

High-speed winds produced instrument errors by which a pilot believed he could squeeze over an approaching mountain peak when actually he was below its summit. The unexpected turbulence then sucked the plane into its clutches before the pilot knew what had happened—and kept it there until it was too late to pull out.

Today, scientists compare mountain waves to waterfalls. Air catapulting down a mountainside sets in motion the same types of eddies, vortices, and currents as those that occur in a thundering cascade of water. As a result, pilots now know what to look for and how to swing clear of mountain wave conditions.

This was not the first great discovery of violent winds in the atmosphere. When B-29 pilots raided Tokyo during World War II they discovered that on high-altitude bombing runs their ground speed dropped nearly to zero. As flak began bursting outside, they found to their horror that on the getaway they suddenly were fighting strange

and astonishingly strong headwinds. If the squadron returned successfully to flight base, sharp questions were put to the weatherman.

At first weathermen found the reports that planes had stood almost
still in mid-air hard to believe, as if the crews had fueled on *sake* before
briefing. But the reports persisted, and out of the war came history's
first calculated look at that mysterious and wandering river of air—the
jet stream.

Weather experts have found that the sky-high winds of the jet
stream flow in narrow "rivers" of air in the ten-thousand- to forty-
thousand-foot altitude range. Apparently they play an important role
in the formation and intensification of middle-latitude storms. While
they seem to bear small relation to surface wind patterns with which
we are familiar, increasing evidence is now pointing to jet streams as
having a marked influence on local climates, especially on precipitation.

Though wind velocities along the stream may vary, the winds are
almost always westerlies. There may be a number of streams in the air
at one time, or one jet may branch into several streams. They reach
maximum power approximately over the thirtieth parallel—roughly a
line through Florida, North Africa, Arabia, and Mexico. This does not
automatically mean that Sahara dust can blow via Arabia into American
eyes overnight, but it does show how high-altitude jet aircraft can
utilize these jet winds to advantage and soar through the upper air in
double time.

The precise atmospheric mechanism that makes the jet stream move
the way it does is still under study. The movements and colliding of
great masses of polar and equatorial air must provide some elements of
the causative force. So perhaps do temperature changes. One thing is
sure: riding this maverick gale offers rodeo-like thrills. Its velocities
change suddenly; temperatures jump; zones of turbulence strike hammer blows on unsuspecting aircraft.

One of the first planes to ride it was a B-47 bomber which, guided
by a navigational dead-reckoning device, succeeded early in 1957 in
flying the jet stream from March Air Force Base, California, to Han-
scom Air Force Base, Massachusetts, in three hours, forty-seven minutes—an average ground speed of 714 miles per hour.

With the coming of high-flying, jet-powered airliners, pilots preferred to hug the fringes of the jet stream—and there ran into dangerous turbulence. But once this turbulence was recognized as zones of

friction between air masses moving at different speeds, the danger areas could be predicted, mapped and avoided.

It is only lately that we have come to understand these and other strange actions of the perambulating wind. A century or so ago, very little was known about the origins of wind and weather, and there were no such convenient services as storm warnings and weather forecasts. But even before the first glimmerings of knowledge, far back in time, the sky and its offspring were regarded with fear, respect, and religious awe. The winds, born of Astraeus and Aurora (dawn), became gods in their own right to the Greeks and Romans. The Romans, in fact, dedicated temples to the *Tempestates*.

Winds came from all directions. Hence, how many winds were there? Pliny suggested eight, La Primaudaye sixteen, Du Bartas an infinite number. Finally, twelve were settled on and named. As such they entered into nearly every kind of literature, worship, and prognostication that issued from the pens of men.

Homer wrote of gales and tempests and of Aeolus, keeper of the sea winds. But what was the wind? A "body of dry exhalation moving about the earth," said Aristotle. "A moving current of what we call air," said Hippocrates. And Pliny was convinced that "there be certain caves and holes which breed winds continually without end."

Aristotle got closest to the truth. "The facts bear out the view that winds are formed by the gradual union of many evaporations," he said. "Every wind is weakest in the spot from which it blows; as they proceed and leave their source at a distance they gather strength." And prophetically he stated what was to become the scientific truth: "The sun both checks the formation of winds and stimulates it."

Renaissance thinkers marveled at the wonderful wisdom of God in creating winds and keeping air in motion. If the air were not stirred, said Fulke, it "would soon putrefie, and . . . would be a deadly infection to all that hath breath upon the earth."

The wind has been constantly called upon to illustrate various moods. It was swift and free. It was unstable, wavering, wanton, bawdy. And from Theophrastus on, there have been prognostications to tell whether or not the wind would begin to blow vigorously: dogs rolling on the ground, ducks flapping wings, thunder in the morning, feathers floating on water, and so on.

All things considered, it is natural enough that the winds were deified, and the Mediterranean empires had no monopoly in the matter. By many another group of human beings have the winds been revered and respected, most often as divine powers endowed with tremendous force and with outright capacity for doing good and evil in the world. The Ainus worshiped typhoons. In Hindu and Mayan mythology the wind possessed power to turn men into monkeys. Australian tribes and American Creek Indians considered the wind as a totem. To the Navajo the wind became a character of many traits, a giver of life and therefore motion. Cherokee legends held that the winds, created by the great Manitou, were rulers in their own right.

Jicarilla Apache folklore refers to the whirlwind as a spy or messenger. At Jemez pueblo in New Mexico it was believed that a whirlwind could cause a miscarriage. The Zuñi thought that witches traveled in whirlwinds. Other tribes also associated these dust spouts with evil, as in the beliefs that they were composed of a dead shaman's dust, or that they contained poison, or that they were some evil spirit. To prevent the resultant sickness, bad dreams, accidents, or loss of life, various precautions were taken, such as hiding, throwing dirt or water into the whirlwind, talking, smoking, clapping hands, and stomping feet. In some cases, persons touched or engulfed by a whirlwind were afterwards cleansed by smoke.

For many a moon, the Chinook Indians handed down a legend about the wind that still bears their name. In almost every belief, the winds were great powers to which worshipers offered special inducements for moderation. To make the wind behave, Alaska's Tlingit Indians talked kindly to it. If that didn't work, they offered it a piece of fish. If that failed, they advised their brethren to stop talking about wolverines, since wolverines were supposed to control the frigid north wind.

"'Tis a noble and heroic thing, the wind!" said Captain Ahab in Herman Melville's *Moby Dick*. "Who ever conquered it? In every fight it has the last and bitterest blow. Run tilting at it, and you but run through it. Ha! a coward wind that strikes stark naked men, but will not stand to receive a single blow. Even Ahab is a braver thing—a nobler thing than *that*. . . . And yet, I say again, and swear it now, that there's something all glorious and gracious in the wind."

"Gales have their personalities," said Joseph Conrad in *The Mirror of the Sea*, "and, after all, perhaps it is not strange; for, when all is said and done, there are adversaries whose wiles you must defeat, whose violence you must resist, and yet with whom you must live in the intimacies of nights and days."

For centuries men have lived intimately with the wind, and the winds have had a profound effect on man's affairs and the destinies of nations. Herodotus tells us that a whole nation was lost when it tried, of all things, to make war on the wind itself. "On the country of the Nasamonians," he says, "borders that of the Psylli, who were swept away under the following circumstances. The south-wind had blown for a long time and dried up all the tanks in which their water was stored. Now the whole region within the Syrtis is utterly devoid of springs. Accordingly the Psylli took counsel among themselves, and by common consent made war upon the south-wind—so at least the Libyans say, I do but repeat their words—they went forth and reached the desert; but there the south-wind rose and buried them under heaps of sand: whereupon, the Psylli being destroyed, their lands passed to the Nasamonians."

When Xerxes and his mighty army from Persia and points east were attacking Greece, the Greeks consulted the oracle at Delphi who said, "Pray to the winds, for the winds would do Greece good service." Promptly the Greeks raised an altar at Thyia, and worshiped the winds with sacrifices thereafter.

The Persian fleet sailed along the coast between the city of Casthanaea and Cape Sepias and took up positions there. The innermost vessels anchored inshore, while the remainder anchored offshore, row upon row, eight deep. The weather was fine. The night was calm and peaceful. It looked for all the world as if Greece would be theirs.

But at dawn a violent storm fell upon them from the east, and the peaceful sea became a raging sea. A few sailors on shore managed to drag their ships up on the beach. Elsewhere there was no escape. Ships at sea were blown ashore and dashed to pieces.

More than four hundred vessels were destroyed. A vast treasure was engulfed by the angry waves. No one knows how many men were drowned.

For three days the storm raged on. The Magians offered victims to the winds, but it did no good. They charmed the winds with the help of conjurers. They sacrificed to Thetis and the Nereids. But to no avail—until too late.

On the fourth day the wind lulled and the sea went down. Wreckage and bodies floated everywhere. The survivors who had drawn their ships on shore promptly launched them and proceeded to coast along the mainland.

Peace came again. Greek farmers went down to the shore and there for a long time afterward gathered gold and silver drinking-cups cast up by the surf. Treasure boxes full of golden articles of all kinds washed ashore, and the farmers grew rich. Meanwhile, the Greeks were paying homage to the wind god Boreas who, they were sure, had caused this disaster to befall the barbarians, and they gratefully built a temple to Boreas on the banks of the River Ilissus, near Athens.

Study of the winds was extremely important in man's early history, especially in navigation. But strangely enough, it was not until the American naval officer and oceanographer Matthew Fontaine Maury set up a wind chart in the mid-nineteenth century that the study came out of its infancy. Maury devised a chart showing zones of wind around the earth, and recommended the best routes for ships. What this meant to the sailing world was astonishing. Prior to that time it would have taken 120 days to sail from Europe to Australia—under good conditions. Maury's data made the trip possible in seventy-two days. And so with other routes around the world. Other charts followed Maury's and were improved as time went by.

The sports of ballooning and gliding took man into the air for the first time and he was suddenly compelled to learn about the air currents in order to ride them safely and successfully. Glider pilots took advantage of "slope ascents" to rise into the favorable currents of clouds and then get lifted sky-high.

The Germans did a great deal of research in gliding. In 1929 an Austrian named R. Kronfeld made a flight of a hundred miles, which was shortly exceeded by the Germans.

A glider pilot is dependent solely on wind currents and if he knows how to use them, he may rise on drafts that reach ten thousand feet.

Balloons, first taken into the air in 1783, were fully at the mercy of the wind because of the large spherical surface. In that same year, researchers experimented with ways to steer balloons, but did not succeed, especially in winds above seven miles per hour. Very clearly then, riding balloons successfully depended on knowing the winds and taking advantage of them. Victor Hugo was right: "The balloon is a perfect example of passive obedience to the wind."

An explorer named Andrée tried to steer a balloon to the North Pole in 1897, but as it turned out he placed too much dependence on being able to steer the apparatus. On July 11 of that year, Andrée and two companions left Port Vigo, on the northwest point of Spitzbergen. All would have gone well perhaps, had not meteorological conditions taken a turn for the worse. To make matters more delicate, Andrée's steering apparatus fell off the balloon and into the sea not long out of port.

On they went, disappearing from sight. The next day no word had come. The following day a carrier pigeon arrived with a message that the balloon was in Latitude 82° and drifting east. That was the last to be heard from Andrée and his crew. No one knew what happened until a Norwegian seal-hunting ship many years later found the remains of the expedition at White Island (between Spitzbergen and Franz Josef Land). Andrée's journal revealed that he had abandoned the balloon on August 14 after coming down in 84° 32'. What happened to Andrée and his men is gone with the wind.

In modern times, meteorologists have learned that winds obey well-defined laws. Wind stresses have been studied and the effects on steel towers recorded. A great deal has been learned in wind tunnels, where controlled conditions have been manipulated to answer man's questions about stress, strain, and streamlining.

A great deal has also been learned outside, under exceptionally rigorous conditions. The all-enclosing atmosphere continually roils and writhes with a turbulence man has yet to understand fully. Invisible powers constantly hammer the transient elements of the upper air, the whole impelled by the source of life on Mother Earth: the sun.

To be sure, the sun is big enough to stir up atmospheric winds. Its diameter is more than one hundred times the diameter of the earth. The surface temperature reaches ten thousand degrees Fahrenheit, and the interior may rise as high as forty million degrees. All this is certainly sufficient to convert hundreds of millions of tons of hydrogen into almost like amounts of helium every second, unleashing enormous power.

Of the sun's great output, the earth intercepts an infinitesimal amount —scarcely a billionth. Of that, furthermore, only half—about fifty-six per cent—is absorbed; the rest bounces back into space. Is that insignificant amount of sunshine enough? Evidently so. It adds up to more energy than we can possibly use. So many billions of calories of heat power are received annually by each acre of the earth's surface that surplus light and energy exist, even for the growth of the densest forest.

There is likewise ample energy from the sunshine to move great air masses. Wind means air in motion. Like water, air spills or rises, moves in waves and ripples, spreads, mixes, seeps and penetrates into almost every nook and cranny on earth.

In spite of this perpetual restlessness, or perhaps because of it, air movements can often be outguessed. They can be tracked, calculated, predetermined, and forecast. Yet how difficult to be conscious of the air around us; it is invisible and taken for granted. We little notice it. But without it we die in minutes.

The energy required to drive the atmospheric winds has been calculated to equal that of seven million atomic bombs (Hiroshima size) or the amount of power United States electric plants generate in a hundred years. This uncontrolled power, continually generated and regenerated by the sun, launches and perpetuates a global circulation of giant wind systems.

As the sun warms the land, air on the ground becomes hot, expands, and rises. For every mass that rises, other air rushes in to the original space. The result: wind.

No two regions on earth receive the same amount of sunshine at the same time. The Greenland Ice Cap obtains and radiates solar energy differently than does the Mato Grosso of Brazil. Cities become hotter than suburbs; deserts hotter than oceans. Almost all landscapes slant away obliquely from the sun; even tropic isles are not always squarely hit by the sun's rays. Seascapes reflect lesser warmth back to the air than landscapes, and air layers on mountaintops remain cooler than valley breezes. Everywhere differing amounts of radiation are absorbed and reflected.

The result of this worldwide unequal heating is a gigantic movement of air up from the equator (hottest) toward the poles (coldest). It is the activity between these hot and cold convection currents that makes temperate-zone weather so intemperate.

Nature on the Rampage

Superheated air rising into tropic skies bends over toward the North Pole (or the South Pole as the case may be) and flows at high levels toward polar regions. Were things no more complex than this, the air would circulate toward the poles, come down to earth, and flow monotonously across the land back to the equator, there to rise again. Such a simple pattern would give rise to no storms, no balmy summer days, no autumn hazes—in short, no stimulating changes in weather.

Instead, however, the spinning earth's momentum, its gravity, and the differing relative speeds of rotation on the surface (from a thousand miles per hour at the equator to virtually none at the poles) all push and pull and whirl the air into varied motions. These motions bring changing weather.

Winds at high altitude move rapidly, unimpeded. Low winds, slowed by friction against the landscape, set up invisible currents and eddies. If it weren't for such friction, the low winds would blow at hundreds of miles an hour.

To pin down the varying speed of the winds and describe more adequately the multitude of wind conditions known to exist, man has fashioned a simple means of classifying wind velocity: the Beaufort Scale, named for the British Admiral who first devised it in 1905, and used for official forecasts by the United States Weather Bureau. (See page 31.)

But the question inevitably arises regarding the ultimate speed of the winds. Just how fast do they blow? Ionospheric winds of almost seven hundred miles per hour have been detected by radar sixty-five miles up in the atmosphere. They vary and probably encircle the world, but more research is needed to bring down the facts and detailed patterns. Joint United States-British-Canadian investigations have revealed that the world's record winds speed along in the ionosphere as high as a hundred miles in altitude. On October 28, 1949, Dr. G. J. Phillips of the Cambridge, England, Cavendish Laboratory measured the winds during a magnetic storm and clocked a record-breaking 1,100 miles per hour. But in reality these fantastic winds possess scarcely force enough to blow over a feather. Why? As scientists calculate it, there is only one-millionth of the air in the ionosphere that there is at sea level, so a raging 1,100-miles-per-hour storm up there would exert about the same force as a one-mile-an-hour wind down at sea level.

Such winds rarely affect us directly. The ones that do are chiefly a

BEAUFORT WIND SCALE

NUMBER	TITLE	DESCRIPTION	MILES PER HOUR
0	calm	Smoke rises vertically.	Less than 1
1	light air	Smoke drifts.	1 to 3
2	slight breeze	Leaves rustle.	4 to 7
3	gentle breeze	Leaves and twigs in motion.	8 to 12
4	moderate breeze	Small branches moved; dust and light paper lifted.	13 to 18
5	fresh breeze	Small trees sway; wavelets form on inland lakes.	19 to 24
6	strong breeze	Wind whistles in telegraph wires; large branches move.	25 to 31
7	high wind	Whole trees in motion; walking difficult.	32 to 38
8	gale	Twigs broken off trees; traffic slowed.	39 to 46
9	strong gale	Chimneys down; roofs damaged.	47 to 54
10	whole gale	Trees uprooted; damage considerable.	55 to 63
11	storm	Damage widespread.	64 to 75
12	hurricane		Above 75

result of colliding cold and warm air masses. When air fronts sideswipe one another violently enough, tornadoes start whirling to the ground; in the tropical doldrums spinning air masses move northward, increasing in violence to become hurricanes. These last two wind phenomena are so dangerous and destructive that they are discussed in separate chapters following this one.

Light or strong, the winds go right on blowing, spawned by the heat of the sun, nursed by the moisture of the sea. Scientists have simmered the winds down to two primary types: regular and irregular. Regular winds prevail as trades and westerlies, and as seasonal winds like monsoons, whose actions can be somewhat anticipated. Irregular winds, like hurricanes and tornadoes, result from atmospheric mix-ups that are difficult to study and hence not clearly understood.

The peoples of the world, however, have divided the winds into many more than two simple categories. A wind may be intangible, but to persons who suffer disastrous effects of one, it may be a *thing*, a *being*, a *force*. It may also be complicated because the winds, free as the air of which they are made, sweep across the land irrespective of political and linguistic boundaries. A wind that brushes Europe becomes a *labech* in Marseilles, *libeccio* in Corsica, Grenoble wind at Combe-de-Savoie, and Geneva wind on the shores of Lake Geneva. Another in its travels changes from Lombarde to Galise to mountain-pass to little St. Bernard wind. Others take on village names, as the wind of Arsine, wind of Montmélian, wind of Armenaz. One researcher, delving into the linguistics of Moroccan names for the winds, found fifty altogether; a single *sirocco* goes by the names *arifi*, *irifi*, and *rifi*. What Costa Rican has not heard of the *Tehuantepec*, or Hawaiian the *kona*, or Spaniard the *levanter*, or Chilean the *virazón*, or Tahitian the *hupe?*

One of the world's iciest blasts is the *mistral*, a cold and violent wind that rages across France in spring and autumn. Plummeting down the Rhone Valley it doubles and redoubles in force until it rams through mountain gorges at ninety miles an hour and bursts across Provence with terrifying force.

Not only does it wipe out flocks of animals but has been known to blow stagecoaches into the river. Edgar Aubert de la Rue, in his book *Man and the Winds*, ascribes to the mistral power enough to throw a man off his horse, upset a haycart, carry pebbles through windows, rip branches from trees, blow tiles from roofs, stall river traffic, and even tie up shipping at Marseilles. Sometimes the mistral rages for weeks, freezing and drying the soil, or damaging grain fields and orchards; the Abbé Portalis, so history records, was blown from the summit of the Mountain of St. Victoire and killed by the fall.

On a few occasions the mistral becomes beneficial, but these instances are soon forgotten. Some Frenchmen say that the town of Avignon is unpleasant when the wind is blowing and unhealthy when it is not.

A little farther east and north, in Switzerland, blows the *foehn*, one of the strangest, perhaps, of Nature's calamitous gales. Air masses ascending the southern slopes of the Alps become cool, drop their moisture as rain or snow, push over the summit, descend the northern slopes, warm up by compression, and bring on odd temperature inversions.

The foehn, heating independently of the sun, becomes so dry that it desiccates everything in its path. If this goes on long enough, houses, furniture, and other wooden objects become tinder dry—ready to be fired at the simplest spark. Whole villages declare emergencies and set up stringent regulations from which there is no deviation. Special guards go into action to see that all fires are extinguished. Smoking is *verboten*. So is cooking. Aware of the list of villages that have burned as a result of this danger, each citizen complies happily with emergency orders during the foehn.

For all its parching capacities, the foehn can be a wind of some benefit; driving out winter cold, it melts the snow and touches Europe's countryside with spring. Without the foehn to dry their hay and ripen their fruit, farmers in high, hemmed-in valleys would have an even harder time cultivating crops than they do.

Wind movement, as we have seen, can be disastrous. So can lack of it. Were all the forces which propel the winds to be withdrawn, air movement would die within nine to twelve days. The tropics would begin to burn; the upper latitudes would freeze. Entire cities would suffocate and farmlands dry up. In this oppressive hypothetical disaster, life would be erased from the earth in a span of time no man could predict.

As it is, a few places on earth experience stagnation of air with horrendous results. Dense fogs sometimes settle into valleys and clamp down on residential areas with such heaviness that human beings are eliminated by the thousands. A disastrous fog blanketed London in December, 1952; almost four thousand persons are believed to have died from the direct effects of it, and Dr. Ernest T. Wilkins, head of the atmospheric pollution section of the Department of Scientific and Industrial Research, figured that eight thousand people succumbed later from the after-effects of the fog.

Fortunately, the wind is active more often than not. And it is active with sufficient regularity to permit man's using it for various purposes. Natives once drifted from one south sea island to another, spreading civilization across all Polynesia. The trade winds brought Columbus to America, Cabral to Brazil. In 1486 Bartholomeu Diaz was violently driven around the Cape of Good Hope (he named it the Cape of Storms). The Germans since Otto Lilienthal have mastered the art of gliding. And then, of course, look what the Wright brothers started with the winds at Kitty Hawk.

In the early days, Phoenician and Greek navigators were continually driven back by Indian Ocean monsoons. Nearchus, an admiral of Alexander the Great, played the game safely by following the coasts of the Arabian Sea and the Persian Gulf between the mouths of the Indus and the Shat al Arab and this set an example of Arabia-to-India routing that persisted until the reign of Tiberius.

But coasting was obviously not the straightest distance between two points. Coasting gave way to navigation in the open sea. Sailors became bolder and—if they survived the storms they met—wiser.

As mariners went farther, it became increasingly clear that if one studied the positions of the ports, the state of the sea, and the regularity of the winds, it might just be possible to use the monsoons themselves to sail still farther.

With this discovery, shipping boomed. By the fourth century the sea lanes had reached China. An Arab by the name of Sidi Ali published in 1554 a list showing when the monsoons began at forty different places. Meanwhile, the trade winds—long considered a barrier—were coming to be similarly utilized. And all the while, new developments in sails kept shoving the world's navigators farther afield.

Man had learned to use the wind at sea.

On land, windmills were used by the Egyptians as early as 3600 B.C., and through the years evolved into varied shapes and sizes, grinding corn, pressing oil, drawing up drinking water, and draining and irrigating lands.

Though windmills may never be widely used again, one fact remains: the energy of the wind is practically inexhaustible. For decades, mechanical experts have been intrigued by the possibility of producing electric power from the wind. It was once estimated that a series of three hundred wind wheels spotted along France's Atlantic coast could supply that nation with fifteen million kilowatt-hours of electric energy every year.

Although wind and water have varying velocities, only water can be penned up by dams, yielding constant power. Wind is an invisible force which often eludes the grasping hands of industry. It cannot be funneled readily, nor can its energy be held in place. On prairies and seashores, where little landscape stands in its path, the wind blows at constant speeds and for long periods of time, yet even under the best conditions it varies. Inevitably there will be gales; and inevitably calms. To provide power during calms, a large (and expensive) storage battery is needed; but battery life diminishes when the discharge is too great. Conversely, under high winds the battery may be damaged by overcharge. Although giant wind-turbines on mountain peaks may deliver more than a thousand watts, such towers, subject to lashing winds up to hurricane force, must be tremendously reinforced, which runs the expense up prohibitively.

Icing must be considered—not only on turbines but on transmission lines—and studies show that icing is most serious where wind power would likely be more dependable than solar power. The most promising sources of the future are solar and nuclear power, yet, as it is said, all the power man needs now is in the wind—if it could only be put to work.

With an increase in the world's population going on now and presumably forevermore, the demand for electric energy will doubtless continue on the upswing for as far into the future as men can see. Long after oil and uranium have disappeared as power sources, there will have been developed a self-continuing method of giving the world the power it needs. Until long-range sources become clearer, and perhaps even after, imaginative engineers will probably keep on trying to utilize the elusive energy of the atmosphere.

In the words of Bacon, every wind has its weather. And neither time, nor place, nor temperature can dictate what that weather will be, or with how much severity storms will strike. We shall see later how violent winds influence the desert and stir up disastrous dust storms; what happens when wind-driven waves pile into inhabited seacoasts; and how wind-brewed thunderstorms explode with excessive violence.

There is excess, and plenty of it, for high-speed winds pack a mighty wallop. Even in temperate climates the wind can be intemperate, as when an end-of-January gale in 1853 blew down forty-seven million cubic feet of timber in Scotland. Because of its power to pick up and carry, the wind often becomes a transporting agent. There have been large swarms of grasshoppers, locusts, and butterflies driven from place to place by the winds. In 1939 a violent wind picked up a shower of frogs and splattered them down on the village of Alexandria, Ontario.

More subtly, the pathologic effects of wind upon man have taken a toll. In eastern Iran's basin of Seistan, the summertime "wind of 120 days" blows so wildly and steadily out of the north that trees grow only on the lee side of buildings and the wild melon bunches its branches uniformly in a single direction. Europeans who have endured it claim that it is one of the most trying experiences imaginable.

Depending on the conditions and on the individual human being, persistent winds have been known to help bring on headaches, irritability, epileptic attacks, rheumatism, oppression, fever, heat stroke, and asthma —unsettling the nervous system of some victims to the point of suicide.

Of London's east wind, Voltaire said: "This east wind is responsible for numerous cases of suicide. A famous court physician, to whom I confessed my surprise, told me that I was wrong to be astonished, that I should see many other things in November and March, that then dozens of people hanged themselves, that nearly everybody was ill in those seasons and that black melancholy spread over the whole nation, for it was then that the east wind blew most constantly."

One of the members of Sir Ernest Shackleton's ill-fated voyage and shipwreck in the Antarctic ice sea told of suffering from *amenomania*, or wind madness. He said that the disease took two forms, one that the victim became morbidly anxious about the direction of the wind and jabbered constantly about it, and the other that the victim descended into a sort of lunacy—brought on by listening to other amenomaniacs. "The second form is more trying to bear," he added. "I have had both."

Fiery desert winds—*siroccos, simooms, haboobs, kharifs,* or other names according to locality—are sometimes as devastating as a wildcat grass fire. The capital of Somaliland protectorate in fact was moved from Berbera to Hargeisa because of the sweltering kharif. Under Ottoman Empire law, murder was more pardonable if committed during the blowing of the baleful *khamsin.* More recently, tempers and guns have flashed along disputed borders near Jerusalem, where some of the worst khamsins in half a century have helped to detonate explosive international politics.

What of defense against the wind, against something we cannot grasp or tame or even predict satisfactorily? Because the wind may become a dangerous weapon, men have contrived some ingenious techniques to defend themselves against it.

In some localities house roofs reach completely to the ground on the side of prevailing winds; in other places roofs are held down by stone slabs. Some winds are so severe that houses have to be braced and reinforced. From ancient times, specially planted hedgerows and treelanes as well as brick, stone, and brush walls have helped break the wind's force. Planks, canvas and glass protect delicate garden crops. Holland tulip beds are covered with straw. Michigan farmers sow sheltering rye strips in fields of onions.

Insurance against windstorm is a tricky thing, and every policyowner should double-check to see if his home and furnishings and auto are secured against actual damage by wind. And now is the time to do it— not after the storm.

In the long run, the best way to defend ourselves against the wind is to learn all we can about it. With current researches into thunderstorms, tornadoes, and hurricanes, a great deal *is* being learned.

Yet with the coming of continuous observation by weather satellite, man has passed the threshold of a new era, and can expect new and exciting discoveries about the dulcet breezes and disastrous gales that rake the surface of the earth.

Meanwhile, the all-powerful wind, blowing wildly across vast regions, spreading havoc and damage, good will and bad, will also softly brush the bronze-skinned natives of south sea islands, who tell you as you sail away: "Good-bye, we shall sit together again in the caress of the wind."

3

HURRICANES

Don't worry about us mules, just
load the wagon.
... UNITED STATES NAVY

CHARLEY BEAMER was never a man to take the weather
lightly, or, on the other hand, to fear it. For years Flamingo had held
its present ground, and none of the storms that crawled across the
southern tip of Florida had torn so much as a scrap of paper off his
roof. Waves washed in from out on the bay, but that, after all, was
the reason for the houses' being up on pilings.

"We'll leave if we have to," Charley would allow, "so what's the
use in fixin' now?"

And who should have known any better than Charley? His father
had come as a boy to Flamingo when Henry Flagler's land development scheme had flopped, around the turn of the century, and Charley
had grown up in this land of white sand beaches and yucca flats. He'd
never been able to make much money, at least not enough for a coveted
houseboat down at Tavernier, and he'd long since tried to forget that
the houseboat ever existed. His life was fishin'. He liked Flamingo. And
if a man had fishin' troubles there was always the highway under construction across the keys to Key West. Might get a job over there. In
such Depression days, a family man needed to keep some cards un-
played.

Charley's two loves were Freda, his wife, and their son, Little

38

Charley. On infrequent occasions Charley took the boy along when he fished among the shoals, an idea not to Freda's liking. But she sighed a patient sigh and from her window watched the little boat pull out past the white and grimy markers into the gray-green channel.

It was hot and sultry early that morning, Labor Day. September was the month for hurricanes, but then, you couldn't tell. Some Septembers went by without a single one. Little Charley chattered happily in the bow of the skiff as they headed south, past Oyster Keys. Out there in the shallows beyond the young mangrove trees were mullet leaping from the milky waters.

WBXX TROPICAL DISTURBANCE CENTRAL ABOUT TWO HUNDRED MILES DUE EAST HAVANA CUBA MOVING SLOWLY WESTWARD ATTENDED BY SHIFTING GALES AND PROBABLY WINDS HURRICANE FORCE SMALL AREA NEAR CENTER XX CAUTION ADVISED VESSELS FLORIDA STRAITS NEXT TWENTY FOUR TO THIRTY SIX HOURS XX NORTHEAST STORM WARNINGS REMAIN DISPLAYED MIAMI TO FORT MYERS XX 0930

The weather observer at the north end of Long Key strode across the veranda and down the steps. What hot and muggy weather! It had been that way all summer, or so it seemed. Even the palms were wilted and drooping. He crossed a small lawn patch that separated the house from the beach; on the white coral strand, the sharp limestone crunched as he stepped on it.

At the water's edge he gazed beyond the reef and out across the sea, a hot, spraying, angry sea, chopped into pinnacles of water and troughs of foam. Here and there, masses of turtle grass that had been torn from the sandy bottom were floating in skeins on the surface. Gone was the shimmering aquamarine and the transparent glow of the shallow water. Gone was the reflection from the brilliant tropic sky.

It was mid-morning but the light was pale. The sky to the east had turned gray-black. Loose white clouds skidded by, as if fleeing from some great storm that was imminent yet too far away to be felt.

Earl Slocum, the weather observer, felt uneasy. He looked at the boiling sea. He looked at his house, half a stone's throw from the water, and less than ten feet above mean high tide. Behind it lay a garden flanked by a row of soursop trees, and beyond was a thick wall of gumbo-limbo trees, with bauhinias and jacarandas swaying in the breeze. Through this tangle a path had been cut, and a road led into the jungle toward the overseas highway that was under construction.

Earl shifted his gaze back to the sea. "If those waves—" He started to say it aloud but cut himself short. The ocean, after all, was very shallow out to the reef. It could do little harm.

Or so Earl wanted to think. He must have known that hurricanes had always ravaged the seas. They crossed the Atlantic and Caribbean as evil offspring of the elements, like giant pinwheels spewing destruction. Christopher Columbus must have sailed with a lucky star to have crossed the Caribbean in dangerous October and escaped destruction. Had the tiny and ill-equipped *Niña, Pinta,* and *Santa Maria* entered a fullblown or partly blown hurricane, they would have had as much chance as water-logged chips on a stormy sea. Perhaps an *absence* of storms led the Genoa mariner to discover America when and where he did.

Perhaps only the great god Hunraken knew. One thing was sure. There was hardly such staying of storm fury for mariners after Columbus, or even for Columbus later. He came to know hurricanes, and know them well. History itself was determined from year to year on the basis of the big blows.

The "great hurricane" of 1780 started from Barbados—leaving trees and dwellings flattened—destroyed an English fleet anchored off St. Lucia, ravaged the island completely, crushed six thousand persons under the ruins, swirled toward Martinique, enveloped a French convoy, sank more than forty ships carrying four thousand soldiers, leveled towns and villages, killed nine thousand persons, and devastated Dominique, St. Eustatius, St. Vincent, Puerto Rico, and most of the ships between.

A small, brief Martinique storm in 1891 had packed within it winds of great intensity, and seven hundred people had died. The "San Ciriaco" hurricane, with destructive winds and torrential rains, had stirred up pounding storm waves which passed over the entire length of Puerto Rico in 1899 and snuffed out three thousand human lives.

There was no escape. The winds would rise to a hundred miles an hour and you could not stand up before them. You couldn't see, either.

The roofs would come off tile by tile and plank by plank and go whizzing through the air. Plates and metal strips soared through the streets like giant razor blades, cutting and slicing, decapitating, amputating, maiming, killing.

Before Earl Slocum came south, a hurricane had blasted Miami in 1926 and swept away a hundred lives. Officials set the property damage at a hundred million dollars. What Earl had seen of it afterwards would be long remembered.

Yet he could best remember the great storm of '28, up Kissimmee way. He had not been involved directly, but had gone to Lake Okeechobee to help in rescue operations, and now on stormy nights he would sometimes lie awake remembering. Nearly two thousand people had been killed. Two thousand more had been half-killed or injured, some slightly, some terribly, some who would never recover.

The wind was rising. Shaking off his thoughts, Earl turned from the beach and walked up the sand slope and the limestone and crossed the lawn toward the veranda. It was hot in spite of the freshening breeze, and very humid. He paused a moment to check the wind direction. Northeast. That meant that the center of the storm lay somewhere south of the Keys.

It was time for another advisory, and another report. As he went inside, the rising wind behind him lifted and banged the door.

WBXX HURRICANE WARNINGS ORDERED KEY WEST. TROPICAL DISTURBANCE CENTRAL NOON ABOUT LATITUDE TWENTY THREE DEGREES TWENTY MINUTES LONGITUDE EIGHTY DEGREES FIFTEEN MINUTES MOVING SLOWLY WESTWARD XX IT WILL BE ATTENDED BY WINDS HURRICANE FORCE IN FLORIDA STRAITS AND WINDS GALE FORCE FLORIDA KEYS SOUTH OF KEY LARGO THIS AFTERNOON AND TONIGHT XX CAUTION ADVISED VESSELS FLORIDA STRAITS NEXT TWENTY FOUR HOURS XX 1330

As a long white string of sparsely settled islands arching southwestward from Miami, the Florida Keys fringe the southern edge of Florida Bay like a necklace of pearls. Around the shores of these elongated reef islands the mangrove forests tiptoe into the clear water on arching stilt roots. Overhead on normal days a flock of laughing gulls, in raucous colloquy, wings across the green jungle. Or a speeding flight of ibis glints in the sunlight beyond Key Largo. Or roseate spoonbills preen their feathers on upper and lower Matecumbe Keys. The islands are normally busy and full of life, an Elysium of sun and sand and sea, cooled by the soft trade winds.

But now clouds obscured the sky, and the birds had gone. The mangroves quivered in the rising breeze. Waters pounding against the shore turned murky with mud and broken coral.

Lew Bassett, watching the symptoms from the highway construction camp on lower Matecumbe Key, figured that the storm would grow worse before it got better. He also knew that there were nearly five hundred veterans and their families still in the work camps on the Keys. They were working on the "overseas highway" which, bridging the islands as if they were stepping stones, would soon link Miami with Key West. Wooden and canvas huts formed the permanent work camps, one each on upper and lower Matecumbe Keys. There was also a temporary camp at Rock Harbor, above Tavernier on Key Largo.

Doc Bassett had been physician, surgeon, and father to the veterans ever since they had come from the North. Some were misfits. Some were drunks. Some were disabled, shell-shocked. Most were penniless victims of the Depression. A few had been in the bonus army that marched in Washington. Some went regularly, or at least periodically, to Key West to the bars; others had taken advantage of the Labor Day holiday to go to Miami. But most had remained on the islands, in or around their flimsy shacks and barracks.

They were new to this semi-tropical climate, and unfamiliar with its dangers. They did not realize how swiftly decay and infection spread in these latitudes unless medical care was swiftly and properly given. Healing was not easy. Doc Bassett had never been able to get this idea across as completely as he wished.

The provincial local folks had not taken kindly to the newcomers, but Doc Bassett shrugged off the differences. Even veterans were human beings—that much was constant—and his job was healing them, northern or southern, veteran or not. And if the camps were not evacuated there would be hell to pay when the storm got worse.

From the looks of things, time was getting short.

The palms were bending sharply in the rising breeze. Even the hospital, a flimsy frame building that actually was a hotel—the Snake Creek Hotel—had begun to sway in the wind. As Doc Bassett watched, he wished the building had been repaired before being turned into a hospital. In any case, it should never have held more than twenty-five patients.

"But what can you do?" he would say. "Forty people are crammed in there—men, women, and children—because there's no place else for them to go. You show me where and I'll put them. But you show me."

Doc Bassett picked up the phone at the hospital and listened. A rescue train was being dispatched from Miami to evacuate all the people remaining in the work camps. That made him feel better. Now, in the wind, his patients would have to be bundled up and gotten somehow to the railhead. The train, if it left on time, would be down in an hour. Two hours at the most. If the worst of the weather held off until then, fine, but if the train was delayed, there could be a rough time. He tried not to think of it.

Already men were coming out of the mess hall after lunch. Doc Bassett rounded up some volunteers and went to the hospital. Before entering, he noticed that the turbulent sky was closing in overhead.

On Florida Bay Charley Beamer watched the same sky in the same way. He had seen a lot of storms blow up out there. But this one was black, and the water was black. Already the skiff was dancing on the waves.

Little Charley, on the other hand, was totally unconcerned. When spray from the waves surged over the edge of the boat and struck his face, he started in surprise, but then he laughed and cheerfully slapped the gunwale.

Big Charley was not laughing. Nor was he cheerful. He covered his gear and hauled the skiff about. To the north, in the distance, lay a slim gray line that was Dildo Key, and beyond that, Flamingo, out of sight.

He headed home, fast.

On Long Key Earl Slocum shouted into the telephone.

"Hell yes we got a storm down here! You bet! . . . What? . . . I just read the barometer. It's down to twenty-eight, and still falling . . .

Sure is . . . I know. I don't believe it either . . . Sure I checked it . . . No, there's nothing wrong as far as I can see. We're just in for a helluva big blow. You keep standing by, will you? . . . You hear me? . . . Hello! Hello! Weather Bureau? . . . Operator, get me Miami. Operator . . ."

Outside, the drumming raindrops increased, beating against the house like a barrage of pebbles. What must the storm be like at that very moment, out in the open sea beyond the reef?

"Do you know that you cannot breathe with a hurricane blowing full in your face?" That is what a yachtsman named Weston Martyr once said. "You cannot see, either; the impact on your eyeball of spray and rain flying at over one hundred miles an hour makes seeing quite impossible. You hear nothing except the scream and booming of the wind, which drowns even the thunder of the breaking seas. And you cannot move except by dint of terrific exertions. To stand up on deck is to get blown away like a dead leaf. You cannot even crawl; you have to climb about, twisting your arms and legs around anything solid within reach."

It must have been like that in Galveston, Texas, at the turn of the century. The people of Galveston had been attacked for generations by hurricanes and their city inundated by the waters of the Gulf. Each time they had built anew.

But in 1900 the storm was worse than any before. On September 8, waves surged as usual into houses at the beach, splintering them and shoving debris inland. But then the waves gushed into the streets, lifting and breaking house after house; winds rose to a hundred miles an hour, lobbing debris through the air in deadly projectiles. Men, women, and children—dazed, surprised, shocked—plunged into the waters and scrambled desperately for higher elevation.

But the winds caught them. And so did the water. Chimneys flew to pieces, church steeples collapsed, brick walls disintegrated in avalanches of rubble. Hapless refugees who had managed to survive the first onslaught clung sick or wounded or half-drowned to the wreckage. All through the dark hours they were mauled by the storm—and more and more were blown into the water or buried in cascades of bricks and boards and debris.

When the storm passed, there were only the silence of the dead and the disbelief of the living. No one knows how many lives were lost, or how many people were washed forever out to sea, or how many were mutilated. Six thousand, perhaps? It was by far the greatest toll in any United States hurricane. To Earl it was *the* storm.

The screen door was banging more than ever now, and he went out on the veranda to latch it. The winds had risen and were slicing through the screen. In the twilight he could barely see the coco palms bending to the wind, their pliable fronds flapping like warning flags in a heavy gale.

A hurricane, Admiral Beaufort had said, was a wind "which no canvas could withstand." Earl did not know how fast the fastest winds had blown, because measuring devices were almost always ripped away before the peak of the storm struck. But the gusts were enough to level whatever stood in the way.

He listened to the downpour outside. Millions of tons of rain rode on these winds, and they were driven great distances by hard-blowing gales; but where had it all started? Hurricanes sprang from patches of equatorial ocean calm in which northeast trade winds pulled one way and southeast trades the other. But who could describe an act of nature which no man had ever seen?

Somewhere within the enormous natural hothouse of the doldrums —steaming with vapors, sweltering with heat waves—the air had been stirred by unseen forces. Showers and thunderstorms exploded across the sea, and winds picked up the wave-spray and flung it high. Somewhere in this meteorological mix-up the god of storms had struck the spark that ignited the hurricane.

Heated air rose into the tropic sky and other air slipped in to replace it. Such incoming air, deflected by the earth's rotation, formed a giant whirlpool to which centrifugal force imparted more and more energy. The whole pattern must have been like eddy currents in a great river, where big and little whirlpools constantly form and dissolve. With the earth's whole atmosphere a giant river of air, big and little hurricanes must whirl constantly, some seen and some unseen. Perhaps for every storm that developed, others began, breezed for a while, then evaporated without producing a squall.

Round and round the storm went spinning. In the center, in the mysterious "eye," lay a dead or nearly dead calm that presented a strange paradox. So tranquil a region walled by circumnavigating violence! What a haven it must have seemed to birds thrown into it;

in fact, some old-timers had told Earl that birds. nearly dead with exhaustion often alighted on decks after fighting their way through the storm, and as long as the ship rode inside the eye no sailor or captain could frighten them away. Bedraggled they were, and there to stay, recouping their energy for another battle.

So the whirling gale might once have dissipated had other conditions not lent it power and direction. That direction was toward the Florida Keys.

Earl lighted a kerosene lantern and hung it by the door. Outside the wind had risen in a screaming crescendo and rain was coming in harder. Stones and bits of palm flew into the screen on the porch. Fragments of limestone from near the garden began hitting the house.

He checked the barometer again. "My God!" he exclaimed. "It's going down to twenty-seven!"

He had never seen a pressure reading so low. A fine salt spray blew into the house through crevices by the door and through cracks in the walls and around the windows—spray from heavy waves that had begun piling into the beach.

At suppertime word arrived at the veterans' camp on Matecumbe Key that the train coming down from Miami to pick them up had passed Homestead and was on its way. This brought cheers, but no one ate a hearty supper. Outside, the wind was screaming like banshees. The building shook and reverberated as if it would come loose and be carried away in the gale. When the doctor came into the mess hall and shouted instructions for assembling at the railway, the men headed for the door without any prodding.

At that moment the corners of the mess hall began breaking off and spinning away through the air.

Doc Bassett heard himself shouting: "Take cover! Take cover!"

Someone else shouted: "The building's coming down!"

Wind and rain bore down at a furious pitch. The men had to fight every inch of the way toward the railroad. No one could stand. Few could see. Sand grains struck their faces and drew blood.

The mess hall broke up and disintegrated. Then the canteen collapsed. Wood flew everywhere. Some of the men threw themselves down behind the railroad tracks; there the whizzing wind, laden with debris, plucked at them and loosened their grip and gouged away their flesh, but somehow they held on.

Darkness clamped down upon the chaotic scene. One veteran and his buddy clung to a rock and were holding fast when the sea came in for the first time, roaring up over the beach, pouring through the trees and into the camp in a surging wall. Both men were completely submerged, their grip torn from the rock. Swirling around and around they were carried across the railroad track where both miraculously managed to grab a telephone pole.

It was a precarious perch. The second wave was higher. Then wave after wave of black water washed in. One of the veterans was torn loose.

"Give me a hand, buddy!" he shouted. "Save me! I'm drowning!"

No one could see, or help. To let go was to die. The plaintive call faded away in the darkness and the thunder of the storm, and was not heard again.

Inch by inch the survivors fought their way to higher ground. It was a desperate fight just to keep above water. One man found a pole and took off his belt and strapped himself to it. Suddenly there was a loud swishing noise and a crashing of debris; the barracks roof had fallen on him.

The wind was blowing at nearly two hundred miles an hour, with gusts (as was later estimated) up to two hundred fifty miles an hour. Cabins and buildings exploded and sank into the waves, washing out to sea. Human beings were sucked into outgoing waves and slammed against the razor-sharp ridges of the coral reef.

Somehow Doc Bassett had gotten to his hospital in the Snake Creek Hotel. He had just begun to move the patients when the entire building shuddered in the awful gale and collapsed with a deafening crash. Doc saw vaguely a hole in the wall, and staggered through it.

The wind and debris slapped him like knives, piercing his flesh. He was flung to the ground, where the waves caught him and rolled him over and over. Without knowing just how, he crawled up on the railroad embankment and dropped behind the grade.

"Dig!" he heard himself shouting. "It's the only way to keep your brains from being crushed out!" He meant it. There were timbers flying past at nearly a hundred miles an hour.

But the words were lost in the screaming roar of the storm.

Again and again the sea came, in waves nearly twenty feet high, engulfing the islands like water over a millrace. Men lashed their families in trees to keep them from washing or blowing away; and there the families died from drowning or from exposure to rain that was borne like bullets on the hurricane's wind.

Farther up the keys, the rescue train, chugging southward, was hit broadside by a giant wave. The tracks were washed out. The coaches toppled over into the mud, leaving only the engine standing. The thirteen people aboard took refuge behind fragments of wreckage and shielded themselves against the storm. There they waited for the next wave to suck them into the sea.

Everywhere in the camp, and in the cities along the narrow path of the hurricane, buildings were smashed, trees were snapped off, road-beds were ripped up, docks and bridges destroyed. Rescue boats and houseboats and pleasure boats crumbled into debris in the blackness. And everywhere were the bodies—swirling and catching in the mangroves, or being pulled out to sea never to return.

The hurricane's eye, passing over Long Key, brought a strange quiet to Earl Slocum's cottage. It was the heart of the storm. He knew it as soon as the gale died. Waves still boomed and pounded on the beach but now there was almost no wind. The storm had been suddenly silenced. Where before were untold violence, beating of wind and rain, rocking of the house, shrieking of the storm, now he heard only a strange quiet. The elemental hand of the weather had released its grip and the storm seemed over. But it was not.

Many persons now would be stepping from their houses or their huts or their places of refuge, rejoicing that the storm had gone and they were still alive. If he could only shout to them: "Get back! Get back! Stay inside!" How many would be caught unaware when the winds blasted in from the opposite direction—from the other side of the storm?

Earl's cottage, by some odd benevolence of Nature, had remained where it was during the first half of the storm. He wondered suddenly if everything would hold when the hurricane continued. The second part of the storm, he knew, was the worst. North-blowing winds would be combined with the northward surge of the storm.

He thought he heard the sea rising and growing louder. Contrary to his own advice, he went outside, crouching against the wind, and aimed his flashlight in the direction of the beach. Then he froze. Reflections glinted from a high wall of water towering over him.

Earl spun around and ran for the steps of the cottage, but it was too late. The water thundered down upon him and dashed him against a coco palm, to which he clung as the surf surged back to sea. Waves lifted the cottage and settled it again. Earl held on until the wave subsided, then sloshed his way back inside. The wind rose again with a blast from the southwest. The eye was gone.

The gale howled beyond the windows and rain pounded and waves threatened to rise again. But Earl, oblivious of the roar of the storm or the creakings of the cottage, sat at his desk and entered descriptions of the storm in his journal.

He glanced at the barometer and, disbelieving, took it down from the wall. 26.35 inches. He would have bet anyone then and there that it was a record low. (It was—for the Western Hemisphere.)

He didn't have time to speculate long on the matter. Water foamed up through the floor and poured across the veranda. The kerosene lantern fell into the water and the room was plunged into darkness. The house began to break up. Earl dropped the barometer and with the collapse of the house the winds and water caught him and swept him outside into the sea.

Somehow he managed to catch the broken fronds of a palm and cling to them as the spitting rain and lashing wind pulled and plucked and almost tore him loose. Suddenly something flying through the darkness struck the side of his head. He saw exploding suns, and then the roaring noise of the wind and waves began to fade as he drifted into unconsciousness.

Twenty miles to the north, angry waves from Florida Bay rose again and again into the fishing village of Flamingo. Wind and wave and spray pushed over the coastal prairie and salt flats and plunged into the buttonwoods, ripping bark off the trees, twisting trunks and stripping away foliage. Mangrove forests were devastated. Palms went down. As the whirling hurricane churned northeast in a curving parabolic arc it picked up herons, spoonbills, egrets, and other helpless birds and flung them helter-skelter into the mangroves. How many birds and animals died that night will never be known.

Nature on the Rampage

Charley Beamer and his boy had just made it home ahead of the storm. Freda had gone inland with other villagers. Charley and the boy took refuge in their house, but waves ripped through the pilings. The little house shook and began to go to pieces. When peak winds struck, the house toppled and Charley found himself waist deep in the driving water—with his boy clutched to his chest.

It was all he could do to keep Little Charley's head above water. Timbers hit them from nearly every direction, both in the air and in the water, and since he could not see in the darkness there was no way of knowing from which direction he would be struck. He heard shouts, but the noise of the storm overwhelmed the voices.

His only thought was to make for the nearest buttonwood patch, even though it offered scant shelter. He could only stumble. The biting rain stung his eyeballs and he could not open his eyes. The power and force of the wind took his breath away. Wave after wave poured in from the bay, each rising higher and higher, and presently a giant wave caught him from behind and spun him around. His feet were torn from under him, and as he toppled into the mud and foam, Little Charley slipped from his arms and disappeared in the roaring, watery darkness.

Miami, Sept. 3. More than 100 deaths were reported last night along Florida's hurricane-swept keys as a tropical storm, raging northwestward along the West Coast, whipped up winds estimated at more than 100 miles an hour at Boca Grande.

Tavernier was nearly demolished.

Deaths among veterans began mounting at Rock Harbor and in camps on Upper and Lower Matecumbe Keys. Rescuers speeding toward the scene were blocked south of Homestead by high tides and washed-out roads.

Meanwhile, the steamship *Dixie*, aground on Carysfort Reef with 410 persons aboard, continued to be pounded by mountainous waves.

The *Reaper*, a 6,400-ton Texaco tanker, notified Coast Guard Headquarters in Jacksonville that it was proceeding full speed to help the *Dixie*.

The Coast Guard vessels *Carrabassett* and *Saukee* also were speeding to the rescue, but were being hampered by heavy seas and high winds in the hurricane's wake.

Captain Einer Sundstrom, using emergency communications equipment, radioed that all was well, however, aboard the *Dixie*.

This news gave a surge of relief to Morgan Line officials in New York and to friends and relatives of the besieged passengers. It also eased the sleepless vigil kept by Captain Sundstrom's wife and two daughters.

"Father is a seaman of the old school," said one of the daughters. "He has always said that if his ship ever went down he would go down with it."

"In 40 years of the sea, Einer's never lost a ship," Mrs. Sundstrom said confidently. "He won't begin now."

The second day remained gray and dreary along the Keys. Rain fell in a drizzling blanket as the first rescuers arrived in the late afternoon at Snake Creek. Both the rail and highway bridges, which connected the southern Keys with civilization to the north, had gone and only the naked abutments remained. The veterans' work camps were isolated. Winds howled and waves crashed in a booming thunder, but cries for help could be heard in the distance. One of the foremen of the camps, arriving from Miami, where he had gone for the weekend, surveyed the scene from the north bank of Snake Creek and plunged straightaway into the water. The current pulled him away from the bank. He fought with all his might to reach the first bridge abutment but it was no use and he was forced to return to the bank while he could still reach it.

Someone brought up a rope and another man, with a line around his waist, started out into the stream, the current tugging at him every stroke of the way. Meanwhile two other men, salvaging a boat from the bottom of the stream, righted it, floated it, and fought their way past the abutments to the other side. In a little while more boats arrived and refugees began collecting for the trip across Snake Creek to safety.

The first to be ferried across was a pale girl of six, her clothing tattered and ripped, her face scarred and smudged and tear-stained. Her legs were caked with blood. What was her name? Dorothy Van Ness. Her mommy and daddy? No answer. Could she tell what happened?

Yes. Her father, her mother, two brothers, and a sister had taken refuge in the hospital before it fell. In a broken voice she told of the building being blown away and how in the darkness, she had clung with her mother to broken timbers to keep from falling in the water.

"You've been out there all night?" they asked.

"Yes."

"Where is your father?"

"Papa is gone."

The wind screamed through the gumbo-limbo trees and the water roared and clawed at the white rock banks.

"My big brother is gone, too," she said. "So is Katherine and so is Gene. All are gone except me and Mama."

Mrs. Van Ness arrived on the third boat. Her face was tired and drawn. She broke into sobs as the little girl ran up to her and took her hands.

On Lower Matecumbe Key Doc Bassett worked continuously. In his back throbbed a sharp pain where he had been struck by a flying timber during the night. His tools and equipment were gone. He was using rags for bandages, broken lumber for splints. There was no water, save what could be collected in buckets, and he used sparingly all he could find—for drinking and for cleaning wounds.

Moving through the camps, fighting exhaustion, he helped pull the dead and the injured from where they had been caught in trees, and supervised the lifting of bodies from water and wreckage. Where treatment was needed, he treated. Where it was too late, he murmured a prayer and went on.

"I tried, Doc," the timekeeper said. "I tried to make a human chain to the railroad track to get the women and children out, but I got washed into the Gulf by a high wave. I swam back as fast as I could and got to shore just as the hospital fell in."

"Your wife was in there." Doc said it gently.

"Yeah. I heard her calling my name. She was close but I couldn't find her. I could hear her as well as I can hear you now. But I couldn't get to her in time."

"What about your daughters?"

"We found them a while ago. All dead, all of them."

"And your grandchildren?"

The timekeeper looked away and closed his eyes.

They found George Sherman later that day. George had gone through the war unscratched, and like the others, had been eking out a living on the Keys. He thought the world of his dog, a fuzzy little mongrel, and wherever he went, it went, too. When the storm broke the little dog fell into the waves, and George, without thinking, plunged in to save it. George had never learned to swim.

After the storm, his body was found near the hospital. And there, too, was the grateful little dog, licking its master's hand.

As the rain ended and a new day came, the hot sun came out. More rescuers arrived. They found hundreds of bodies, some still up in the trees, some floating in the sea, mingled with debris.

Veterans—grimy, bearded, shaken—roamed the broken camps. They dug in the sand with sticks, hunting bottles of beer that had been covered by the storm. When a bottle was found they would sit and drink it. It was hot, but they liked it. Some of the men huddled in the mud at the foot of a railroad trestle. Others limped along over jagged rocks on bruised and swollen feet. Some had gashes on their heads and bodies, wounds that had not been treated after two days.

One man was found sitting against a wall with a piece of two-by-four running completely through him, under his ribs and out over the kidneys. He was still alive. The doctor asked if he wanted a shot of morphine before the timber was pulled out. The man said no. He asked for two beers, got them, drank them. When the timber was pulled out, he said, he would die. He did.

The storm recurred across northern Florida and spent itself over the Atlantic. At Tavernier a dozen houses remained out of four hundred.

Offshore, rescue crews got through the rough seas to the ill-starred *Dixie*, and took off her passengers and crew. The Captain stayed behind to help ascertain the damage to the ship—later estimated at half a million dollars—and the passengers were taken to New York by train.

On Long Key Earl Slocum had regained consciousness during the first night and found himself lodged in a tree twenty feet above the ground. Nothing remained of his house but the foundation. His garden was gone. The bauhinia and jacaranda trees were broken and stripped. Yet probably they would survive. And probably Earl would rebuild his house in the very same place and plant his garden again—

and perhaps the new house would be kept more neatly painted than the old one. He would also need a new desk and a lantern.

And a new barometer.

Except for the little red cap, no trace was found of Charley Beamer's boy at Flamingo.

The death toll rose to four hundred, and in the semi-tropical climate the bodies promptly began to decay. There was no transportation to take them away. Neither was there any way of digging graves in the solid limestone. The stench of crematory fires soon filled the limpid tropic air.

Winds of hurricane force had extended over an area only twenty to thirty miles in width. Yet in the end, the laughing gulls returned, as they had after every storm, laughing, and ibis flocks rose into the sunshine, and frigate-birds returned to their places in the bright blue sky over Windley Key.

As the most widely disastrous of all Nature's rampaging storms—bar none—the hurricane owes its destructive wallop to the fact that it travels so far and covers such tremendous territory. Tornadoes pack their brief power in a lethal swath several hundred yards wide and at most a few hundred miles in length. But a hurricane may last for weeks and travel thousands of miles, scattering destruction wherever it goes. Ivan Ray Tannehill, a specialist on the matter, says: "Words fail to present an adequate description of the fury of a great hurricane."

This fury rages, as a rule, for about nine days, but the time from origin to decay may be much longer. August, September, and October are principal hurricane months, with September by far the period of greatest frequency. In some seasons only one or two tropical storms may be produced, but in 1933 there were twenty-one. Usually no more than half a dozen get big enough to worry about.

They whirl counterclockwise (clockwise in the Southern Hemisphere) and their tracks assume no definite pattern. In the early part of the season (June and July) they generally boil out of the western Caribbean and steam across the Gulf of Mexico. Later, they issue chiefly from the vicinity of the Cape Verde Islands and may go anywhere. Some curve back into the North Atlantic before striking the continental United States, but why and how are moot questions.

Meteorologists believe that a hurricane is guided, partly at least, by other pushing and shoving air masses.

But the storms do not always turn magnanimously away from the coast. On the fourth of September, 1938, in a remote and isolated section of the Sahara desert, the pressure of the air dropped slightly. In the neighborhood of Bilma Oasis, a desert village in French West Africa, no one seemed to notice. There was scarcely a sway in the palm leaves, or a flicker among the tent flaps. Yet the motions of earth and atmosphere had set off a whirlwind that silently grew and drifted across the coastline out to sea.

There, clouds began to form in circular bands. Lightning flashed, thunderstorms exploded. Spinning westward and gathering steam the storm aimed straight across the Atlantic toward Miami.

This was the front-page news. Said the New York *Times*: "A tropical disturbance of dangerous proportions roared westward over the Atlantic tonight. . . ." and the Weather Bureau warned that "all vessels in path and all sail craft, Cape Hatteras to Florida Straits, should remain in port until storm danger passes."

A flurry of hammers turned elegant Miami into something akin to a ghost town as residents boarded up their windows, nailed down shutters, anchored lawn furniture, and buttoned up ships in the harbor. They knew what was coming. Emergency relief organizations and the Red Cross augmented preparations by private citizens. Radio trucks cruised the beaches to report the storm's progress.

Then, unexpectedly, the storm veered north in a sharp curve above the Bahamas—and gave scarcely a whiplash to the coast that had prepared so well for it.

Next morning the New York *Times* confined the storm news to two brief reports on page 27. (1) The hurricane would hit the Virginia Capes and the southern New Jersey coast. (2) A predicted gradual turn eventually would take the center of the disturbance into transatlantic shipping lanes.

That's what usually happened. The northern states could hardly be considered in danger, could they? Hurricanes were tropical storms; they did not come so far north, certainly not to New England.

Yet no one bothered to consult the historical record, or recall the events of 1821. What was worse, there were in 1938 no radar, no reconnaissance aircraft, no way of checking up on the hurricane to find out what it was doing.

Late in the afternoon of September 21 nearly all of Long Island was plunged into darkness. The storm, moving at an extraordinary fifty-six miles an hour and packing interior winds of 186 miles an hour, struck like a pinwheeling battering ram, unleashing tons of moisture and shoving high walls of sea water before it. Along the whole length of the island, trees were uprooted and strewn over highways, live wires were snapped and flung down, and floods poured into streets and cellars.

The wind clutched a fifty-five-year-old man working atop a sixty-foot tower at Inwood and blew him away. A fifty-nine-year-old woman became panic-stricken when waves began pounding her house. Her husband bundled her into the family car and steered cautiously across a causeway to the mainland where she collapsed and died of a heart attack.

Waves thundered entirely over Fire Island, sweeping homes, cottages, and even the Coast Guard station into the sea. In the churning maelstrom one woman on a small schooner found herself about to be swamped in Port Washington harbor. She threw overboard three anchors, one after another, but none of them held. Taking charge of her plight like a latter-day Artemisia, she tied a rope around her brown terrier and tossed the dog into the sea. It swam ashore with the rope, where waiting rescuers pulled the craft to safety.

The hurricane charged into Connecticut coastlands, gutting seaside resorts, fishing fleets, summer homes, and industrial areas. Flying limbs and chimney bricks were spat like machine-gun fire through the air. As far inland as twenty miles salt spray destroyed vegetation, and salt traces were later discovered nearly fifty miles from the sea. Winds far over a hundred miles an hour raked the peaceful New England countryside, uprooting some 275 million trees, destroying or damaging thousands of buildings, and chopping up thousands of miles of telephone lines.

A New Jersey man stood on a bulkhead of his summer home, normally well above high tide, when a wave rolled in and swept him away. A return wave dumped him back on the bulkhead with little injury, but his watching wife collapsed from shock.

The storm blasted into a stunned populace. No one had been

warned. The people were inexperienced, unable to cope with the on-slaught. A French countess, wife of the French consul-general in New York, clutched her baby and waded with a retinue of servants out of her summer cottage on Long Island just before it collapsed. In the battering of the storm she discarded her overalls to make better prog-ress and arrived at a neighbor's house wearing nothing but underwear.

When all was over, railroad routes between New York and Boston lay blocked for days while ten thousand workers filled a thousand washouts, replaced nearly a hundred bridges, and cleared away as-sorted houses, cottages, boats, and other accoutrements of civilization sprawled across the tracks. Four hundred million dollars' worth of property had been destroyed. Nearly seven hundred people had died. It was a calamity of unprecedented dimensions for a part of the nation that considered itself hurricane-free.

Nor had the north country had the last word from the great god Hunraken. Nearly ten years after World War II the region was sacked again. Hurricane Hazel in October, 1954, moved into North Carolina with winds of 150 miles per hour and swirled on up to Canada spitting drenching rains and wreaking damage estimated at more than 250 million dollars.

And then the following year New England received a double punch. During the summer of 1955 widespread abnormalities in atmospheric circulation (doubtless having something to do with the jet stream) stirred up two hurricanes in rapid succession—Connie and Diane, both in August—and brought them far enough north of the equator for their trajectories to plunge them squarely into the United States.

Both were laden with moisture picked up from warmer-than-usual seas. Connie dumped heavy rainfall from North Carolina to New Eng-land (over twelve inches at New York's La Guardia Field), saturated the ground, filled the streams, and prepared the landscape for an enor-mous flood which, exactly a week later, was delivered by Diane. After such preparation and with her own heavy moisture, Diane became tremendously destructive. Damage estimate: 755 million dollars. Donna, in September, 1960, was worse yet—to the tune of more than a billion dollars.

Not since 1869, said the old-timers, when a September blow had wrecked New England from Boston to Maine, had there been storms so vicious. But in 1869 not nearly so many people or as much industry had been concentrated in the region. Unless these storms were freaks (as some thought), New England had become shockingly vulnerable to tropical storms. If so, something must be done at once.

Yet the fact was that people had been trying to do something about hurricanes for more than a century. Such an elemental force so fully capable of eradicating human beings and their property wholesale had long attracted attention. A storm so violent that it could sink an entire fleet was something no admiralty dared ignore.

For many a decade, any storm that struck a particular region was presumed to have originated there, i.e., formed out of thin air, spent its fury and blown itself out on the spot. The idea of storms *moving* from place to place was a puzzling concept, slow to be accepted and slow to be understood.

In the early days of sailing vessels, tropical disturbances were scarcely segregated, either in name or in form. In the North Atlantic and Caribbean they came to be called hurricanes, perhaps from the Carib Indian word for "big wind." Columbus was the first European to use this term, and he may have gotten it from Arawak Indians who returned with him to Spain; possibly he heard them utter it in terror when the ship was engulfed in a howling storm.

On the other hand, gales rising out of the Pacific and crossing the China Sea were called typhoons. But whence the name? From the Greek Typhon, father of dangerous winds? From the Chinese *t'ai fung*, great wind? From the Arabic and Hindustani *tufan*, a tempest?

In the pirate days of William Dampier, at the end of the seventeenth century, typhoons and hurricanes were barely differentiated and little was known about them. Dampier was a lean and keen-eyed buccaneer who had been orphaned early in life. He got his start with the master of an English sailing vessel and became a swashbuckling hero from the East to the West Indies and from the Americas to Australia. During all this time he noted the natural history and scientific phenomena around him with an accuracy that was unusual for the seventeenth century. Among other things, he became history's first mariner to define correctly the basic nature of a tropical storm. He described a typhoon in the China Sea as a kind of violent whirlwind, which it is. Furthermore, he knew of no difference, he said, between a hurricane in the Caribbean and a "Tuffoon" on the coast of China. When one considers the size of these storms and how difficult they are to understand close-up, Dampier's accomplishment and insight seem little short of remarkable.

But defining their rotatory nature was insufficient. Mariners needed to know much more before even the slightest defenses could be planned, for as long as man's ships crossed the bounding main Nature's hurricanes would depredate them.

And except for a Connecticut saddler's apprentice—a landlubber at that—the first theories of storms might have been much longer in coming. His name was William Redfield and he was the son of a New England sailor who many an evening had recounted to his children tales of storms at sea. Peleg Redfield had died in 1802, leaving a widow with six children, a family too poor to buy candles for light at night.

William, the eldest, was forced to leave school to help support the family, and he soon apprenticed himself to a saddle and harness maker. Each night, bone tired, he fell to the hearth and there in the soft red glow of the fire he read. Night after night, book after book, his mind unfolded to a realm of science that was as real to him as the clouds in the sky, and as thought-provoking as the patter of rain on a window sill.

The world about him became a laboratory. Every day was a new chapter in an open book of Nature whose pages needed only discerning eyes. Wherever he went in pursuit of his saddling—down country lanes, across ridges and valleys, through gentle forests of the Connecticut countryside—he talked and inquired and listened, and began to understand what was meant by the movement of storms.

On the third of September, 1821, his world was torn asunder by a violent hurricane that blustered in from the southeast, wrecking New York City and slamming into the towns around him—Middletown, New London, Springfield, Worcester.

The wreckage was appalling, particularly the swaths of trees felled in the path of the storm. As Redfield went from village to village he rode past forests where giant oaks and pines and maples had been twisted and cast to the ground. After several days of riding he noticed something curious. Near Middletown the trees lay fallen like dominoes, toppled toward the north. Yet little more than a day's ride away they had all fallen toward the south.

He inquired as he rode along, and learned that the violent winds had blown in completely different directions—at the same time in the same storm. Tracking carefully, tracing the path of the hurricane as best he could, Redfield judged it to have come as a giant whirlwind, invading the land from south to north, with winds that circled counterclockwise. What had been theory was now evidently fact. There lay the trees in witness. And he had heard the testimony of the village folk.

Redfield went on amassing evidence through the years—reports from stricken vessels, facts from log books, notes from interviews, details from correspondence—evolving laws of storms and establishing the world's first comprehensive knowledge of hurricanes.

When his papers were published in the *American Journal of Science*, they caught the eyes of scientists and laymen all over the world, including Lieutenant Colonel William Reid of the Royal Engineers who, by correspondence, confirmed Redfield's findings. Reid had superintended reconstruction of hurricane-felled buildings on Barbados, and had been appalled by the destructive power of these storms. He was trying to learn more about them. He also was instrumental in getting the East India Company to send a man named Henry Piddington to Calcutta, a remarkable case of the right man in the right place at the right time.

Piddington was interested in storms, and fortunately for him, there is hardly a deadlier bay in the world than the Bay of Bengal. Because the natural contours channel relentless storm waves directly into Calcutta and other towns on the Ganges delta, many a wave has flooded the coastal lowlands. One in a single day destroyed the town of Coringa and its twenty thousand inhabitants. Another, forty feet in height, smashed twenty thousand craft of all descriptions and reputedly cost the lives of three hundred thousand persons. Years afterward, another was to drown one hundred thousand and leave in its wake cruel epidemics to account for at least that many more.

In such lethal gales, Piddington found fertile ground for his work. As curator of the Calcutta Museum, and later as president of the Marine Courts of Inquiry, he was able to analyze in detail the reports of storms that twisted across the Indian Ocean. He coined the word "cyclone" (based partly on the Greek *kyklos*, a circle), which he intended to apply to the coiling storms of the Indian Ocean.

Piddington also had a highly original and unconventional idea. He suggested that men go forth and tackle these storms aggressively to find out what they were like. And he meant it. "The day will yet come," he wrote in 1845, "when ships will be sent out to investigate the nature and course of storms and hurricanes. . . ."

Meanwhile, the lighter touch was provided by Oliver Wendell Holmes, who wrote of an 1841 storm:

> Lord how the ponds and rivers boiled
> And how the shingles rattled
> And oaks were scattered on the ground
> As if the Titans battled
> And all above was in a howl
> And all below a clatter,—
> The earth was like a frying pan
> Or some such hissing matter.

While ships were the only means of crossing the oceans (and sailing ships at that) it was hardly safe or simple to enter a hurricane and come out with dependable storm data. Captains and crews had to fight for their lives, and only after the mariners' early laws of storms had been advanced by Redfield, Piddington, and their successors did seamen begin to comprehend the magnitude of the elements and learn what to do about impending storms.

The next step was to anticipate the approach, or even the course, of a storm, and to forecast it so that men would have time to get out of the way—or to brace themselves for battle.

After the destruction of a fleet of his supply ships in the Black Sea, Napoleon III ordered the French astronomer Urbain Leverrier (known to posterity as discoverer of the planet Neptune) to make a thorough study of weather, with forecasting in mind. Leverrier did so, and in 1855 showed that a system of weather reports and warnings could be and ought to be established. The Emperor approved. Although weather warnings had been issued before, this was one of, if not *the*, first official organizations to do so. Soon afterwards, the British were following the example.

The American attitude was less emphatic. In 1842, Congressman John Quincy Adams, as an influential ex-President, summarized weather progress as "crack-brained discoveries in meteorology" and called "interloping" a proposed weather-study office under the War

Department. The proposal lay dormant until, after continued pleas and further scientific studies, Congress in 1870 set up funds for a Federal weather service, attaching it to the Signal Corps of the Army; in 1890 it branched off on its own and the Weather Bureau was born.

For the inauguration of a hurricane-warning system along the American Atlantic coast, much credit is due Willis L. Moore, of the United States Weather Bureau. At the beginning of the Spanish-American War, Moore informed President McKinley that more ships had been sunk by weather than by war, and that a weather warning service should be put into force. Shortly after that McKinley is said to have remarked: "I am more afraid of a West Indian hurricane than the entire Spanish Navy. Get this service inaugurated at the earliest possible moment."

It was. In the years that followed, the Weather Bureau's Hurricane Warning Service developed as each new tool of communication was made ready—first telegraph, then radio. Special hurricane-season teletypewriter circuits connected coastal Weather Bureau offices from Brownsville, Texas, to Portland, Maine.

But this only gave warning of the storms *after* they reached the coast. What about details on hurricanes while they were still out to sea? If only data could be assembled and a storm course predicted in advance of danger to land, then coastal areas could be evacuated.

True, ships had been caught in hurricanes and typhoons and had made observations, as Piddington has told us. But these ships had been unable to examine the storm as a whole and even if so, to transmit their findings swiftly to land. Progress at this point awaited two major breakthroughs in the history of hurricane research.

One was radar. During World War II these electronic transmitters had been developed for detecting enemy aircraft, and for some time men had been cursing the "weather clutter" on their screens. At length, military and civilian weathermen began to perceive definite patterns in this "clutter" and soon realized that there on the radarscope was a complete picture of the storm, that bands of rain or lines of squalls echoed radar transmissions and reproduced themselves perfectly. Thus, for the first time, a whole hurricane could be examined, at least that part of it within the radar's range of two or three hundred miles.

The second major breakthrough in the history of hurricane research took place on July 27, 1943, near Galveston, Texas, when an AT-6 training plane rose into the boiling black clouds of a hurricane and headed for the eye of the storm. At the controls was a man named Joseph Duckworth.

Colonel Duckworth, Georgia-born and raised, onetime flight captain for Eastern Air Lines, had wanted to fly from the time his parents took him as a child to watch the flight of a Wright-type biplane. He grew as flying grew, through Brooks and Kelly fields as a cadet captain, through the fabulous twenties when Lindbergh flew to Paris and Byrd to the South Pole.

In those days, with the parallel development of radio, the science of instrument flying was still in its infancy. There was no "flying the weather." When storms arose, planes stayed on the ground. After war came in 1940 Duckworth, who held a reserve commission in the Air Corps, entered active duty with the notion that war could not be called off when the weather was bad. With ambition, fortitude, and uncountable skill he spearheaded the establishment of an instrument flying instructor's school at Bryan, Texas.

From there on the morning of July 27, 1943, he took off with a young navigator named Ralph O'Hair. Neither had planned the trip. There had been reports of a hurricane somewhere near Galveston and, come to think of it, nobody had ever flown into a hurricane before. From this casual beginning one would never have realized that a historic flight was in the making.

Duckworth did not take one of the new, powerful B-25's. That would have required elaborate authorization. He took instead a single-engine trainer (under his own authority), disregarding advice he might readily have given his cadets: never enter a severe tropical storm in a craft with one engine.

Duckworth and O'Hair flew into scudding black clouds and squalls and turbulence. Thick rain torrents drove against the engine, threatening to cool it and stall it. The sky grew black. The choppy air became choppier. The plane leaped and danced and skidded sideways, and gusts of wind pummeled it unmercifully. When they must have thought the plane could take no more, it broke out of the spinning clouds into a quiet, white-walled world that was the calm and eerie eye of the storm.

Looking down they could see ground, the open Texas lowland

somewhere between Houston and Galveston. Above, they saw the subtropical sky.

But it was not strictly a sightseeing jaunt. One could not stay here forever, so back they plunged into the maelstrom of hundred-mile-an-hour winds. Tossing about, as Duckworth put it, like a stick in a dog's mouth, they set a course for Bryan Field and, with little more ado than if they had been barnstorming, touched down safely after a flight that was epic in the history of hurricane research.

As it happened, a lot of flying went on that day. When Duckworth reported back to the field, the weather officer frowned. If only he could have been along, too! Whereupon the colonel packed him aboard the trainer and forthwith repeated the entire trip. And then, as Duckworth discovered a year later, some of his instructors, checked out in B-25's, had slipped clandestinely into the heart of the same storm.

It was a busy introduction to the saga of the "Hurricane Hunters," and was not to be construed as a parlor game (Duckworth was awarded the Air Medal for his flight). Once men in aircraft had proved that the mighty wall of a hurricane could be penetrated, it became instantly obvious that flight reconnaissance was the quickest, surest way to follow a storm and predict its path. But it was far from easy and far from safe. As one flier later admitted, flying a hurricane was like going over Niagara Falls in a telephone booth.

In any case, everybody was interested now. The Navy had ships on the high seas and was obliged to care for them the best it could, which is why early flights were made at elevations of three hundred to seven hundred feet.

The Air Force not only analyzed upper air patterns, but laid elaborate plans for evacuating bases and warning Army units. And all the while, there were the weathermen, poring eagerly over the results, reading the charts, plotting, predicting, hopping statistically jump by jump ahead of every storm. But the payoff was significant: better and more effective public notice of impending storms.

On the other side of the world the same thing was happening. Typhoons were generically identical to Atlantic hurricanes, but more of them could originate over the wider Pacific and each could travel farther. Typhoons were therefore harder to hunt and track because of a broader search area and because several might be in motion simultaneously.

These complications didn't stop the Navy, however. During the late stages of the war in the Pacific, after the United States fleet had been badly damaged by a typhoon, the Navy began flying storm missions in four-engine, land-based bombers. To the crews soaring out to tangle with them, it soon became apparent that no two storms were alike. Each might be big or little, fast or slow, severe or light, forming or dying out. The hurricane hunters' mission was to find out what was going on. How close? How soon? How much?

The more immediate problem was how to concentrate on weather instruments or make notations on charts when your plane pitched and yawed like a bucking bronco, and flew with all the stability of a storm-tossed leaf in a raging wind.

One navigator, pummeled within an inch of his life, uttered a classic understatement: "In my opinion a hurricane is not the place in which to fly an airplane."

"We were getting slapped around like a punching bag with Joe Louis on the prod," observed a flight engineer. ". . . You're so busy hanging on and trying to keep from getting thrown on your face that there isn't much time to think whether you're scared or not. . . ."

"When you are near the center," a navigator said, "about all you can do is brace yourself and hold on to something that won't pull loose."

Reaching the calm eye was a pleasant enough experience, but only the birds caught in that weird refuge cared to stay there. Weather observers wanted out fast, and in standard Navy jargon the intercom conversation went something like this:

"Stand by to leave the eye—report when ready."

"Don't worry about us mules, just load the wagon!"

In 1952 the Navy officially commissioned an Airborne Early Warning Squadron at the Naval Air Station in Jacksonville, Florida, and tropical storm reconnaissance became more than a sometime thing.

The Hurricane Hunters found abundant reasons for existing, and plenty to keep them busy, for a batch of catastrophic hurricanes shortly plowed across the densely peopled areas under their charge. There was a fearful toll of life, but without proper warnings each calamity would most certainly have been worse. During Hurricane Hazel, in 1954, for example, the Squadron flew twenty-one missions in ten days and made a total of 148 center fixes on the storm. This was coverage of 22½ hours out of every twenty-four hours that the storm moved over water.

Then after more storms ripped into heavily populated New England, the stricken public began to inquire in bewilderment why there had been no hurricanes in this area for decades, then suddenly a whole series. It must have surprised many inquirers to find out not only that the reason for this is unknown, but how little we actually know about the subject altogether. Out of the catastrophe came a public awareness of what weathermen had been trying to tell Congress for a long time: that real control of hurricanes would never be feasible unless we first pried out the facts concerning hurricanes themselves. Each storm was like an enemy during wartime. If you knew all about him you could predict his actions in a given set of circumstances and then put up offenses and defenses to stop him.

One result was the establishment, in 1956, of a comprehensive National Hurricane Research Project at West Palm Beach, Florida, sponsored and coordinated by the Weather Bureau and utilizing the best brains of the Army, Navy, Coast Guard, Air Force, and public and private meteorological laboratories. It was an excellent start, and the only danger that could be expected after it got under way was an old enemy which periodically plagues such projects: public apathy after a few seasons without disasters. The human mind likes to forget unpleasant things.

But unpleasant things like hurricanes have been around for a long time, and about them the fertile minds of men have fashioned explanations, conjectures, and drama. Aristotle assumed that hurricanes rose up when winds were blowing and other winds fell on them, adding to their velocity. Lucretius, in the century preceding Christ, averred that the wind wrapped itself in clouds and imitated the "prester," a hurricane or whirlwind attended with lightning. "When this prester has let itself down to the land and has burst," Lucretius wrote, "it belches forth a whirlwind and storm of enormous violence; but as it seldom takes place at all and as mountains cannot but obstruct it on land, it is seen more frequently on the sea with its wide prospect and unobstructed horizon."

"Good God!" wrote Alexander Hamilton, who as a studious youth of less than fifteen, witnessed the heart of a Caribbean hurricane. "What horror and destruction—it is impossible for me to describe—or you to form any idea of it. It seemed as if a total dissolution of nature was taking place. The roaring of the sea and the wind—fiery meteors flying about in the air—the prodigious glare of almost perpetual lightning—the crash of the falling houses—and the ear-piercing shrieks of the distressed were sufficient to strike astonishment into Angels."

The Dominican Jean-Baptiste Labat wrote *Memoires des Nouveaux Voyages Faits Aux Isles de l'Amérique,* in which he explained hurricanes as caused either by the sun moving around the earth, or vice versa, or else by a compression of winds. Of one thing he was sure, they were not here by accident.

But the very fact that they *were* here allowed the litterateurs to develop tales about them. Charles Nordhoff and James Norman Hall carried South Seas tragedy and Polynesian passion to a stormy climax in *The Hurricane,* in which the natives referred to such storms as "the wind that overturns the land."

In *Typhoon,* Joseph Conrad said that a storm-wracked ship gave every appearance of having been used as a running target for the gun batteries of a cruiser. A typhoon to him was many things, ". . . a ragged mass of clouds hanging low, the lurch of the long outlines of the ship, the black figures of men caught on the bridge, heads forward, as if petrified in the act of butting. The darkness palpitated down upon all this, and then the real thing came at last.

"It was something formidable and swift, like the sudden smashing of a vial of wrath. It seemed to explode all round the ship with an overpowering concussion and a rush of great waters, as if an immense dam had been blown up to windward. In an instant, the men lost touch of each other."

Nicholas Monsarrat, in *The Cruel Sea,* called it more than a full gale. To him the stormy sea was "a great roaring battlefield with ships blowing across it like scraps of newspaper. The convoy no longer had the shape of a convoy, and indeed a ship was scarcely a ship, trapped and hounded in this howling wilderness. The tumult of that southerly gale, increasing in fury from day to day, had a staggering malice from which there was no escape: it was as if each ship were some desperate fugitive, sentenced to be lynched by a mob whose movements had progressed from clumsy ill-humour to sightless rage.

"Huge waves, a mile from crest to crest, roared down upon the pigmies that were to be their prey; sometimes the entire surface of the water would be blown bodily away, and any ship that stood in the path of the onslaught shook and staggered as tons of green sea smote her upper deck and raced in a torrent down her whole length. Boats were smashed, funnels were buckled, bridges and deck-houses were crushed out of shape: men disappeared overboard without trace and without cry, sponged out of life like figures wiped from a blackboard at a single imperious stroke. . . ."

Perhaps the finest rhetoric came from Herman Melville, who wrote in *Moby Dick*:

"Warmest climes but nurse the cruellest fangs: the tiger of Bengal crouches in spiced groves of ceaseless verdure. Skies the most effulgent but basket the deadliest thunders: gorgeous Cuba knows tornadoes that never swept tame northern lands. So, too, it is, that in these resplendent Japanese seas the mariner encounters the direst of all storms, the Typhoon. It will sometimes burst from out that cloudless sky, like an exploding bomb upon a dazed and sleepy town.

"Towards evening of that day, the *Pequod* was torn of her canvas, and barepoled was left to fight a Typhoon which had struck her directly ahead. When darkness came on, sky and sea roared and split with the thunder, and blazed with the lightning, that showed the disabled masts fluttering here and there with the rags which the first fury of the tempest had left for its after-sport."

Artists likewise have been strongly impressed with these awful storms and their effect on men. Winslow Homer's *After the Hurricane*, painted in 1899, interpreted with bold strokes the black clouds receding in the distance and the dirty gray sky sinking into the troubled sea. In the foreground upon the white sand beach a fragment of skiff lies amid the debris that has been washed ashore. Sprawled awkwardly across the wreckage is a man stripped to the waist, lying on one arm. Compelled by the scene, one is left to wonder if the man be dead, or collapsed from exhaustion. Human fragility, as it was viewed in those days, seemed a permanent thing.

Since man is fragile, the most immediate and practical problem is how to act when a hurricane approaches, what to do when it is going on, and what to beware of after it has passed. There are many proved ways to die; but there are also some sensible rules for survival.

WHAT TO DO WHEN A HURRICANE STRIKES

Before the storm . . .
1. Follow official weather reports, and avoid listening to rumors.
2. Get away from lowlands along coastal rivers and from seacoasts; when the word for evacuation comes, move!
3. Once away from the lowlands, remain in a well-braced or well-constructed house safe from flooding, and cover the windows either with storm shutters or well-fastened boards.
4. Store in a food supply, particularly food that can be consumed without cooking; chances are that electric power will be blown out by the storm, or shut off deliberately to avoid fire. Thus your refrigerator will be off. So will your water pump, and your heating system. You may eat out of cans, but you will not go hungry if you are prepared.
5. Store as much drinking water as possible. Sterilize the bathtub and fill it. Fill all the jugs, bottles, pots, and cans you can find but be sure you store *clean* water; there is chance enough for disease after hurricanes without inviting contamination in your own home. The water may have to last for quite some time if the city's water mains are damaged and polluted. Even when service is restored, be sure to boil tap water until city authorities pronounce it safe.
6. Keep a flashlight handy, with an extra supply of fresh batteries. Candles should also be available.
7. Check for anything that might come loose outside and turn into a deadly missile: tools, signs, furniture, trash cans, awnings, bricks, lumber, loose tiles on the roof.
8. When the storm strikes, beware of the calm center. Don't go outside thinking the winds are over. They may suddenly and violently return from the opposite direction.

After the storm . . .
1. Get medical care at disaster stations or hospitals for anyone injured.
2. Report loose or dangling power lines to the police or power company. Don't touch!
3. Report broken sewer, water, or gas lines.
4. Check food and water for spoilage or contamination.
5. Remove broken or hanging tree limbs or other debris.

6. Unless you have any business there, stay away from disaster areas. Rescue workers, police, and doctors have no time for amenities.
7. Watch out when driving your car; sections of pavement undermined by moving water may collapse as you drive over them.
8. Be careful with fire, more so than usual. Water pressure is likely to be lower than normal, insufficient for coping with widespread conflagrations.

True, this is all hard work and much trouble and great expense. But the alternatives of death or of severe injury make the work worthwhile.

Considering a natural phenomenon so violent, there may seem little future but to sit and take the punishment, or, as Marcus Aurelius said, the breeze which heaven sends we must endure, and toil without complaining. Yet we cannot help asking whether, with all the weapons modern science commands, there may be a way of battling these storms before they run out of control.

One suggestion might be to patrol the Atlantic and lambaste suspicious whirlwinds with everything from minié balls to guided missiles. However, splashing the United States Navy across the wide Atlantic would hardly give sufficient coverage, even with the British Navy added for good measure. And besides, both navies have other duties.

There is also the embarrassing fact that no one knows what to look for in the first place. Some nimble whirlwinds undoubtedly do steam up into full hurricanes. That drop of air pressure over Africa's Bilma Oasis in 1938—which turned into one of New England's worst hurricanes—how did it start? Which of a thousand atmospheric circumstances led to it? We don't know. Perhaps whole regions of doldrums also erupt on a broad scale. Under such conditions it seems decidedly Quixotic to attack weather so unknown, so unpredictable, and so intangible.

Is there a possibility that nuclear explosions could modify hurricanes? To be sure, the staggering power of thermonuclear explosions beggars description and can hardly be shrugged away. The Weather Bureau explains, however, that we do not yet know enough about hurricanes even to guess what would happen. If the hurricane's incipient stage (the critical time to be flinging our bombs about) were more obvious, it would be different. But tropical rain and squall areas appear much alike, with only a few slated by the gods to develop into full strength. We thus scarcely know which to bomb.

Furthermore, the storms that do build up derive their energy partly by release of heat from the formation of rainfall. If heat from a nuclear device were added to all this, we might—of all things—make the storm worse.

By the time the hurricane reaches full size, its winds are circulating over hundreds of square miles, and the power it has generated has become so enormous that even a hydrogen bomb would have little effect on it. Or no effect at all. Worse yet, should the hurricane be diminishing, unleashed nuclear energy might heat it up again and move it along with renewed vigor. Or if the storm were vanquished but the rain became radioactive, we should have a Cadmean victory indeed.

In spite of all this, man's efforts to modify hurricanes are not entirely hopeless, and he knows it. He also is painfully aware that success in the venture lies clearly in solving the mysteries of these tremendous sea-borne tempests. Perhaps long years of time will be necessary to deduce the inner secrets of hurricanes. And then perhaps not. Our hopes lie in the fact that weathermen are patient people, and they have time. Someday they will know.

To men like Charley Beamer, who have lost their loved ones to a storm, it may not matter any longer. Or where the memory of a little grimy girl with lacerated legs still remains vivid, we quietly say to ourselves, "An Act of God."

Yet the deaths and hardships have not been in vain, for they have helped to spur the building of effective warning networks which have saved the lives of countless human beings already and will save the lives of countless more in times to come.

We must also remember that hurricanes once remained mysterious only because no plane had flown into them. Hence, we may at present merely have aloft an insufficiency of weather-observing satellites. Ultimately the laws of hurricanes will be understood, and in fact the wagon may well be loaded already. We are simply waiting for the patient mules to solve another intriguing puzzle of the wandering forces of Nature.

But let no smug inlander feel superior to this whole affair, and think himself secure on his dry and dusty plains. For bearing down upon him from behind is another kind of raging whirlwind which is nearly as deadly as the hurricane, just as dramatic, and just as mysterious.

4

TORNADOES

Big whirls have little whirls that feed on their velocity,
And little whirls have lesser whirls and so on to viscosity.
. . . L. H. RICHARDSON

NOTWITHSTANDING mistrals and hurricanes, no windstorm on earth can do what tornadoes do—with such finesse and finality. Each year, with the roar of a thousand banshees, these furious funnels slam into towns and villages and blow them to smithereens, whirl across the countryside clipping and uprooting trees, and in general raise more commotion in more concentrated form than any other wind on the rampage.

"I opened the door and saw a great wall that seemed to be smoke," one woman said of a tornado, "driving in front of it white billows that looked like steam. There was a deep roar, like a train, but many, many times louder."

She had been visiting a friend in a restaurant, according to the Associated Press report, when the sky outside had suddenly grown dark.

"The air was full of everything," she continued, "boards, branches of trees, pans, stoves, all churning around together. I saw whole sides of houses rolling along near the ground."

Her first thought was to reach her two children, then in school. Bending against the wind, she started out into the street.

"Then the storm hit me," she said, "and I was blown back into the restaurant against the stove. The building rocked back and forth and then it began to fall in. Fire flashed in great puffs from the stove. I tried to get away from it. I was afraid I would be burned to death. But the wind blew me back against it. Then the walls fell in. The roof fell. Something hit me on the head.

"How long I was unconscious I don't know. When I came to I was buried under boards and timbers. Near me was the body of a red cow which seemed to be holding some of the weight off of me."

The butcher came in then, looking for his sister who worked in the restaurant. "He saw me," the woman said, "and lifted some of the heavy boards . . . and pulled me out. I got up and looked around. There on the floor . . . was his sister, with a great wound in her head."

At the school she found a great crowd, milling amid the ruins. "Children were screaming and crying. Mothers and fathers were weeping silently. But everybody was trying to dig out their own children. I found mine. They were both hurt, but, thank God, they were alive."

Anything can happen. Tornadoes have sucked rope, buckets and water out of open wells. They have pulled a team of horses from a wagon and left the driver uninjured; ripped bedding and mattress from under a sleeping boy; plucked a wheel off an automobile; blown a house away so cleanly that not a splinter remained; picked up a farm hand, plastered him with mud and set him down a hundred feet away; carried a dresser a hundred yards without breaking the mirror; rammed a six-by-nine timber four feet into the ground; blown a car two hundred feet, a horse three hundred yards, the lid of a compact forty miles; demolished a schoolhouse and carried the children 150 yards without killing any of them; carried a pair of trousers containing ninety-five dollars thirty-nine miles; blown another man's trousers containing $1,400 into a nearby cave (along with a hog, a pump, and a washing machine); pulled up fence posts and stacked them neatly; picked up a rooster and set him down in a flock of hens several miles away; split open a tree, jammed in an automobile, and clamped the tree shut again.

There is the case of a woman who once took refuge in a closet under her back stairway and opened the door at the end of the storm to find that the closet and stairway were all that remained of the house. Another woman jumped into a bathtub and pulled a mattress over her; and she, the bathtub, and the mattress were all that survived. At Ponca

City, Oklahoma, a twister lifted a house in which a man and his wife were at supper, exploded it, and settled the floor back to the ground without injuring the occupants.

In the barnyard, chickens have been stripped of their feathers. The tiniest flying objects become as deadly as a hail of bullets; small missiles have rammed into the sides of barns, into houses, trees, animals and people. So powerful is the propulsion that planks are driven into trees and through solid iron, and even wheat straws have been jabbed more than an inch into the trunk of a tree.

Most of these fantastic pranks seem unbelievable but the United States Weather Bureau takes considerable pains to check not only the reports themselves but the integrity, veracity and reliability of the observers.

Of course, not all the damage is freakish. Most tornadoes deal death and disaster of an entirely believable and terrible kind; they create casualty lists and damage estimates that are sickening enough without being freakish. On June 28, 1924, a destructive tornado rolled from Sandusky, Ohio, out across Lake Erie and straight into Lorain, Ohio. People, horses, autos, high-lines, trees, and clouds of debris hurtled through the streets. Within forty minutes, ninety-three persons were killed and property worth thirteen million dollars destroyed.

Automobiles, with their occupants aboard, were blown off highways into Lake Erie. One couple, more fortunate, drove on toward Lorain until a tangle of fallen trees made further progress impossible; then they got out and walked.

"The town was a wreck," said one, later. "I had an uncanny feeling as I looked at houses without roofs or without walls, as I picked my way through the wreckage in these streets.

"I recall looking into one house from which the front wall had been blown out. I could see into the bedrooms, and I noticed that the bed stood there neatly made. In the distance we could see some houses in flames, although there appeared to be no general conflagration."

The police chief was having different trouble. And he wasn't fooling about it. "We've found some men robbing bodies," he shouted through a megaphone. "From now on I'm giving orders to shoot to kill anybody found looting the dead."

The storm came as a cloud, a queer yellow cloud from off the lake. One man in his office heard a noise he thought was an airplane flying through the streets. He put his head out the window to see what was up. Something hit him in the back, and suddenly he was in the street.

"Lie down!" he yelled, seeing some of the other members of the office force also in the street. "Lie down! Flat on your face!"

They did. When the twister had passed, they got up and found that they were sixty feet from their office.

Meanwhile, three miles east of town, a freight train of seventy-eight cars was being blown off the tracks.

Most of the casualties occurred in the State Theatre, which collapsed at about five o'clock, between the afternoon and evening shows. The lights went out but the girl at the piano, good trouper that she was, kept right on playing.

"My first impression," said a woman who had been in the audience, "was that a stage trick, possibly announcing the approach of the villain, was in process."

But it was no stage trick. "That's a tornado!" her husband exclaimed.

"But these children," she said, looking around her. "What if they stampede? They might be trampled."

They got up and started toward the lobby, which was full of freshly fallen bricks. Looking up they could see the sky.

The woman saw a pillar at the rear of the lobby. "We can't get through here," she said. "Let's go to that pillar."

Bricks were falling and cascading. Some were crunching on scalps, and cutting them. Plaster fell into everybody's hair. Gravel filled their pockets. Dust filled the lobby.

The woman's clothes and her husband's clothes had been torn to tatters. They waded through the bricks, and the sharp, broken edges cut their shoes. They found a place where plate glass had been broken, and stepped through the opening.

Outside, water was nearly knee high. Automobiles lay overturned and wrecked. Debris was everywhere. They could hear screams of the injured.

"Look," the woman from the theater said to her husband, "those who are not hurt seem more shocked than those who are." Some of the injured were calmly making their way to a drugstore for help and treatment.

After a while a man came along with his hand on the shoulder of a boy about twelve years old. The boy's clothing was torn and he was obviously frightened.

"I've found him! I've found him!" the man shouted. "I've found my boy. He was in the State Theatre and he ain't hurt a bit."

A twister tore into Akron, Ohio, in 1943 and left almost a thousand buildings damaged, including war plants so severely hit that several had to be shut down. A pre-dawn storm in 1940 ripped up the business district of Albany, Georgia, in a quarter-mile swath that took eighteen lives, injured three hundred persons, left a thousand homeless and ruined more than three million dollars' worth of property.

Through the years Chicago has seen six tornadoes, one of which jumped erratically from Joliet through Melrose Park and into Lake Michigan, leaving twenty-eight dead, three hundred injured, and three million dollars' damage in a single hour.

West of Missouri, tornado tracks are usually short, but one midnight in May, 1927, a violent storm tore up more than a hundred miles of Kansas sod before abating. It flung a five-thousand-gallon, 165-foot-high water tower to the ground, pitched and rolled a five-ton tractor, blew down a steel bridge span, and obliterated (among other things) thousands of plains rabbits.

Few tornadoes have been reported in terms of such terror as two which struck Irving, Kansas, almost simultaneously in 1879. No one knows exactly how many casualties or how much damage were experienced, but the inky blackness, the overall destruction, the "end of the world" tension, the smoke and fumes, the rumbling of the storm and rocking of the ground, all contributed to an almost unbelievable chaos. Says Snowden Flora, United States Weather Bureau tornado expert: "The horror . . . was not forgotten for years. Night after night following the storms hundreds of persons never went to bed, but peered into the darkness watching for a recurrence of the scenes through which they had passed. Every dark cloud . . . filled them with foreboding. . . ."

This psychological aspect of tornadoes is often apparent in survivors of disasters. On Saturday, December 5, 1953, at about five-thirty in the afternoon, a tornado swung into Vicksburg, Mississippi, and demolished a theater in which a number of children were watching the movies.

"They won't go anywhere without me, except to school," said one parent of his children later, as reported in a study made by the National Academy of Sciences.

"Janie won't sleep by herself," said another; "she sleeps with her daddy."

Another reported: "Nothing about school ever distressed her. Now there's always something wrong. She won't go to the bathroom, even with all the lights on, without someone being with her."

Others would not go to school, especially if there was a dark cloud in the sky.

Great numbers of tornadoes can occur at the same time. A cluster of thirty-one storms ravaged six states from Missouri to Alabama in 1952, leaving 343 dead, 1,409 injured, more than 3,500 homes torn to shreds, and a fifteen-million-dollar damage bill. Five tornadoes once struck Charleston, South Carolina, just as the inhabitants were getting up, having breakfast and leaving for work. Thirty-two people never made it, 150 others were injured, and two million dollars in damage resulted.

Dozens of combines, automobiles, and airplanes were mangled in 1949 in a vicious twister in Amarillo, Texas; the storm demolished fifteen farmhouses and blew twenty-eight boxcars off the railway tracks. .

The business district of Gainesville, Georgia, was almost completely erased when two tornadoes merged and cut a disastrous path through the city, killing 203 persons and destroying thirteen million dollars' worth of property. It was not the first time Gainesville had been plundered by twisters; another in 1903 had taken twenty-eight lives, and one in 1884 caused some damage. Nor was it the last time. In the spring of 1944 a storm took forty-one lives and more than a million dollars in property.

Observers who cherished the notion that mountain regions were immune got a rude shock in June, 1944. A family of tornadoes cut loose over Pennsylvania, West Virginia, and Maryland mountain country, killed 153 persons, injured hundreds more, and destroyed or damaged more than a thousand homes.

St. Louis has been through two of the worst tornadoes in history. On May 27, 1896, the toll was 306 dead, $12,904,000 in damage. The second storm struck in 1927, killing seventy-nine persons and destroying no less than twenty-five million dollars' worth of property.

Hangars and aircraft are sitting ducks. Two twisters five days apart tore into Will Rogers and Tinker fields near Oklahoma City in 1948 and demolished over sixteen million dollars' worth of buildings and aircraft.

Minneapolis has had five tornadoes, Oklahoma City eight, Indianapolis five, New Orleans six. In populous New York State a destructive twister once plowed through Jamestown; others have edged up to West Point and to Niagara Falls. A tornado once brushed close enough to the Tennessee State Capitol in Nashville to smash several windows.

Nearly every state has experienced tornadic weather of some kind. Here's the United States Weather Bureau's forty-two-year official record from 1916 through 1957.

Kansas	1,220	Michigan	201	Arizona	26
Texas	1,159	Wisconsin	181	New Jersey	22
Oklahoma	959	Ohio	154	Maine	19
Iowa	588	South Carolina	151	Idaho	19
Arkansas	443	North Dakota	148	New Hampshire	17
Missouri	427	Pennsylvania	141	Connecticut	17
Nebraska	421	Colorado	141	West Virginia	15
Florida	377	North Carolina	110	Vermont	11
Alabama	302	Wyoming	80	Delaware	10
Mississippi	297	Montana	71	Washington	9
Illinois	289	Virginia	70	Utah	9
Louisiana	283	Kentucky	69	Oregon	8
Georgia	269	New Mexico	69	Nevada	6
Indiana	253	Maryland	61	District of Columbia	4
Minnesota	215	Massachusetts	50	Hawaii	2
South Dakota	205	California	29	Rhode Island	2
Tennessee	204	New York	28	Alaska	0

United States total	9,861

Although the United States is the world's chief battleground for tornadoes, it does not have full corner on the market. Similar storms have been reported from many parts of Europe, from Australia, India, Russia, China, Japan, Bermuda, the Fiji Islands, and South Africa. More than fifty occurred in Great Britain within the last century, but none on the scale of death and destruction of United States storms.

After long study, meteorologists are convinced that America's specific combination of plains, mountains and seas sets a perfect stage for tornado make-up. Sea air from the cool expanses of the North Pacific moves into Washington and Oregon, and across the Coast Ranges, condensing into clouds and precipitating buckets of rain. Over the Rockies almost the last bit of moisture is wrung from the moving air. Sliding downhill onto the Great Plains, the air advances as a dry mass, the lower reaches warmed by compression, the upper levels cool. No one seems to notice—except weathermen, who recognize familiar signs and begin to feel a little uneasy. Communities in the path of the air enjoy fair days, brisk air, clear skies—weather for a picnic perhaps, or a ball game.

But at the same time, an air mass that has for days been soaking up humidity over the Gulf of Mexico begins to move north. Dark clouds expand angrily from it, unleashing rain torrents along the Texas coast. Ahead of the storm, weathermen begin issuing tornado alerts.

The two air masses, one clear and cool from the north, the other hot and moist from the tropics, spin toward each other like giant whirlpools. Separately, they rotate on a broad scale—like any other storm that glides across the surface of the earth. As high or low pressure areas they have been affected by the earth's whirling motion. Their own consequent spinning, while not exceptionally violent, provides part of the tornado's motive force when at length, over the plains country, they collide.

If neither storm has gained substantial momentum, if either or both have been blocked and hemmed in by adjacent air-pressure masses, then this encounter will be a tempered one, probably resulting in nominal thunderstorms and nothing more.

But if neighboring air pressures recede, as it were, and permit either or both of the revolving air masses to gain momentum, then their circular outer winds may increase to considerable force. On one side of the line of contact between the two advancing air masses, winds blow at gale force from the south or southwest; on the other side they blow from the west or northwest. Where these upper-air gales sideswipe, a vortex of wind currents develops and tornadoes are born.

There are more than a score of other origins but this process is evidently most common. Because the Great Plains lie so close to mountains that cool and dry the oncoming polar air, they become a perfect spawning ground for tornadoes. No other region in the world has physical conditions as perfectly matched for the birth of these funnels.

Tornadoes have been reported in all months of the year and at every hour of the day or night. Mostly they form in warm weather, but one in Utah's Wasatch Mountains once roared across snowfields, turning white as it scooped up snow. Tornadoes move uphill or down, across ravines and valleys, up and over cliffs, or alternately between water and land—all without losing force.

There is one classic eyewitness account of what the weather is like inside a tornado. A Kansas farmer named Will Keller, after watching a twister jump over his storm cellar near Greensburg on June 22, 1928, said: "I looked up, and to my astonishment I saw right into the heart of the tornado. There was a circular opening in the center of the funnel, about fifty to one hundred feet in diameter and extending straight upward for a distance of at least half a mile, as best I could judge under the circumstances. The walls of this opening were rotating clouds and the whole was brilliantly lighted with constant flashes of lightning, which zig-zagged from side to side. Had it not been for the lightning, I could not have seen the opening, or any distance into it.

"Around the rim of the great vortex small tornadoes were constantly forming and breaking away. These looked like tails as they writhed their way around the funnel. It was these that made the hissing sound. I noticed the rotation of the great whirl was anti-clockwise, but some of the small twisters rotated clockwise. The opening was entirely hollow, except for something I could not exactly make out but suppose it was a detached wind cloud. This thing kept moving up and down. The tornado was not traveling at a great speed. I had plenty of time to get a good view of the whole thing, inside and out."

Observers have detected winds on the order of two hundred miles an hour whirling around the vortex, and winds in exceptional tornadoes may reach five hundred miles per hour. Wherever this revolving chaos strikes the earth, damage is instantaneous and complete. So low is the air pressure inside a tornado that the very center of the whirl becomes a near-vacuum. As a tornado passes over a house the outside pressure is suddenly released, the pressure inside the house bursts outward, and the house is as explosively demolished as if it had been hit dead-center by a blockbuster.

Nobody knows the lifting power of a tornado, but railway coaches (weight about seventy tons) have been lifted off their tracks and flung into ditches eighty feet away. Tornadoes move slowly across the countryside, or they move rapidly. They "bounce" along, or they plow up a continuous track. The average cross-country speed is forty-five miles per hour, but this varies greatly among different storms as well as in the same storm. Some funnels remain stationary for a while, then roar on. The slowest tornado on record: Pratt, Kansas, 1930, five miles per hour. The fastest: Albany, Kansas, 1917, sixty-five miles per hour.

The length of the path varies. Some tornadoes drop, touch once, bounce up and dissipate. Others move long distances, veer up, and plow down again. The longest: Mattoon, Illinois, May 26, 1917—293 miles from Louisiana, Missouri, to Jennings County, Indiana. The width of the path changes as the tornado travels, and has varied from around a hundred feet to one or two miles. Average width of a tornado path is 396 yards.

The noise is ear-splitting. According to some ear-witnesses it is "pure pandemonium." To others the clatter is like a dozen factories filled with buzz-saws, or the approach of a railway train, or like a hundred locomotives or the roar of a thousand cannons.

Tornadoes over water become waterspouts, or, as Pliny said, a "cloud which draweth water to it, as it were into a long pipe." Generally, waterspouts appear as thin translucent columns over a basal mushroom of spray, and travel about twenty miles an hour, although sometimes reportedly speeding as fast as eighty miles an hour. Sometimes they have odd shapes, like an hourglass or, as was once reported off the coast of New South Wales, coiled like a serpent.

Not much is known about them, primarily because waterspouts—especially those far out to sea—are seldom seen and rarely leave evidence of their passage. They seem to be far less predictable than land tornadoes; they form in high- or low-pressure regions, in good or bad weather, warm or cold temperatures, night or day. From the Gulf of Mexico north they usually ride the Gulf Stream from May to October. As many as fifteen have been reported in the same vicinity at the same time. They last about fifteen minutes ordinarily but can hang on for an hour. Snow, hail and ice occasionally plummet down from them, the ice building up into chunks as big as six inches in diameter.

Sometimes they do approach land. Frank Lane, in *The Elements Rage*, lists five ships sunk by waterspouts in Tunis harbor in 1885, and tells of the barque *Lilian Morris* encountering a spout five hundred feet in diameter which tore away masts and canvas and swept a crewman overboard. Off the United States seaboard waterspouts have wrought their damage, too, as in the case of a steamship struck amidships off Cape Hatteras in 1902. In no case has a ship been lifted out of the water and dumped any distance away. A canoe perhaps, but not a commercial vessel.

Probably the most astounding outcome of waterspouts and tornadoes is the rainfall of live animals on towns and villages. Fish have cascaded on parade grounds. Five-inch perch once fell in the streets of Providence, Rhode Island, and were scooped up and sold. Toads have fallen at Châlons-sur-Saône, France; jellyfish at Bath, England; lizards at Montreal, tadpoles in New York, rats in Norway, worms in Sweden.

Tornadoes strike twice in the same place, and often. Baldwyn, Mississippi, was shattered by two storms twenty-five minutes apart in 1942; almost the same thing happened to Austin, Texas, twenty years earlier. Probably the most coincidental set of events in tornado history closed in on the little town of Codell, Kansas. It was barely missed by a tornado in 1915. On May 20 of the following year a twister struck the town. On May 20 of the year after that the same thing happened. And on May 20 of the *next* year the same thing again. All at about the same hour of day. Jinxed Codell residents were beginning to write off May 20 as their black-letter day, but not a twister has troubled them since.

The worst tornado in United States history was one that did not follow all the rules. It originated in Reynolds County, Missouri, early on the afternoon of March 18, 1925, as one of about eight tornadoes that ransacked the central lowlands that day. It moved at about sixty miles an hour across Illinois to Princeton, Indiana, breaking up after 219 miles and over three hours of destructive rampage. Along its mile-wide path the devastation was enormous: 689 persons dead, almost two thousand injured, a property loss of $16,632,000. Eyewitnesses reported blackness, flying tree limbs, and turbulent clouds—but no clearly defined tornado funnel, no sign of anything more than a "blackberry storm." It was one of those treacherous twisters in which an easily identifiable vortex cloud did not appear. Even so, had there been a warning system approaching that in readiness today, the casualty list would have been much lower.

City after city was a "picture of ruin," reported the Chicago *Tribune*. "Scores of buildings are demolished and the streets are strewn with wreckage. Tangled wires and splintered trees litter the streets. Naked walls from which the rest of the structure has been torn stand out as grim silhouettes. And all of this thrown into fantastic contortions by the flames from a dozen fires which spring up here and there among the ruins."

Miners streamed in from the mines, just outside West Frankfort, Illinois, to seek their wives and children. In some cases, entire families were wiped out. Eyewitnesses said that the tornado was so severe that some bodies were blown a mile and a half out of town.

"City of Gorham destroyed by tornado," wired one mayor to another. "Town burning up. Impossible to estimate number of dead and injured. All people are homeless. What is needed immediately is a Red Cross unit, doctors, and nurses and 500 tents for the homeless. We are transporting as many as possible to Grand Tower. The roads are nearly impassable."

Three towns were virtually annihilated. "It was hardly more than a rain cloud that hovered above De Soto yesterday afternoon," wrote one reporter. "In less than five minutes after the storm struck nothing remained of the village except ruins, not a single building escaped the winds of destruction. . . . Fire is still eating the piles of lumber and debris which fills the townsite. . . .

"When bodies were taken from the wrecked schoolhouse and laid out, row after row, there was no one to claim the lifeless forms. The children's parents were either dead or on the way to hospitals. . . .

"In a field on the outskirts of the town two babies about seven months old were found. The bodies were crushed. A tourist on the highway was caught by the twister and his Ford sedan was picked up and hurled against the railroad embankment 50 yards away and both occupants instantly killed. Boxcars standing on the tracks were lifted from the wheels and carried away, leaving the wheels in place on the tracks. . . .

"Surviving members of various families do not know the fate of the persons living under the same roof with them. There was a spot swept clean with a lone smoke-blackened man standing on it. He turned his eyes skyward and exclaimed, 'Here was my home, my wife, my mother and my baby—I wonder where they are?' "

A fourteen-year-old girl told about her day at school: "We were in a classroom and it suddenly got so dark we couldn't see. All the children rushed to the windows. Teacher was mad. She made us go back to our seats again. All that we could see at the windows was that it was black—like night almost.

"Then the wind struck the school. The walls seemed to fall in, all around us. Then the floor, at one end of the building, gave way. We all slipped or slid in that direction. If it hadn't been for the seats it would have been like sliding down a cellar door."

The girl burst into tears. "I can't tell you what happened then. I can't describe it. I can't bear to think about it. Children all about me were cut and bleeding. They cried and screamed. It was something awful. I had to close my eyes."

A man, unkempt and haggard, watched doctors at the hospital working over his child, a little golden-headed girl who had suffered a fractured skull and fractured leg. But the doctors were too late. "Her mother's dead," the father sobbed. "All the others are crippled."

A workman put his arm about the father's shoulder and led him outside.

One doctor examined a woman for injuries, and found them to be slight. "All right," he said. "You're O.K. You can go."

"Go?" she said, examining the doctor with vacant eyes. "Where shall I go?"

The doctor didn't answer. The woman turned and walked back to her cot.

"Believe me, I prayed," another woman said, "and I'm not ashamed of that. I thought the world had come to an end."

One victim lay in a Masonic hall, his leg fractured in two places. "Where's your home?" asked a newsman.

"Buddy," came the reply, "I ain't got none now."

The circulation manager for a newspaper asked one boy why he wasn't hustling out along his route with the extras.

"How can I?" the boy replied. "My route's all blown away."

Six men at a general store were sitting around talking when the crash came so suddenly that the shock of ripping timber and falling stone numbed all pain. A wood-burning stove immediately set fire to the debris, beneath which four men were pinned. Flames swept over one man and he died as a friend tugging at his sleeve was forced to retreat. Afterwards an old woman wandered for long periods of time through the ruins, poking here and there, looking for her son.

"Virgil was thirty years old," she would say, "and a fine boy to me indeed, sir."

All that remained of Virgil was his watch.

At the numerous burial services there was little to say in so great a shock, so mass a series of burials. "It's God's will," came the hushed tones in the wind. "God's will be done."

Yet even though few standing buildings remained, the hardy people clung on. "I was born in this little town," said an old man. "I raised my family here and I've been away very little. This time I was spared, but I don't want to die anywhere else."

And as the years would pass and the wounds of body and spirit would heal, there would be those whose stories could add a lighter touch to the tales of the great storm. A Griffin, Indiana, man had seen the storm coming and ran for the railway station. "As I took hold of the doorknob," he said, "that storm just naturally jerked the station right out of my hand!"

WHAT TO DO WHEN A TORNADO STRIKES

Since 1870 the United States Government has been grappling with the responsibility of trying to tell its citizens when a tornado will strike and where. The United States Army Signal Corps first issued warnings or "probabilities" (despite fears that such forecasts would engender public panic) and the job has since been taken over by the United States Weather Bureau. The Air Force, with its own weather eye peeled, has also shouldered the responsibility of helping work out a dependable tornado-warning system.

The trouble is that tornado conditions exist over a wide stretch of territory while the actual tornado describes a small line or pin-point in that territory. Since tornadoes ransack the countryside so erratically, weather observers are hard put to guess where the next vortex will form. Predicting the path, once a tornado appears, is even worse, for the storm can swerve in circles, curve in arcs, go straight, U-turn, or touch and dissipate, all of which is like trying to predict which way a football will bounce.

Warning networks have been set up in states where the hazard is most serious, yet the quick wit and presence of mind of the man on the street is still incalculably valuable. On the day after Memorial Day, 1947, a telephone official spotted a funnel bearing down on Leedey, Oklahoma. Figuring promptly on the best way of bringing the populace out into the streets, he sounded the town fire alarm, corralled volunteer firemen for emergency duty, announced the approaching tornado over a public address system, then hustled into a storm cellar— as did most of the citizenry. As a result, there were only six casualties in a town where there could have been many times more. Two-thirds of Leedey was wrecked.

Citizens of other towns have also escaped disaster by heeding advance warnings and getting to safety in a matter of minutes. But there are still twisters that arrive unheralded in darkness or under cover of a blanketing storm. Against such sneak attacks men have little defense.

Undaunted, meteorologists have worked out—and are still working to perfect—a more and more accurate tornado warning system. Warnings and alerts, even if issued only a few minutes in advance, do immeasurable good. Citizens with eyes toward the sky before such disasters are more apt to head for the cellar in the nick of time. They may spend a number of nights there needlessly but they know all too well how easy it is to become an entry in the casualty lists when the sky turns black and blustery.

Here are the rules when a tornado is sighted:

1. Get to the storm cellar. As far as is known, no one who did has ever been killed by a tornado. (Want to build a storm cellar? The Red Cross recommends that it be concrete, eight feet long, six feet wide, seven feet high, completely or partly underground, either connected to the house by a tunnel or having its own entrance facing northeast; locate it near the southeast corner of the house and provide drainage for it—a water-filled cellar won't help much when a tornado comes— and an escape hatch-ventilation opening. Be sure it has a strong door and strong lock.)

2. If no storm cellar, crouch in the southwest corner of the basement. (Debris almost always drops in the northeast corner of the basement.)

3. If you live in a masonry house, run. Tons of brick or stone cascading down upon you can make the cellar a sepulchre.

4. If no basement, flatten out on the floor, preferably under a desk or table or bed, or even in the bathtub under a mattress. Above all, stay away from windows, through which flying debris can plummet with the speed of a guided missile.

5. In a car, you have two choices: (a) turn around and outrun the storm or at least speed off at right angles to its path; (b) stop, get out, and fling yourself in a ditch. A rolling, pitching, twisting automobile becomes a death trap.

6. In open country, find a small ditch, get into it, and lie face down. Any depression, however slight, gives you at least a fifty-fifty chance of survival.

7. In the city, if nothing better offers, crouch in a gutter on the side of the street toward the storm. Get away from brick buildings if you can; dive into a basement, or take refuge in a steel-reinforced structure. Stay away from windows; cities are loaded with whizzing debris during the melee of a tornado.

8. Schools: in the city get the children low against partitions in closets and storerooms away from windows. In the country, if a school is readily collapsible or contains large windows through which death can roar at five hundred miles an hour, get the students outside if there is time and have them lie down in a ravine or ditch.

9. Factories: when an alert is broadcast, post a guard in some conspicuous place to watch for the tornado and give immediate warning if one approaches; then go into a prearranged survival plan to locate the employees in safe places in the quickest possible time.

10. Build safe buildings. Time and again it has been demonstrated that adequately constructed houses and other buildings can survive the rampages of a tornado. Ask your architect. If you live in a tornado-proof house, you can feel relatively at ease when the twister strikes. Provided you're at home, that is.

5

DESERTS

> The wind is the very life of
> the desert.
>   . . . GAUTIER

ONE September day, Bill Falls, twenty-two, lifted his light plane into the bright blue California sky and banked toward the east. As San Diego dropped behind, he looked out to the yellow radiance of the lands ahead. Destination: Phoenix. Terrain: some of the richest —and cruelest—desert in the United States.

Cruel, that is, if you make it the way Bill Falls did. First he got lost. Then he ran out of gas. Then he crashed.

Bill Falls survived the crash, but only to embark upon eleven days without food, shelter, or water. Eleven days of heat that shimmered the purple mountain ranges until they seemed like wobbling masses of jelly. Eleven days of crawling and groveling in the sand and dust and rocks, of brushing against cactus and creosote bush, of sidestepping sidewinders and sharing ledges with lizards.

Bill managed to reach the Gulf of California and there went swimming. The water was warm, and it was wet. It staved off dehydration for another hour, another day. But by then, time was running out.

Thirty-eight miles away lay a fishing village. Bill Falls didn't know this. If he had, he could have made it in a couple of days. Half dead, maybe, but able to be revived. But Bill Falls did not have a map. He had no idea of where he was or in which direction he should have walked to reach the nearest settlement. He had no water. He didn't even have a signal mirror, and apparently didn't attempt to use anything else as a signaling device.

His diary told the story. And when rescuers finally came upon his body, trouble still dogged Bill Falls' trail. The rescuers, in trying to take off in the sand, cracked up their plane. One of them then walked sixty miles overland for help. It was the kind of chain reaction of trouble on trouble that can occur when just one man gets lost.

To Bill Falls the desert was a merciless enemy. He did not understand it. He did not prepare for it. He lost.

But does this mean that those who do understand the desert are better off? That the desert is kind to those who know it?

Once upon a time in the Mojave Desert, when temperatures ranged between 120 and 130 degrees, four men rode in a jeep, four experienced desert travelers. The jeep broke down. One man, who waited until evening as he should have, started hiking the fifteen miles to a highway and fell dead after five miles. The remaining three managed to get three miles to a salt flat (where they would be more conspicuous). Next day their water gave out. One man became unconscious. Another began walking, and wandered in circles until he died. The following day a helicopter rescued the survivors. Said one: "It was the worst thing I've been through in twenty years in the desert—but I've learned this: after so many years on the desert a fellow gets sort of careless."

Whether we know it intimately or not at all, the desert can be delightful or disastrous. It may be dry or fiery, or dusty, or windy. And its victims are usually convinced, as Shakespeare was, that "sometime too hot the eye of heaven shines."

Books have been written about deserts; motion pictures have been filmed in them; and careful scientific studies have been made on their flora, fauna, geology, history, and prehistory. But the fact is that no one knows all there is to know about deserts.

They occupy more than twenty per cent of the earth's land area. But only four per cent of the earth's population lives in deserts, a figure that will undoubtedly change with the wider dissemination of refrigerated cooling. Every continent, hot or cold, has a desert—a place where moisture is normally scant and vegetation limited.

A desert is essentially a deep basin in the earth's crust and has interior drainage only. True, the Colorado, Nile, and Indus rivers provide external drainage to some important deserts, but for the most part any moisture falling in a desert runs a while and disappears into the ground or into the air.

Climate is the other factor—climate with moisture so meager that the ground is barren, or nearly so, or is covered with vegetation adapted to severe dryness. Deserts lie generally beneath the evaporating trade winds, or in the shelter of mountain ranges—the so-called rain shadow. Rain, when it does come, is in brief and often violent bursts.

Thus deserts are characterized by broad basins, interior drainage, and aridity. Within those limits it might be possible to include Arctic tundras, certain temperate plateaus, and the ice-coated Antarctic. Still, the best-known method of identifying a desert region is by its ferocious heat and—as you may often hear—by its interminable sand dunes.

Yet dunes are not common. Only one-seventh of the Sahara's three million square miles is covered with blowing sand; the rest is rocky plain. Organ Pipe Cactus National Monument, created on the United States-Mexico border to preserve a virgin segment of true North American Desert, abounds in cactus, grass, shrubs, trees, and herbaceous plants, but not dunes. Southern California boasts extensive reaches of pure dunes, as do a few other isolated American localities, but for the most part deserts are not barren, at least not completely.

The dunes that do exist throughout the world reach considerable proportions—600 feet high at Great Sand Dunes, Colorado, a thousand feet high in the Sahara. They are the most ambulatory features of the natural landscape—so movable in fact, that given enough time they encroach upon villages and cover the works of man. Indeed, whole cities have so perished. From the steep face of a dune, sand spills over the top with the wind, extending the dune slowly to leeward. The stronger the prevailing wind, the faster the dunes move, some as much as a hundred feet a year. Excavations in India, Mesopotamia, and the Syrian desert have revealed ancient cities entombed for posterity beneath desert dunes. Dunes sealed the fate of the ancient cities of Acre, Tyre, Tortosa, and Laodicea on the Mediterranean. It is estimated that thousands of square miles of towns and cities in central Asia are buried under windblown sand. So it is with Egyptian villages in the Libyan desert. At Abu-Simbel, the great rock temple of Rameses II has been threatened by drifting desert sands. Even today, moving dunes constantly encroach on the Suez Canal. Sahara dunes are slowly filling Lake Chad. Cities like In-Salah, in southern Algeria, and villages in Chinese Turkestan are on the verge of being buried in a slowly encroaching avalanche of sand.

Dunes hold mysteries. One still night, deep in the interior of southwestern Egypt, a caravan made camp for the night—three hundred miles from the nearest habitation. Darkness crept in like a sluggish sand lizard, and the shimmering dunes were blotted from sight. In an immense wasteland of sand, not a living thing moved beyond camp, hardly a breath of air stirred the wilderness.

Then from the silence came a rhythmic sound, faint at first, low, slow, casual—but rising in crescendo. Soon rumbling and roaring, the noise boomed louder and before they knew it the men of the camp were shouting to be heard by each other.

For more than five minutes the booming sound continued. Then, echo by echo, it faded. Silence returned to the lonely camp, and the ground ceased to tremble.

On the following morning no footprints were to be found, no disturbances on the sand, no evidence that an enemy tribe had crept up to camp and conducted an ominous ritual. Signs of activity beyond the camp were as absent as a drop of rain.

Whence came such a demoniac symphony of sound? The pealing of bells from a monastery buried beneath the sand? A song of sirens, as the natives believed, luring wayfarers to a waterless doom?

Charles Darwin gives something of an answer in describing a visit he made to the valley of Copiapó, in northern Chile. "I heard an account," he said, "from several of the inhabitants, of a hill in the neighbourhood which they called 'El Bramador,'—the roarer or bellower. . . . The hill was covered by sand, and the noise was produced only when people, by ascending it, put the sand in motion. The same circumstances are described in detail on the authority of Seetzen and Ehrenberg, as the cause of the sounds which have been heard by many travelers on Mount Sinai, near the Red Sea. One person with whom I conversed had himself heard the noise: he described it as very surprising; and he distinctly stated that, although he could not understand how it was caused, yet it was necessary to set the sand rolling down the acclivity. A horse walking over dry coarse sand, causes a peculiar chirping noise from the friction of the particles; a circumstance which I several times noticed on the coast of Brazil."

The booming of desert sands remains to this day one of the enigmas of the sand country. Perhaps a breath of wind sets the sands in motion. Sometimes footsteps on a beach cause pips and barks, and walking on desert sands brings a swelling boom. Although the physics of this phenomenon remains obscure, scientists think the booming comes from the lower part of a sand avalanche flowing down the steep face of a dune—an avalanche triggered by simple gravity, by a footstep, or by a breath of wind, its sound amplified beyond proportion by the desert's solitude.

On the other hand, there is no mystery about one of the desert's chief characteristics—temperature. The highest average annual land temperature in the world is at Lugh, Italian Somaliland: eighty-eight degrees. The hottest temperature ever reported comes not from there but from Azizia, Tripolitania, North Africa, where the record stands at 136 degrees. Hottest record in the United States is Death Valley's 134 degrees. There have been reports of land temperatures as high as 170 degrees but these are not substantiated.

Of the sands themselves, Emile Gautier reports that in the battle of Metarfa the dunes were so blisteringly hot that soldiers were unable to take a prone position and were exposed to enemy fire and killed. The floor of the desert may heat up to two hundred degrees. Air a foot above this is thirty degrees cooler and the sand beneath the surface is cooler yet. Then, too, if you wait until night the desert temperature will drop sharply to become pleasant, if not downright cold.

In fact, it may be more appropriate to characterize the desert by its contrasts rather than its high temperature alone. Snow falls in deserts which at other times are famous for their heat extremes. Hailstones that measured 1¼ inches in diameter eighteen hours after a storm were once seen on the Gobi.

The same contrast is true of moisture. In some places the relative humidity may fall to below five per cent during the day and stay that way for a week. Then again, floods may occur from violent summer thunderstorms, sweeping down on and drowning unsuspecting people, horses, sheep, and cattle.

Where clear air remains dry for long periods of time, only rarely do cloudbursts fill the arroyos and gullies and dry washes. On some deserts, like the Atacama of South America, so little rain falls that the natives say it never rains. On the other hand, just because a place is surrounded by water is no sign it will have much rainfall. Islands like St. Helena, Ascension, and the Galapagos have deserts. Key West receives little moisture in winter, but is drenched in late summer and fall during the hurricane season.

The world's *least* average rainfall exists at Arica on the northern desert of Chile and measures .02 inch per year, although many a year passes during which no rain falls at all. (On the other hand, at Bahia Felix, just north of the Straits of Magellan, rain falls on an average of 325 days a year.)

United States weather records give the United States as a whole an average 29.1 inches of annual precipitation. Dwellers in some communities, perhaps, would appreciate a more equable distribution of this moisture: the record for the longest dry spell in the United States is held by Bagdad, California, which (during 1912-14) went 767 days without a drop of rain.

There have been places where no rain has fallen for years in the Sahara, but this also has happened: On the fifteenth of January, 1922, an evening wind slammed into Tamanrasset, in southern Algeria, followed by torrential rain. Water gushed through the village, ripping up dwellings and gardens bordering the *wadi* and carrying them downstream. Roofs collapsed and the natives rushed to refuge in the fortress; but a wall crumbled and buried twenty-two persons, killing at least eight and injuring eight.

Cairo has gone through numerous individual years without any rain, including seven consecutive years from 1909-1916. When a rain does come, it melts the houses of unbaked brick, pours mud through Cairo's streets, and may stall tramways in mud up to their windows.

Water, or the lack of it, in th hirsty nd has always been a problem. Rameses III built an elaborate bronze and pine-wood cistern in the Ayan desert. In some parts of the world moisture is at such a premium that certain native tribes send expert horsemen galloping after a distant thundercloud to catch the rainfall as best they can.

Far-flung and priceless are the oases. A few of them are fed by surface waters, but most are artesian or deep-seated waters rising to the surface from deep underground. These underground channels are rock faults or fractured zones into which water from the infrequent heavy storms sinks and percolates. Sometimes the water amounts to very little, but it gives life.

Before the first white man set foot in the American Southwest there occurred what is probably the most disastrous drought in American history or prehistory. By A.D. 1276, prehistoric Indian groups had achieved an astonishing height of culture, as evidenced by tree-ring dating methods, cultural remains, and the architecture of their ruined dwellings. A period of deficient rainfall set in and continued for twenty-three consecutive years.

This condition may have been imperceptible at first. Perhaps one fewer thunderstorm than usual; maybe just a few weeks late. But the next year was no better, and the following year was worse. And on it went. Since the subsistence of most tribes came largely from agriculture, the entire civilization was doomed by this persistent dryness. Crops and natural foods withered. Springs dried up.

One by one, and by the hundreds, the pueblos and cliff cities and smaller sites of the Southwest were abandoned, as the ancient people sought more reliable springs and streams elsewhere. Their cities crumbled into ruin over the years, and the only record of the drought lay in the tightly packed growth rings of the pines and junipers—thin rings denoting years of dryness.

No one can say why the droughts came so regularly or stayed so long. Perhaps a persistent offswing of the jet stream. Perhaps an unfortunate and repeated grouping of high and low pressure areas.

A drought is a drought, yes, a period of deficient rainfall; but how deficient, and where? Ohio's worst might have been abundant rainfall for the Indian country. Droughts are not cyclic and have no apparent historic patterns. Or do they? Some are local, some are widespread. Sometimes there has been much rainfall beforehand, sometimes a succession of lesser droughts.

There was a time—as settlers swarmed to the dry lands and plowed the dusty plains—when putting land to crops was thought to increase the atmospheric moisture. Planted lands absorbed and gave off moisture, it was believed, so more rain would come, and more snow. But the rain did not fall and the sun shone without mercy and the hot winds blew, scorching the land and the crops. Drought—and the wind—had taken over.

Ever since history's first farmer scanned his withering crops, looked up to the sky, and began to plead, there have been countless methods, devices and contrivances thrown into action to induce rainfall. Arizona's Hopi Indians undertake elaborate snake dances each August to bring down desperately needed moisture, and these dances usually succeed because August is one of the wetter months on their plateau anyway. A cloudburst or two at the right time may be all that their corn and peaches need.

In Australia the Duri draw blood from the wizards and sprinkle it on other tribesmen, together with bird down, to make them look like clouds. Some primitive people, supposing frogs to be rain-gods, beat them with clubs to make them do something about the drought. Zulus, in fact, bury their children up to the neck in the ground, hoping the rains will come in pity.

Americans have also gone to elaborate measures. In a bold and daring gamble in 1891, Congress appropriated nine thousand dollars to see if rain could be made artificially. Dynamite was exploded over Texas and gas-filled balloons were cut loose, but the only rain that came was some that the Weather Bureau said would probably have come anyway.

Large quantities of hydrogen have been released, on the theory that the lighter-than-air property would cause it—and large masses of air— to rise, precipitating moisture. That didn't work either. Giant blowing devices, attempting to get the circulation moving faster, have also failed. In fact, during the great drought of the thirties many people were convinced that the new national pastime, radio, was sending so much electricity into the air that rain refused to fall. They proposed shutting off all transmitters for a while to see if the rains would come again. Probably if another great drought grips the country there will be proposals to explode a dozen super-hydrogen devices in the north Pacific in order to create a low-pressure area that would subsequently drench the United States.

In spite of all the methods and proposals for producing moisture, there are still localities in the world where desert persists as desert, and where climate resists the efforts of man to make it anything else. Irrigation has brought unbelievable paradise to otherwise inhospitable land, but elsewhere hot and dry winds ravage the plains and forests, reducing the humidity and pushing the temperature so high that little plant life can survive. The heat is oppressive. Even leaves on trees are burned so badly by the wind that they crumble to dust on being touched. Against such conditions man can do little.

Where desert lands are geared to perpetual dryness, man and Nature can and do get along together. But when severe drought strikes the plains country, with hot winds fanning the green lands, the damage mounts at an appalling rate. The drought of 1934, for example, lowered water levels in rivers, impeded navigation, reduced Lakes Michigan and Huron to the lowest levels on record, diminished crop yield by almost half, and resulted in an agricultural loss of some five billion dollars.

When intense dryness reduces tree-lands to tinder conditions, blow-ups occur. The forest burns like gunpowder, and then it is gone. So is the undergrowth. So is the grass. So is the wildlife. Some of the soil still remains, but one disaster leads to another, and here is what can happen:

A twelve-inch rainstorm once fell upon a mountain range in California; dividing, it sped down two canyons. One was forested and chaparral-covered, and in it most of the waters of this terrific rain were absorbed. In the other canyon, which had been burned over by fire, the soil lay bare, waiting to be picked up and flung downstream. It was. With no grass or shrubbery or trees to hold it back, the flood roared down the treeless canyon and rammed into a town, sweeping away two hundred houses and thirty-four lives.

The drying and parching of agricultural lands by winds devoid of moisture may scatter devastation far and wide, creating sinister havoc on the most grandiose scale of all: famine.

Owing to the modern-day brotherhood of nations (however tenuous) and a general economy of abundance, famine has little chance to destroy as many lives as it used to. In drought-prone places like India and China, where millions of lives are concentrated in vastly inferior conditions, human beings have died so rapidly and by such numbers that burials sometimes became impossible. Whole populations have been wiped out in a single stroke. A severe famine in North China in 1877-78 destroyed nine and a half million persons. The great famine in Bengal (1769-70) obliterated ten million.

South America has had its share of drought, and in a violent way. Darwin describes one about which he learned during the voyage of the *Beagle.*

"The period included between the years 1827 and 1830 is called the 'gran seco,' or the great drought. During this time so little rain fell, that the vegetation, even to the thistles, failed; the brooks were dried up, and the whole country assumed the appearance of a dusty high road. . . . The lowest estimation of the loss of cattle in the province of Buenos Ayres alone, was taken at one million head. . . .

"I was informed by an eye-witness that the cattle in herds of thousands rushed into the Parana, and being exhausted by hunger were unable to crawl up the muddy banks, and thus were drowned. The arm of the river which runs by San Pedro was so full of putrid carcasses, that the master of a vessel told me that the smell rendered it quite impassable. . . . Azara describes the fury of the wild horses on a similar occasion, rushing into the marshes, those which arrived first being overwhelmed and crushed by those which followed. He adds that more than once he has seen the carcasses of upwards of a thousand wild horses thus destroyed."

Part of the trouble is that droughts are all too common. They are ordinary manifestations of the circulation pattern of the world's winds. And the winds are indeed the very life of the desert. Winds bring moisture, and take it away. Winds hasten evaporation, which over the centuries cause desert plants to assume bizarre and fantastic shapes to conserve every molecule of priceless moisture. Winds make and remake dunes, lifting sands that gouge and scrape and polish—and even glaze—the parched terrain.

Stories of caravans annihilated by wind and sandstorms may be simply legends, but desert winds are severe. Boxwork, pedestals, pinnacles, spires, cathedrals, gaps, and natural bridges are sculptured by the eroding wind. Winds carrying sand may frost and destroy glass windows, or cut down telephone poles to the level of the ground. So severe is this eroding power that Egypt's Sphinx and pyramids will eventually be shapeless; they have long since lost their sharp outlines.

And what is more, we have stark and convincing evidence that droughts have been common for millions of years. Geologic history records millennium after millennium of dryness in which windblown sands spread out across thousands upon thousands of square miles of the earth's surface. Changing climates, plus wholesale destruction and renewal of landscapes as recorded in rocks, have shifted the circulation, and therefore consequences, of desiccating winds.

This may have guided, to some extent, the evolution and destiny of plants and animals. Though no one knows for sure, the giant dinosaurs, which became extinct at the end of the Mesozoic Era (sixty million years ago), might have succumbed as a result of slow and insidious climatic changes when mountain-building deprived the winds of moisture. Even slightly reduced rainfall could slowly have dried the swamps in which many of these monstrous reptiles lived.

We don't know. Our theory today is expressed in much the same terms that Aristotle used to express it over two thousand years ago: "The same parts of the earth are not always moist or dry, but they change according as rivers come into existence and dry up. And so the relation of land to sea changes too and a place does not always remain land or sea throughout all time, but where there was dry land there comes to be sea, and where there is now sea, there one day comes to be dry land."

With all the evidence past and present, we may well wonder why man ever dared go into deserts and make homes there. Of course, our modern emigration to the desert may be largely because air conditioning now mitigates the cruelest desert temperatures. But some races of human beings have never left the desert. As a matter of fact, Western civilization has had its very roots in the desert.

That there were once vast civilizations and elaborate cities in the desert we know to be a fact. Hence, the desert cannot be as hostile as we have seen. Either the climate was different in ancient times, which from various evidence does not appear to be the case, or archeologists who interpret these things have badly erred, which is not true either.

What then?

The situation becomes clearer as intrepid anthropologists trek into the fierce deserts of the world and stay there long enough to make some concrete studies and interpretations. One such researcher was Dr. Nelson Glueck, who initiated and completed the archeological mapping of all Transjordan, discovered King Solomon's copper mines in the Wadi Arabah, directed excavations of King Solomon's important Red Sea port and industrial city of Ezion-geber, and dug out the Nabataean temple of Khirbet Tannur. Then he turned to the exploration and mapping of the fierce Negev Desert, in southern Israel. By this time Dr. Glueck had made certain discoveries about ancient life on the desert and he recorded them in a history of the Negev called *Rivers in the Desert.*

One astonishing insight was that a population of as many as a hundred thousand people may have lived in the Negev during a single historic period. Dr. Glueck admits that it is hard to understand at first how any sort of life could exist in the Negev. The rainfall is two to eight inches annually, and daytime temperatures rise to levels excruciating to man.

Yet the glaring desert at noon is not the same desert at four P.M., when refreshing winds arise, or in the morning when low-lying mists blanket the landscape. Though the rains are rare, their occurrence is a miracle of rebirth. "The grass and flowers," says Dr. Glueck, "fairly spring up after the first shower or storm, and the grim desert becomes a colorful garden overnight. It is as if a magic wand had been passed over the face of the earth. Flocks of birds suddenly make their appearance then, to sing and to swoop about in happy flight, and bands of gazelles and ibexes graze and cavort through the lush green. Camels and goats and sheep and their young wax fat. They drink their fill at pools of water collected in hollows, making it unnecessary for months on end to find other supplies for them. Springs flow more strongly, wells rise to their highest levels and the underground water is replenished in the wadi beds, there to remain long after the flowers have faded and the grass has withered and gone."

The wadis (dry stream beds) collect the moist soil washed down from the hills and store it like a sponge after every storm. Where Bedouins erect a small dam, there the water sinks and remains within reach of roots. Even into late summer the fig and pomegranate trees thrive on this moisture. Besides the rare and violent tempests, dew falls nearly every summer morning, sustaining life for the wild melon or the delicate crocus. One has but to look. The life is there.

"All this," Dr. Glueck states, "was known and appreciated by the ancients, who, undeterred by the unfriendly appearance of the land, terraced and dry-farmed the wadi beds and cultivable slopes above them and built thriving agricultural economies in much of its expanse. I have found wadis hidden in the heart of the Negev alive with waving stands of golden wheat, far from settlements of any kind."

The more the ancient people lived in this land, the more proficient they became at gathering, storing, and utilizing the moisture of the desert. The secret of their success was to use dams, terraces, diversion-ary walls, and channels, aqueducts, cisterns, reservoirs, and whole hill-sides as catchment basins, and to employ extensive water-spreading devices.

Dr. Glueck dispels the notion that climates then were more moist than now. "I could show you," he says, "a thousand or more sites of an-tiquity in Transjordan which existed during and after the time the land was supposed no longer to be able to sustain them because of radical, pronounced and permanent climatic changes. The settlements on them flourished in spite of currently popular theories of a steady diminution of rainfall that made permanent, sedentary, agricultural occupation pro-gressively impossible."

What then? Frankly, the same old problem of man against man. Ele-gant desert cities like Palmyra sprang up and flourished because they were in the crossroads of very profitable trade routes.

But the trade routes that built the cities also furnished avenues for the invading armies that destroyed them. And this, in essence, is the thesis Dr. Glueck expounds. "They . . . succumbed to conquest by arms and not to uncontrollable forces of nature. The resulting diversion of trade to other regions and routes drained away their economic lifeblood, and not the drying up of their lands because of a sudden lack of water."

So perhaps the desert is not wholly inhospitable after all. Perhaps the secret lies in knowing when to move and when to rest. Once that has been mastered—and once we learn to sit and think and reason—even being lost in the desert may not turn into tragedy.

Yet many a human being, confined to the luxury of advanced civili-zation, has suddenly been thrust into the midst of a vast and burning desert with nothing to live on but his own and the desert's resources, both of which are usually limited. The matter then becomes clearly one of survival.

Because they can move away from excessive temperatures, animals—including man—at least have a chance of avoiding the heat of the desert. Not so the plants. For this reason, some of the world's most unusual plants grow on deserts, where extremes of xeric adaptation have forced them to take on outlandish safeguards against disastrous desiccation. The needles of cactus are merely modified leaves, so reduced that pre-cious moisture cannot evaporate from them. The spindly ocotillo's first small leaves turn into spines. The creosote bush, one of the world's most successfully adapted dry-land plants, has leaves covered with a heavy wax that prevents loss of moisture.

Broad-leaved plants do not survive in the desert unless, like the ubiquitous cottonwood, they sink their roots in or near a stream bed or beside a spring or, like the palm, at an oasis. In leafless plants the functions ordinarily carried out by chlorophyll in broad leaves are carried out by chlorophyll in the trunk, limbs, and spinelike branches of species like the palo verde and crucifixion thorn.

And yet, perhaps it is this very bizarreness—not only of plants but of temperature and moisture extremes as well—that makes the desert awe-inspiring—a landscape that holds unfading fascination for the human mind.

Scientists have found that the temperature in which man best operates is sixty-eight degrees, though temperatures of 120 degrees are not insufferable provided humidity stays low. When the humidity rises, the direct comfort of perspiring human beings is related to the all-powerful wind. A hot and humid wind fails to increase evaporation from the skin, and thus becomes irritating.

Survival in the desert, at best a touch-and-go proposition, is possible, though, and the Desert Branch of the Air Force Arctic, Desert, Tropic Information Center has analyzed survival experiences and conducted research into the business of staying alive in an environment where only the rattlesnake and antelope may roam. Says the *Survival Book* *: "The intelligent, foresighted traveler can live in the desert for days, weeks and months at a time—but always on his own terms, not on the desert's terms. He always plans in advance for possible and probable emergencies. He carries his shelter, sleeping bag, and supply of food and water. He learns in advance where wells or water holes could be expected and he keeps his friends posted on the area in which he is working."

If you are suddenly stranded in the desert, miles from nowhere, getting out alive is a matter of following some simple rules.

1. *Keep in the shade*. If there is no shade, use your clothing as a shield against the sun. Save your energy. Walk only at night because travel by day takes two to three times more water. This is no idle sug-

* Paul H. Nesbitt, Alonzo W. Pond, and William H. Allen, the *Survival Book*; D. Van Nostrand Co., Inc., Princeton, New Jersey. Copyright 1959 by D. Van Nostrand Company, Inc.

gestion; it is a life-or-death lesson we have learned from desert animals. Midday is siesta time for them, and they pass the hottest part of the day asleep in cool burrows.

Yet this is perhaps the most difficult rule for lost persons to follow. The natural tendency is to run pell-mell for help, without the slightest idea of which direction is which. This uses up precious energy. To sit is to think. To think is to reason. And a lost person who retains his reason has the best possible chance either to rescue himself or to be rescued. Very few crash survivors have died of starvation or exposure when they stayed at the scene or followed a well-defined trail. The wreckage may be sighted quickly—but not the man who leaves it and wanders aimlessly.

2. *Ration your sweat, not your water.* Every gallon of water you have means another day of life. Don't skimp. The water does more good in you than in your canteen. You can kid yourself by chewing gum or sucking pebbles if you wish; they do no harm and may help you feel better. But they do not provide moisture.

Heat in itself is not the worst killer. It contributes to a more sinister malady: dehydration. Two main things are required to prevent this— shelter from the sun, and ample drinking water.

How much heat and dehydration can the human body stand? One man survived eight days on a vast stretch of Arizona desert and struggled 150 miles under temperatures that rose to 120°. He lost twenty-five per cent of his weight (half that loss is often fatal), and crawled the last eight miles completely naked. So thick did his blood become that cuts did not bleed until he had consumed considerable water on rescue. How he did it, no one knows. He used none of the survival techniques, and in fact did everything wrong. How then could he possibly survive? Two answers remain: the will to live—and the grace of God.

3. *Cut open a cactus?* Yes, if you can find one. It may be mushy and bitter, but there's *some* moisture in it.

Hunger is not usually much of a problem, since rescue is likely before the victim starves. Besides, what with the shock of crashing or getting lost, many persons are not apt to be hungry, at least not for a day or so. There is the possibility of living off the land, and that is not as farfetched as it seems. Even the desert may abound with natural foods.

The fruit of all cactus plants is edible. According to researchers, the species most useful to a thirsty desert traveler is the barrel cactus, or bisnaga. Pads of prickly pear, stripped of thorns, are eatable, though with the taste of an average dishrag. The danger is that in parts of the world other than America some plants that look like cactus are not. Warning: if they have milky juice, leave them alone.

In 1942 a marine lieutenant parachuted out of a burning plane, landed in the Arizona desert, and roamed for five days. He tried several kinds of cactus before finding one that was entirely satisfactory. Scraping out chunks and chewing the water from them, he found the taste to be good but eventually monotonous. Though he carried them for several days they still retained moisture for drinking. He also rubbed his body with pieces he had chewed. This kept him cool and reduced perspiration.

4. *Avoid drinking alcohol, sea water, or urine*—even in desperation. The added salt soaks up fluids in your body, increasing dehydration. More water is required to carry off the salty wastes that have been added. And when you're in the desert, you haven't that kind of moisture to spare.

Doctors say that the amount of water you need depends on your size and weight. If you are average, you need two quarts or more daily, in hot weather more than that, and in hot deserts a gallon a day.

5. *Beware of taking salt*. The body itself regulates the amount of salt lost through perspiration. Other than a slight increase in salt intake the first day or so, you need not shove down salt pills to stay alive. Salt is a great dehydrator and should be taken only when plenty of water is available.

6. *Keep fully clothed*. The penalties for overexposure (whether by direct or reflected rays) are eye injury, sunstroke, and heat prostration. Sunburn is seldom, if ever, fatal, though the miseries it occasions are legion, and much depends on individual sensitivity.

Clothing makes a difference, and on this score we can get some ideas from native tribes who spend their lives in the desert. People of the Sahara prefer white wool or white cotton. The Tuaregs, with their typical blue-black apparel and protective face veils, wear white cotton undergarments. In the winter, sheepskin coats help combat icy desert winds.

7. *Know where you're going*. Learn the geography and carry a com-

pass so that you can walk in a straight line to the nearest water. You may not have distance to spare. Maps of deserts are not always reliable, however. Check as closely as you can, and handle yourself accordingly.

8. *Signal!* Search planes may be on the prowl. Spell out an SOS by footprints or boulders, or leave arrows to track your progress; if you can make a fire it becomes a beacon at night or a pillar of smoke by day.

Obviously the best piece of equipment is a portable radio receiver-transmitter. Lacking that, the best thing to have—according to authorities who have studied the matter carefully and analyzed many survival incidents—is a simple mirror, or anything that will act as a mirror. A British pilot once downed in the Red Sea signaled for help with the lid of a ration can. At night, a flashlight is indispensable. There is no mistaking this when viewed from a searching aircraft. The flashes represent trouble.

The *Survival Book* says that "a signal mirror is the best, the simplest, the most important piece of survival equipment ever invented for the desert." Two men flying between Los Angeles and southern Utah once crashed in the desert. Both were unconscious during the night. Next morning the passenger came to, assessed the situation, and decided to go for help. Before leaving, however, he put a mirror in the pilot's pocket. At length he arrived at a ranch, and shortly afterwards search planes were out over the area. But they could not find the plane. After a while one pilot saw a flash of light some eighteen miles from the wreck. He flew lower. It was the lost pilot signaling with the mirror.

Use a mirror even on hazy days. Flash at the sound of an aircraft, even if the plane cannot be seen. Flash at the horizon, too. You may safely assume that searchers are out in numbers. The point is that by making yourself conspicuous and disturbing the natural order of things you will attract the eyes of rescuers.

9. *If you find a trail, follow it.* All deserts have trails. One of them may lead to a hidden source of water—or to habitation.

10. *Protect your eyes.* Desert glare may cause a kind of "snowblindness." Wear sunglasses, make crude slit-goggles, or shade your eyes with a low hat or cloth headpiece.

Were we chuckwallas, or desert tortoises, we would know how to handle ourselves. We'd be prepared. But we are not chuckwallas and we are not always ready for a duel with the sun. The desert must be respected and appreciated for exactly what it is. Expect no mercy. Ask only for its finer attributes and learn how to live with the rest. That way, life on the desert can be one of the most thrilling experiences on earth.

Yet suppose that man does not choose to go to the desert. Suppose that the desert comes to the cool green lands he loves so well. A great share of the earth's populace resides in temperate climates where rainfall is plentiful and the vegetation is lush. These people rarely concern themselves with high temperatures and scarcity of water. Why should they? Nature is bountiful. And so they are unprepared when the rain ceases and the sun shines unbearably day after day and week after week, and the crops begin to wilt and shrivel. The rain, so taken for granted, has refused to fall.

Drought hangs over the land. Puffs of dust rise from the drying soil, and soon the sky grows yellow, then brown, then black. The people, watching helplessly, begin to pray. As surely as if man had gone to the desert, the desert has come to him.

6

DUST

Real estate for sale at this office, by the
acre or bushel.
.·. . JUNCTION CITY, KANSAS, *Union*, 1873

"WE'RE THROUGH," said the Southwestern farmer.

He watched a wisp of dust curl up into a small cloud and join the other dunes in the burrows.

"It's worse than the papers say. We know we made a mistake plowing up all that land, but it's too late now to do anything about it."

Halfway around the world, a Syrian farmer paused in his work and looked up. The day was abnormally calm. The air was oppressive .and heavy. On the horizon he saw a yellowish mass and as he watched, it increased in size and became a high opaque wall, floating nearer and nearer.

Suddenly he was brushed by strong blasts of scorching air, which picked up the dust about him and swirled it in every direction. Then, as quickly as the air blasts had come, a sinister calm settled down. The yellow wall had reached the sun and blocked it out. Darkness settled.

The wind rose again. Fine sand cut into the farmer's flesh, and blew into his eyes, ears, nose, and mouth. He started running; the nearest shelter lay more than a mile away. The wind snatched up all the dust that it could raise from the ground, and as the cloud struck in all its fury the farmer could hardly see in the blinding, choking mass.

As he neared the village a strange thing happened. When he could

106

squint and see a few feet ahead he noticed that there was an almost continuous sheet-lightning of great brilliance, with flashes about every ten seconds. As he dashed into a dark entranceway he heard the thunder. It was not like other thunderclaps he had heard, but like the continuous pounding of giant waves on a rocky shore.

When the storm had passed and the thunder and lightning ceased, not a drop of rain had fallen. Instead, dust lay everywhere in the village, and formed little dunes inside the tightly closed houses.

The earliest journals of civilization call attention to dust clouds, if only for reverent purposes. It was on the Thriasian plain of Greece that Dicaeus the Athenian and Demaratus the Lacedaemonian once chanced to be standing when a cloud of dust advanced toward them, a cloud such as a host of thirty thousand men might raise. They wondered who the men might be, when suddenly the sound of voices was heard, singing the mystic hymn of Bacchus. Presently the dust became a cloud and rose into the air to sail away to Salamis, an almost sure prediction of ill for their enemies and good for themselves.

Homer mentions dust storms. So does Virgil. Early legends said that shifting sands buried whole caravans and marching columns. Though such reports were wildly exaggerated, the fact remains that sandstorms can be dangerous to travelers struck without warning.

Dust storms come big and small—from clouds that blanket wide areas to smaller dust devils and whirlwinds. These latter rise from the ground on hot days, singly or in groups, and may form at any time of the year. All they require are slight breezes, warm ground, and hot sun. Sahara dwellers call them waltzing jinns. They may reach a hundred feet in width and six hundred feet in height, and may be propelled with enough power to blow a Bedouin out of his tent. But they rarely result in severe damage.

In most localities, sand and dust are almost always on the move. They are picked up, blown a short distance, and settled to earth again. That great amounts of dust are carried thousands of miles becomes spectacularly obvious in "black blizzards," and the measurement of radioactive particles around the earth after nuclear explosions clearly shows that dust moves vast distances. Someone has ventured to say that every square mile of the earth's land surface probably contains rock particles brought by the wind from each of the remaining square miles. So-called dust hurricanes stir up the Russian steppes. Dust-filled winds drive across the Pampas in Argentina and in South Australia, bringing fiery heat waves in January and February. Erosion and dust storms produce severe economic loss in Canada, Russia, Asia and Africa.

Borne on far-flung winds, Sahara dust storms become exceptionally widespread. In 1901 a mass of dust estimated to weigh 3,610,420 tons was spread in a thin mantle across North Africa and Europe. An estimated ten million tons fell on England in two days in 1903. Ships on the Red Sea and far out in the Atlantic have been brushed with dust from the Sahara. Pacific vessels have been dusted by wind-borne particles from the deserts of China. New Zealand has received contributions from Australia—1,400 miles away. In Kodiak, Alaska, five inches of volcanic dust fell during one night in June, 1912, from the eruption of Katmai volcano and ash was dropped on Seattle, 1,600 miles away. Dust from Krakatoa, an East Indian island blown sky high in 1883, traveled around the earth for years before settling.

And there's the economic side. A South African engineer once went to a place near the Port of Luderitzbucht, German East Africa, to determine commercial possibilities of alluvial diamond grounds in that neighborhood. The grounds looked good, but there was one disturbing factor. He prospected a patch of ground and found it very promising; then a high wind picked up the surface sands and swept the property bare. He stood in the door of his hut and watched diamonds, sand, dust, and landscape in general go flying past, settling on property lower down. After that the engineer quietly retreated from diamond hunting in windy lands.

Dust on the move produces some odd effects. Red rains and red snows are in some places comparatively frequent—the product of dust accumulations encountering humid air and condensing to douse broad areas with reddish sediment. Millions of tons of Sahara dust sail along at high elevations to moist climates and then precipitate widely, as in December, 1859, when over 15,600 square miles of Germany were blanketed with reddish snow.

The first inquiry into the amount of dust in the atmosphere was made by the British physicist John Aitken in 1880. He demonstrated that if there were no dust particles, water droplets would not form, even in supersaturated air. This suggested that dust nuclei were essential to the formation of raindrops and other forms of precipitation.

Aitken devised atmospheric tests which were conducted all over the world, and led to the determination that nowhere was air completely free of nuclei. And over some of the world's cities, there were as many as a hundred thousand dust particles per cubic centimeter.

Later investigations showed that most dust nuclei were not attracting moisture but repelling it, hence were not inducive to condensation. However, such particles as chlorides of sodium (i.e., salt) were effective in the production of precipitation.

"Dust itself is nothing new," said the climatic historian Paul B. Sears in *Deserts on the March*. "Like the circle, it is a symbol of eternal time."

For millions of years the atmospheric winds have picked up dust and hauled it elsewhere. Throughout the world lie vast deposits of fine sediment called loess, often hundreds of feet thick. In other places, sandstone strata with sloping bedding planes attest to wide expanses of desert throughout hundreds of millions of years.

The American physicist W. J. Humphreys, in his book *Physics of the Air*, brings up the intriguing speculation that dust from volcanic eruptions has so permeated the primeval atmospheres as to alter climates altogether. These variations could have been of sufficient magnitude to bring on glaciation. We do have pyrheliometric measurements of solar radiation changes that took place after the eruption of Krakatoa in 1883 and the subsequent worldwide spread of dust from that volcano.

Today the dubious honor of suffering the world's most disastrous dust storms belongs to the United States, whose Great Plains, product of erosion and glacial retreat, have had a nip and tuck history of grass and grassless expanses since long before the coming of man. Although clouds of dust have raided the primitive flatlands for centuries, it was left for man to plow and sift and replow the soil to the consistency of flour, after which the plains *really* got up and moved—on a gigantic scale.

Colonial settlers first met the dust on what were to them strange "dark days," when reduction in atmospheric visibility and brightness occurred. These murky conditions elicited comment as early as 1716, although the colonists could not have known that their dark days resulted from dust storms a thousand miles beyond their farthest frontier.

Yet even on the colonial frontier the damage had begun. "Our lands," said George Washington, "were originally very good; but use and abuse have made them quite otherwise. . . . We ruin the lands that are already cleared, and either cut down more wood, if we have it, or emigrate into the Western country."

"Are you ignorant," Duquesne demanded of the Iroquois, "of the difference between the King of England and the King of France? See the forts that our king has established. You can still hunt under their very walls. . . . The English, on the contrary, are no sooner in possession of a place than the game is driven off. The forest falls before them as they advance and the soil is laid bare."

With the passing of the colonial period and subsequent probing of western America by early explorers, it became apparent that the lands beyond the Mississippi River were not quite as fruitful as those to which the early settlers had become accustomed.

"It might be possible to introduce a limited population," said Zebulon Pike, setting out from St. Louis in 1803.

"Altogether valueless," said Lieutenant Joseph Ives of the Southwest in 1858, ". . . a profitless locality."

But then—after the explorers—came the pioneer families to set up housekeeping on the plains. They, too, found the land hostile. "We have had some strange weather in Kansas," came the news. "No rain yet. The air, in consequence of the winds, is filled with dust—a very strange appearance to those of us who have lived always in the States, and have been accustomed to seeing rainy and muddy weather at this season."

In 1870, Kansans began to believe that their state was being distributed to the world at large. Yet even as great clouds of fine dust filled the sky and blotted out the sun, the rare good humor of the plains people asserted itself. No use getting all riled up and choked on the dust; no use admitting that this *wasn't* always a plush Utopia. The dust could be something to laugh about. It might even be something to *brag* about!

"Zephyrs are our strong point," said one newspaper. "They lift ten-pound boulders and two-year-old mule colts off the ground—the squawking flocks overhead may be geese, may be jackasses. . . ."

"The streets were filled all day long," said another, "with so dense a cloud of dust that you couldn't see your cigar before your face; and so deep was the artificial darkness, that several men who owe this establishment, passed directly by the office door without seeing it. The

Lawrence *Journal,* which is a standard authority on the subject of weather, says the wind blew seventy miles an hour in Lawrence, from which we conclude that its speed diminished about one-half after leaving this point."

The spirited frontier plainsman forgot most of the bad weather and played up his territory as a land of milk and honey. Above all it was free. New settlers flocked in year after year. New lands opened up.

And then in 1890, disaster struck. Crops failed all over the southern plains. They failed again in 1891. And in 1892. Hordes of grasshoppers swooped in on the winds, leaving not a blade of grass; they were so thick that wagon riders had to scrape them from the spokes of wheels.

Always the people figured next year would be better. In 1893 there was a panic in the East, and the cattle markets crashed. 1894 was dry. 1895 was worse. The sun and wind, masters of the plains, had asserted their awful power.

People began to pack up and leave. Some counties in western Kansas had only half as many people in 1896 as they had in 1891.

But then came ten years of good weather, and everybody forgot the drought. In fact, the general conviction was that droughts had gone for good, that the plains would become a land of Canaan. So more people came and once again the cattle ranges were mutilated and the grass and sod broken up and plowed over and over and over. . . .

In 1908 some crops failed. Drought spread across the land in 1910. Rain-making experiments from 1911 to 1913 failed. Then came the dust.

There had always been dust, of course, rising from dry washes and grassless areas; but now the plowed fields added more soil and dust and sand to the winds. The storms became more menacing and more damaging. Wheat was seared and pulled out by the roots. By 1912 dust had piled up everywhere, and in some cases had to be shoveled like snowdrifts.

With the war, demand for wheat skyrocketed. Nineteen fifteen, happily, was a bumper year, but the next two years were poor ones. Because of the war, few crops were planted in Europe—so America's farmers plunged into the fight on the agricultural front; it was up to them, they were told, just as surely as it was up to the doughboys "over there," to help win the victory. That, plus economic incentives, plus increasingly effective planting and harvesting equipment impelled a sod rip-up as never before. Bumper crops came in. More acreage was planted. New records were broken. At last the war ended, but the threat of famine pressed the cry for "Wheat! Wheat! Wheat!"

And the United States farmer, raping the grasslands, complied.

With the improvement of harvesting machines, Great Plains prosperity spread. The crash of 1929 did little to hamper destruction of open lands; the great plow-up went on. Farm machinery became more effective. Corn, wheat, and cotton sprang up wherever tractors could go. Nineteen thirty-one was the best year and wheat poured in by millions of bushels.

Then tottering prices began to loosen the bottom of the wheat market, and granaries filled to overflowing. Hard times arrived and to combat starvation the only thing the farmer could do was plant every last square inch with wheat. At exactly that moment—the spring of 1932— a late freeze came; then violent storms tore at the wheat stalks and left them ruined. Cutworms followed; then drought. The market stayed low. Creditors banged on doors, and to meet their demands the farmer tore up more sod and planted more crops.

Thus began America's fabulous and notorious Dust Bowl era.

On April 14, 1934, the wind raged in from the north, whipping the powdery dust at first into small ground-hugging clouds, then into one great blanket that shut out visibility. Rolling over and over, the tumbling jet-black cloud raced across the plains, driving wild birds before it—not quite catching the stronger ones, engulfing and destroying the weaker. Daytime turned into midnight. Dust filtered everywhere—into houses, into stores, into autos. Blue-green light played around automobiles on the highway; sparks jumped from metal to metal and fluttered around the plumbing.

"This weather's just generating electricity," the ranchers said. Some vowed that dust storms were less the work of man than explosions of lightning absorbed by the earth.

Food was ruined, even in cupboards and refrigerators, and clothes and furniture became covered and saturated with silky dust. Street lights were turned on but did little good. As the worst darkness passed, the dust thinned a little. Hours later it was over and the sky cleared— but only briefly.

A few days later a high-powered flanking wind mass moved in from the west and picked up dust in a sky-high cloud that spread out for thousands of square miles from Texas to North Dakota. As the swirling winds moved eastward, Chicago was covered with a thin dust pall. Then the Ohio Valley. Then the eastern seaboard, obscuring daylight over New York, Baltimore, and Washington. Then dust fell on ships three hundred miles out to sea. By estimation this storm picked up 350 million tons of plains topsoil and spread it across half the earth.

Back on the plains, disaster lowered on every side. A Kansas schoolboy got lost in the storm and perished in a shifting dune. A woman was killed when a chicken coop blew over on her. Travel was disrupted. Cattle and poultry lay dying, crops burning and blowing away. Family after family plunged into bankruptcy and joined relief lines. President Roosevelt pushed through a 525-million-dollar drought-relief program.

Nineteen thirty-four was one of the driest, searingest years on record. The rains never came. Streams dried up, springs failed, trees withered. Record lows in precipitation were recorded. Pastures began drying up. Thousands of emaciated cattle were destroyed by squads of humanitarian Texas ranchers.

Still the farmers dusted off (or dug out) the tractor, hitched up the disks, and went out in the fields. There was new wheat to plant. Next year would be a good year.

But it wasn't. On February 25, 1935, the dust rose again in a storm that traveled forty or fifty miles per hour, damaging and killing, moving out into the Gulf of Mexico and Caribbean to sprinkle ships with dust. Again and again came the dust and the wind. During that single year, Dalhart, Texas, was struck by sixty-one storms. Now the dust was drifting and piling, obstructing railways and roads, banking against barns and houses, burying tools and fences and animals and people. It stopped engines and watches. It helped bring on sinus infections, laryngitis, pharyngitis, bronchitis, and other maladies, and surgical operations were even suspended when dust seeped into sterilizing apparatus.

"It represents a waste so stupendous," said the Baltimore *Evening Sun*, "that the human mind is incapable of comprehending it."

By this time, about the only thing that could grow was the tumbleweed, and it was having a hard time. Farmers began leaving by the thousands, to escape the dust and disaster and find greener pastures elsewhere. And yet, surprisingly, not all hopes were broken, and not all sod-busters became refugees. There had never been anything wrong with the soil itself—just the mobility of it, induced by breaking up, lack of rainfall, and hot sun. Or was it really lack of rain?

Agriculture experts began to take second looks at the countryside and heed the old voices which warned against tearing up so much land so fast. They learned that the prosperity of the country did not necessarily depend upon how much water remained in the lakes and ponds after spring rains had come and gone, but rather how much remained *in the ground* beneath crops.

Some land, ill-suited to cultivation, clearly needed to go back to grass. Then if the ground were properly plowed so as to hold moisture more deeply, and if protective stubble were left to prevent the wind from scouring out furrows, the problem might be licked. By hindsight, it seems simple. But the concepts were new and mistakes were many.

Early in 1936 a concerted fight against the dust began. Farmers were paid by the government to contour-plow their sloping lands, following what natural gradients and configurations their fields took, to catch and hold whatever moisture came. Wheat was plowed under, and the stirred-up clods caught some of the flowing dust and settled it in rows. Settled dust was not blowing dust, at least; a start had been made. Reseeding of grasses on the poorest soils was begun. When the farmers saw for themselves that this rampaging phenomenon could be harnessed, the battle gained renewed vigor. Federal and state agencies worked overtime. Conservation practices were devised, tried out, adopted, circulated.

Meanwhile the ruination kept on. In 1937 Guymon, Oklahoma, had 110 destructive dust storms. Next year the grasshoppers came—so thick and numerous that they piled in drifts three feet deep. They slicked highways, clogged windshields, ate crops. Texas called out its National Guard, but neither that nor poisoning nor special killing contraptions did any good.

Just the same, 1938 saw much wheat harvested in spite of the plague. Slowly things were getting better. Soil-conservation laws were adopted. Crop-insurance programs went into effect. Demonstration farms were set up to provide examples. The Government purchased millions of acres of windblown land and retired it to grassland. Multiple crops were planted, including strips of sorghum to provide wind protection for the soil and for other crops. New drought-resistant grains were developed. Once again the grass grew tall. Terrace and furrow farming held the water in place, and moistened the soil to greater depth. Wheat yield increased.

Then came the shelterbelt trees (which had been proposed as a wind-stopping technique more than thirty years before). Though considered fantastic in 1934, the project, at the insistence of the President, was set up, with the idea of planting trees in lines or belts around farms to break the force of the wind. Hundreds of miles of saplings were planted—ponderosa pine, cottonwood, elm, hackberry, locust, green ash, and shrubs like Russian olive. These plantings thrived best in the eastern part of the Dust Bowl where moisture conditions were a little better. Elsewhere the trees survived only in favorable locations or where extra moisture was provided. Many trees did not survive, of course, because much of the region was too dry.

Nevertheless, where before lay barren, blowing land, now stretched a few tree-lined lanes.

Finally the rains came again, so heavily in places that the cry "mud bowl" was heard on the land. They were as rampageous as the dust had been. A housewife told what happened on Memorial Day, 1935:

"At four that morning it clouded over darkly and poured down hail. It covered the ground in places to a depth of four inches. I thought it would flatten the house, it hit so hard. Finally it stopped and a dust cloud blew up. It was so thick we had to eat lunch by lamplight. The electric power was off. The creek was up, plunging and roaring, but you couldn't see it for the dust.

"Early in the afternoon it hailed again—big stones this time, and dirty. Then it rained. There is no describing it. A year's rain in a day, they say. No gauge could keep track of it. Some claim to have caught as much as thirty inches in tubs and cisterns.

"The bridge went out like a snapped match, and the creek came over its banks. At three o'clock my husband said, 'The house is going. It hasn't a chance.' We got out, wading with the children and whatever we could throw together over to the old cabin, on higher ground. It was like a fire. We took along such things as [our daughter's] doll bed, but forgot to take anything to eat.

"I never expected to see this house again. The water reached it but didn't move it. Below here, things were even worse. The wash from these slopes swept fifty buildings out of the town . . . and drowned some people. . . ."

And so the great drought had broken. There would be lesser droughts afterward, of course, but nothing as widely ruinous as in the thirties. During World War II the rains were better than ever, fortunately for us and for a famine-stricken world.

The occasional droughts of postwar years have helped to stimulate public attention to dust storms and their control. But was control possible?

To harness these moving dust basins, the soil conservationist has a pocket answer worked out by experience: get those unproducing lands out of crops and back into grass. Give them a rest—for good. Get the marginal lands back into grass, also, if only for brief regular periods. And on land that is plowed, leave the stubble in place during windy months.

No one knows if this will work throughout the entire region but the Department of Agriculture and the Great Plains Agricultural Council intend to find out. Under Public Law 1021, the Great Plains Conservation Program was established to help farmers minimize climatic hazards and protect their land from erosion and deterioration by natural causes. It was a long-range project to establish permanent cover, plant windbreaks, build waterways and terrace systems, improve dams or ponds for irrigation, and stimulate strip-cropping and contour cultivation, among other items. By 1961, 5,422 contracts involving 14,-462,152 acres of land in the Great Plains had been negotiated under this program.

Today the winds blow as they always have, and dust bowls still reflect man's folly and careless ethics toward his source of life—the soil. The fact remains that he *can* do something about it. Not one farmer, but many. So many, in fact, that when the plains are inhabited by erosion-conscious farmers practicing proved soil-conservation techniques, the danger of severe dust storms will be sharply reduced.

There is a limit to what a certain type of land in a certain climate can do. If someday giant atomic pumps force filtered sea water through "big inch" pipelines to these interior badlands, it will be quite another matter. Until then, the choice is clear: conservation or desolation.

"The face of the earth is a graveyard," said Paul B. Sears, "and so it has always been." All living things return to the soil whatever they have borrowed to give them form and substance. Dust thou art, to dust returneth, and as a rule, Nature manages these borrowings and repayments in an efficient way. But when man, with his mechanical genius and exuberant vitality, breaks Nature's gentle grip, the forces of the earth spring forth unleashed—to destroy at will.

7

RAIN

~~~

Some people are weatherwise but most
are otherwise.

... BENJAMIN FRANKLIN

"SIR, HIS MAJESTY, taking notice of an opinion enter-
tained in Staffordshire, that the burning of ferne doth drawe downe
rain, and being desirous that the country and himself may enjoy fair
weather so long as he remains in these parts, His Majesty has commanded me to write to you, to cause all burning of ferne to be for-
bidden until His Majesty be passed the country."

Thus wrote Lord Chamberlain to the sheriff of Staffordshire in
1636, pending a visit of King Charles I. If only the sheriff's compli-
ance could produce the desired results! If burning or not burning ferns
would control rainfall we should have solved one of man's oldest and
most distressing problems: how to get the right amount of rain at the
right place at the right time.

In Nature's never-ending cycle from cloud to earth and sea to sky,
rain (or snow) inevitably falls on almost every spot on earth. Manhattan gets forty-two inches per year, Los Angeles fourteen, Washington
forty-one, Seattle and Chicago thirty-two, Miami (Florida) fifty-nine,
and New Orleans sixty-three.

Some places get so little rainfall they literally dry up and blow away.
Death Valley receives 1.9 inches a year. In parts of Peru and the Sahara not a single drop has fallen for years.

But as sure as rain falls, sometimes it plummets down by the bucket-and barrelful and pours out some astonishing world records.

For a long time, the wettest minute in history was claimed at Opid's Camp (Los Angeles County), California, where .65 inch of rain fell on April 5, 1926, in a span of sixty seconds. Then a summer cloudburst at Jefferson, Iowa, in 1955 broke the record by a fraction of an inch.

But at Unionville, Maryland, on the Fourth of July, 1956, came a flooding cloudburst which, at its height, dropped 1.23 inches of rain in a single minute. This walloping cloudburst may stand for some time as Nature's greatest and most sudden aquatic punch.

Rain once pelted Holt, Missouri, for forty-two solid minutes and unloaded a total of twelve inches. One afternoon near D'Hanis, Texas, the skies opened up and dumped twenty-two inches on the Edwards Plateau in less than three hours.

For a single day, the Philippine Islands hold the record; on July 14, 1911, forty-six inches fell at Baguio. On two consecutive days a storm on Formosa once doused the island with seven feet of rain.

And the Caribbean can be just as wet. In 1909 a storm hovered over Jamaica's Silver Hill plantation for almost a week and dropped 122.5 inches.

No one knows exactly why the skies open up and flood the unsuspecting earth with these freak downpours and continuous torrents. It might be due to the magnitude of some temperature difference, the speed of various air movements, the intensity of convection currents, or perhaps some unexplained vagary of the overall weather pattern. About all to be said with sureness is that high humidity (wet air), high temperature (hot air), and lack of movement (still air) are the breeding grounds for tempests that crash around our ears.

Meteorologists have long suspected that if they could pry out the inner secrets of a single thundercloud they might be able to forecast excessive rainfall. Although no cloud or storm can be brought into the laboratory for microscopic examination or surgical dissection, it is possible to take the laboratory aloft, and scientifically equipped aircraft have done just that. Much has been learned on these flights but no plane or human being can plow headlong into a violent thunderstorm and remain there still enough or long enough to discover why any storm goes to excess.

Nor even how much excess. Around the world, heavier rains and deeper snows have occurred than any measured by official weather stations. The United States Weather Bureau points out that across the nation there are some 14,000 rain gauges which, placed together, would cover scarcely half a city block. Scattered as they are across country they record a regional sampling, not always Nature's biggest rainstorms at peak downpour.

Weathermen may not know precisely where the heaviest rainfall of all time has occurred, but they have a couple of choice places in which to look. One is Mount Waialeale, Kauai, Hawaii (elevation 5,080 feet), which gets around 476 inches a year.

Another is in India. East of the Ganges and Brahmaputra rivers rise the Khasi Hills, an east-west spur paralleling the Himalayas for 150 miles. Here in the northeasternmost province of India the Khasis soar to 6,500 feet and meet a northward continuation of the Arakan-Yoma of western Burma.

Between these ranges lies a broad funnel-like depression toward which, from vast swamplands in the steaming Ganges delta far away, come air masses heavily laden with moisture.

On a plateau overlooking the plains of Assam sits the little village of Cherrapunji. When the full force of the monsoon roars out of the Bay of Bengal and across the swamps of the Ganges it is funneled into the hills around Cherrapunji and forced to rise. Precipitation begins, and the average rainfall amounts to some 450 inches a year. (Heaviest in the United States, on the lush Olympic Peninsula at Wyoochee, Washington, is 155 inches a year.)

The wettest single month in world history occurred at Cherrapunji when 366 inches fell in July, 1861.

And during a single year there the rains once came in a colossal deluge totaling 1,042 inches—which would equal a wall of water eighty-seven feet high!

The climate of the central Shillong Plateau is very salubrious, but the low hills in parts of the district are malarious. Nor does the rain pour constantly; practically all of it occurs during the six months from May to October. After all, Cherrapunji is at the same latitude as Miami, Florida, and is thus entitled to a temperate zone variation in climate. So long as there is no prolonged drought during the other six months of the year, the dense vegetation persists and thrives.

It seems surprising to see so much grass on the Cherrapunji Plateau, where the precipitation is so excessive. One might expect deep rain forest instead. This is explained by the existence of a violent wind that blows much of the year, and by the near-perfect runoff conditions, which allow the massive rains to run away quickly without appreciably raising the humidity of the soil.

However, farther down the valleys there is a dense arboreal vegetation, and here one finds large palms on which climb the spiny rattan palms that erect their leaves like ostrich plumes above the big trees.

In a radius of ten miles around Cherrapunji can be found more than two thousand species of flowering plants and 150 kinds of ferns. This, as a botanist will attest, is a fantastic variation. Moreover, there are more than 165 kinds of grass, a number of them bamboo. Clusters of pandanus often form remarkable features of the countryside. And there are small wooded patches of laurel, bramble, jasmine, and oak scattered throughout the high country. In some places grow rhododendrons and chestnuts, covered with a profusion of epiphytic orchids.

In this delightful floral environment, warmed by the sun, nurtured by the rain, live numerous wild animals, some of which, like the tiger, would chill the spines of city dwellers anywhere. Elephants lumber across the lowlands and valleys, sharing their domain with rhinoceroses, bison, wild buffalo, deer, goats, and bears.

In *Le Plateau de Meghalaya*, Shiba Prasad Chatterjee says, "The leeches are so numerous during the rainy season that it is impossible to escape their attack when one is outside. Before sucking blood they are very thin, and they creep across the socks toward the skin in such a way that the victim does not see them, and death has resulted from the bleeding they cause. The author, despite precautions he took, found each evening on returning from work at least a dozen of these animals stuck to his body. They died as soon as they were powdered with common salt."

The differing climates of this strange country affect the people who live there. The Khasis of the high central plateau are strong and healthy, but those in the more humid and malarial "Bhoi country" to the north, and others in the west, are stunted and sickly.

How do the Khasis live under the buckets of rain that come plummeting down upon them? Apparently they do not find the rain any more confining or deleterious than do other native tribes of humid regions. Their villages consist of substantial thatched cottages with plank or stone walls, raised on a plinth two or three feet from the ground. Such villages are generally built just below the summits of the hills, chiefly for protection from the winds and storms. Surely the rain must cramp their style sometimes, but they no doubt grew used to the climate long ago.

In the state of savagery where human intellect was at an early stage of development, it was not strange that man looked upon the great sky forces with awe and superstition. To primitive peoples the flashing and flooding violence of the sky was superhuman (as opposed to supernatural), and the aboriginal mind fostered supermen, super-animals, and super-peoples to control it. Some tribes reckoned thunder to be caused by the flapping wings of a large and unseen bird; and lightning was the glance of his eye in seeking prey. The Sioux made use of *waka*, a prefix denoting mysterious, wonderful, incomprehensible forces which their primitive philosophy could scarcely grasp or understand. Even the simple rainbow was a banner of violence, death, disease, drought, and war.

All polytheistic religions have included gods who ruled the weather. But that was only a start. Says S. K. Heninger in *Handbook of Renaissance Meteorology*: "Always the natural processes of the atmosphere, both usual and unusual, have formed an integral part of the traditions within any culture that man has developed."

All over the world there exist and have existed for centuries numerous and complicated magico-religious ceremonies for the control or manufacture of rain. The highest gods of Greece and Rome were deities of rain. Images were cast into the Tiber by Romans in order to induce rain. Ancient Teutons poured water over naked girls. Buddhist priests symbolized rain sinking into the earth by pouring water into holes in the temple floor. Indians sprinkled water on images of frogs and snakes. Celtic druids went by procession to magic wells or springs and dabbled water over special stones.

Years ago, the Mohammedans of Iran would sometimes set their babies and lambs apart in a field and let them wail, thinking that the innocent might prevail upon God to make it rain, whereas the adults had sinned so much that their prayers had little chance of being answered.

Natives of the Moluccas shook water from a stick to encourage rain.

Ojibway Indians fired flaming arrows at the sun. Or, if you were a Shawnee in want of rain, you simply dipped a buffalo tail in water and sprinkled the water on the ground.

Perhaps for want of buffalo tails, man's efforts eventually became more serious and more costly, as we have seen in the discussion of deserts and droughts. Perhaps as man becomes proficient at weather control, a dream as old as civilization will be achieved.

Like all other weather phenomena, rain and rainbows found their place in literature; in the Bible rainbows betokened peace and accord between God and the world (*Genesis* 9:11-17). Falling rain became tears of lament. And it was written in Deuteronomy: "My doctrine shall drop as the rain . . ."

One of the best known books to make rain its central theme is Louis Bromfield's *The Rains Came*, set in Ranchipur, India. Bromfield described a city and its people in the throes of monsoon, earthquake, and flood. The characters were deftly divided into two groups, one rising to meet the catastrophe (thereby kindling a spiritual rebirth), and one incapable of coping with the situation. Typical of Bromfield's descriptions:

"He had plenty of money and not a tie in the world, yet he stayed on and on through the burning heat, waiting for that day, if it ever came, when the skies would open and the floods descend and the fields and jungle would steam and writhe and grow in the incredible wet heat which was worse than the hot dusty dryness of the winter season. . . .

"The branches of the mango tree whipped black against the wild glare of lightning, and the water fell in torrents on the parched thirsty earth. Tomorrow it would be green again, miraculously green with the miracle of the monsoon."

In the normal course of affairs, Nature brings down her moisture in various ways, usually as rain or snow. But sometimes a narrow range of temperature and moisture occurs and rain freezes on contact with the ground, coating trees, wires, highways, and everything else with a dangerous sheet of ice.

An outbreak of continental polar air touched the Texas panhandle in 1940 and a severe ice storm settled over the landscape. Wires iced up to a thickness of five inches before collapsing. Power was severed.

Flying ice chunks injured pedestrians. Doctors performed operations with flashlights in heatless hospitals. Not a newspaper, with either a report or forecast, could be printed. The people were literally frozen in their tracks.

Sleet is no more than frozen raindrops, simply water particles that solidified before landing. Graupel, or "soft hail," is a round, snowlike lump of frozen moisture which bounces on the ground and usually falls apart. True hail is disastrous enough to deserve separate discussion.

Thunderstorms have been going on since the earth was born, constantly changing and shifting, periodic or cyclic, but never static because weather itself is never static. That is why, in the long view, it seems odd to ask: is our weather changing?

Of course it is. Climates have been changing millennium after millennium. If they had not, things would be in an astonishing fix at the present time. In the words of Harlow Shapley: "An absolutely steady sun and earth-crust for the past 400,000,000 years might have left us living as Silurian ooze-browsers, unambitious, deprived of climatic stimulation."

Throughout the geologic past, great periods of glaciation have spread out from the poles, one as recent as that of the Pleistocene, which began a million years ago. Giant deserts, thousands of square miles in extent, have seared the earth in one place and another. Countless fossil corals occur today in limestones at altitudes and latitudes which long since have passed from tropic to temperate or cold.

What alters climates? Variations, probably, in radiation from the sun, although changing conditions on the earth's crust (uplift and erosion of mountain ranges) have some effect. It takes only a sunspot or two, or any slight change in the steady stream of solar warmth and energy, to stir up long-lasting and widespread climatic changes. A few degrees' difference for several decades will suffice to send glaciers creeping out from the poles.

There are short-range factors, though, that have been noticed within the span of a generation. The first half of the twentieth century has demonstrably been a period of warming up. Glaciers have been melting. September has become a summer month. There has been more precipitation and wider dissemination of death-dealing storms, such as more hurricanes in New England. Something has happened. But it is nothing new.

It may be merely a general thawing as we enter an inter-glacial ice stage. It may be the clearing of the upper atmosphere after eruptions of Krakatoa, Katmai, and other volcanoes which filled the air with volcanic dust decades ago. Or the output of solar energy may be undergoing some long-range variation.

No matter how well man gets acquainted with weather patterns and learns how to predict them, it may still be a while before he learns how to push air masses where he pleases. Until he does, the unleashed watery elements of the sky will batter the earth with rampaging fury and affect every inhabitant, human and animal.

Would that the control of such elements were as simple as the Tsimshian Indian prayer: *"Lusega naksenalgent, semagrid, dem wul gakset!"*

"Hold in thy breath, Chief, that it be calm!"

8

HAIL

I wield the flail of the lashing hail,
And whiten the green plains under;
And then again I dissolve it in rain
And laugh as I pass in thunder.
   . . . SHELLEY, *The Cloud*

IN NATURE'S powerful arsenal few weapons are deadlier than hail. Accuracy is unnecessary. One heavy fall of hail may so blanket the ground that anything caught in the area is mangled, battered, stripped, or destroyed. Throughout the United States greater property damage results from hailstorms than from tornadoes.

Hailstorm losses are staggering. Windows may be smashed, trees cut to ribbons, neon signs shattered, buildings riddled. In some years losses from hail exceed fifty million dollars and come surprisingly close to the destruction wrought by hurricanes.

Excepting drought and frost, hail is Nature's greatest menace to thriving farm crops, and no place in the United States is immune. Hail has smashed cotton fields in Arizona, fruitlands in California, melon patches in Georgia. Orchards have been hopelessly lacerated, and cornfields so completely ravaged that not a stalk was left standing.

In warmer climates, tobacco crops suffer heavily because the broad leaves break at the stalk and lose value instantly when punctured or torn. Since even an acre of tobacco is worth a tidy sum, not much of

126

a storm is required to erase a season's profits. Without hail insurance, the tobacco farmer is financially finished.

And imagine how you would feel about hail if you were a grower of grapes, with your fruit bursting on the vine. Ivan Tannehill, in his book *The Hurricane Hunters*, tells how Italian grapegrowers around the turn of the century conceived the idea of shooting at storms to prevent buildup of hail. They thought first, so the story goes, of lobbing heavy cannonballs into the clouds, but this plan was spurned by sensitive neighbors who resented the possibility of being wiped out along with the hailstorms.

The vineyardists then crammed their cannons with gunpowder and fired for all they were worth. Great plumes of smoke rose into the sky and mingled with the storm clouds. And sure enough, no hail fell. The project worked—they thought.

With this cheerful news spreading from country to country hail-shooting gained a substantial coterie of adherents. There was even an international hail-shooting congress. But after a few devastating storms on which guns had no effect, the shooters began to have doubts and the sport declined for a while. In 1962, the Moscow newspaper *Komsomolskaya Pravda* announced that the Russians were shooting rockets into hailstorms in an effort to protect Georgian vineyards.

Hailstorms occur in all parts of the world and virtually all altitudes. Most of them develop in the afternoon and evening, and usually in summer, but can come pelting down any time, any month, advancing or retreating with the vagaries of weather. And it seems an angry twist of fate that the heaviest United States hailstorms arrive at a time when crops are most vulnerable—July in the corn belt, August in the northern wheat country.

No man has yet determined the precise mechanics by which clouds manufacture hail. Some scientists suggest that within a violent thundercloud supercooled raindrops are caught in updrafts and lifted into the high, cold regions of the cloud, freezing on the way up. Swooping back downward, they gain a coating of water and are sucked into another updraft, to be frozen again.

Around and around they swirl in an upward-downward circuit, accumulating layer after layer of supercooled water and freezing into solid ice. Finally, becoming so heavy that air currents no longer support them, they plunge to earth as hail. How many layers of ice can form, no one knows. One stone, recovered at Annapolis, Maryland, had twenty-five concentric layers.

The updraft required to keep such enormous hailstones aloft, even momentarily, has been calculated to be about 250 miles per hour. Some researchers, however, suspect that instead of revolving up and down within a cloud a hailstone grows during one continuous drop. They believe it is merely slowed, not lifted, by uprushing air currents, and has time to be repeatedly coated with ice as it floats down through layers of supercooled raindrops. Considering the difficulty of examining hailstorms at first hand, it's a wonder weathermen know as much about them as they do.

Whatever its formation, the hailstone undergoes such elemental turbulence that it may grow to extraordinary size and shape. It may have spikelike protuberances, bristling like a deadly mace. It may be conchoidal, spheroidal, many-sided, or disk-shaped. Some stones contain leaves, nuts and insects, anything capable of being lifted by updrafts and coated with ice.

Perhaps the most spectacular hailstones are those which contain live animals. Fish, turtles and frogs have been found embedded in them and in December, 1933, a fall of iced ducks was noted at Worcester, Massachusetts.

Hailstones may freeze together in flight and come down as enormous chunks of ice, accumulating on the ground to considerable depths. Hail once piled up twelve inches deep in southern Kansas, and just before the turn of the century, several storms in Iowa dropped enough hail to form drifted heaps six feet deep.

The largest known hailstones in history fell in a Potter, Nebraska, storm on July 6, 1928. They plunged to the ground ten to fifteen feet apart and struck with such impact that many were buried. The largest one measured seventeen inches in circumference and weighed 1½ pounds. To verify that it was a single stone, and not several frozen together, investigators cut it open and examined the concentric rings.

In a Pennsylvania storm a farmer once collected a basketful of hailstones that average 8½ inches in circumference, and allegedly bounced ten feet into the air without breaking.

There are claims from India of hail "as big as a millstone," and hail that weighed 7½ pounds, but these may have been stones frozen together.

There is little doubt, however, that hailstones even larger than the one at Potter have fallen. How much larger and where is a matter of speculation.

In Heidgraben, Germany, one measuring almost six by ten inches and weighing possibly four pounds crashed through a house roof, and at Cazorla, Spain, giant hail weighing 4½ pounds has been reported.

That is about as big as hailstones can get and still be kept aloft by wind currents of known velocities.

If hail were to fall straight down, far less damage would result. But frequently it is driven by winds of gale force, and then it smashes windows, batters autos, and mangles machinery on a grandiose scale. Stucco is ripped from houses. Holes are pounded in buildings. Cars are dented and shingles split.

Greenhouses suffer severe losses when hail rams through glass and devastates tender plants under a deluge of cascading debris. After a 1948 storm at Denver, Colorado, twenty carloads of glass were required to replace losses in greenhouses, skylights, windows, and other vulnerable locations. So great is the damage in some places that no adequate estimate can be made.

For the most part, human beings know enough to dive for shelter when hail strikes suddenly, but this is not always possible. A thirty-nine-year-old farmer near Lubbock, Texas, was once caught in open country and pelted so furiously before he could reach safety that he died within a few hours.

Six children were killed and ten others injured by hen's-egg-sized hail which once fell at Klausenberg, Rumania. Twenty-three people died when they rushed to save their cattle during a fall of giant hail at Rostov, Russia. And nearly a score of South African bushmen were killed in 1936 by large hailstones which buried them to a depth of three feet.

The deadliest hailstorm on record swept over Moradabad, India, on April 30, 1888, killing more than 230 people.

Sometimes the damage can be widespread. A set of storms struck the Nirmal Taluk district in Hyderabad, India, in 1939, damaging seventeen villages across thirty square miles. High-velocity winds impelled the hail into great speed, stripping leaves from the trees. Seven hundred tile roofs were smashed to pieces. So were four hundred thatched houses, thousands of acres of crops, two hundred cattle and a thousand sheep.

Yet such massive destruction is by no means new.

The Book of Joshua, tenth chapter, tells how the Lord cast down great stones upon the Amorites, and that there were more that died from hailstones than "they whom the children of Israel slew with the sword."

A hailstorm in 1360 is said to have affected the course of a war between the British and French. Edward III, after failing to take Paris, had withdrawn toward Chartres when the French began to talk peace. Edward was unmoved until a violent hailstorm began shattering his forces, with a resultant loss of a thousand men and six thousand horses. After that, the Treaty of Bretigny was negotiated.

Coronado, the intrepid Spanish conquistador, had his horses stampeded in 1541 when he was exploring the area that is now Texas. If his soldiers had not been clad in armor—an excellent defense—they might have suffered disastrously.

In literature, hail is a well-known emphasizer. The Bible mentions it twenty-nine times. "And Moses stretched forth his rod toward heaven: and the Lord sent thunder and hail, and the fire ran along the ground; and the Lord rained hail upon the land of Egypt."

Antony asks Cleopatra: "Cold-hearted toward me?" And she replies, "Ah, dear, if I be so, from my cold heart let heaven engender hail." Spenser, in *The Faerie Queene*, called hailstorms "horrible and dred." Falstaff, in *The Merry Wives of Windsor*, orders Pistol and Nym to "vanish like hailstones." In *Macbeth*, Ross informs Macbeth that messengers with news of victory came to the King "as thick as hail." And Coriolanus tells a group of citizens that they are no more stable than a hailstone in the sun.

In early days there were recommendations for what to do when a hailstorm struck. The Englishman Thomas Hill advised in *The Profitable Arte of Gardening* that gardens could be protected from hail by the exhibition of a sealskin, a hyena, or a crocodile.

Today about the only known defense against hail is to run for cover, and run fast. While farm crops are at the mercy of hailstorms, homes and other buildings can in some measure be protected. Roofs of shingle, composition, asbestos, and even tile may be shattered to bits, but metal roofs are hail resistant and concrete slab is better yet.

The only sure financial protection against heavy loss and ruination is adequate hail insurance.

Can these shattering storms be predicted? Through observations made from high-floating radiosonde instruments, it is possible to detect areas in which strong updrafts occur—drafts violent enough to produce hail.

Forecasters thus can tell generally where thunderstorms will occur over a given area and whether or not they will contain hail-forming updrafts. But the whole process is enormously complex. Local storms move erratically and do not always strike when and where they are expected.

What can be done with radar is problematical but promising, and experiments by airlines have been encouraging. Pilots have been provided with ample warnings of hail shafts ahead of them. How effective many of these long-distance seeing-eye devices prove will be determined by the thoroughness of continuing research and development, by more orbiting weather satellites, and by better electronic equipment.

Perhaps then we shall have come a long way from shooting at the clouds. Someday we shall understand the make-up of hail and learn why it goes so often and so disastrously on the rampage.

9

LIGHTNING

The voice of thy thunder was in the heaven:
The lightnings lightened the world:
The earth trembled and shook.

. . . PSALM LXXVII

TUNG PO-HUA was his name, and he lived in the city of
Ch'uan-chou. The community knew him chiefly as a brilliant young
chap who frequently wandered off among the immortals for long
periods of time and visited faraway lands. His neighbors pointed out
that while this must certainly be an engaging pastime, it led neither to
the accumulation of earthly wealth nor to the maintenance of a steady
occupation and respected position in the community, and while he
might enjoy the best of both worlds, there was, after all, one's reputation to think of. Tung sometimes disregarded the advice of his neighbors and went right on visiting the nether regions as he preferred, in
his business-as-usual fashion.

One day, an immortal gave him a thunderstone—a pebble endowed
by the god of thunder—and said: "If you want to return home, just
go toward the east and you will find the way. The stone is to be your
traveling money. If you have need of any, just cry 'I am selling thunderclaps,' and, if anybody wants to buy a thunderclap, write a word
into his hand and ask him to close the hand. When he opens his hand
again, he will hear a tremendous thunderclap."

For many days and nights Tung walked to the east, passing through towns and villages and cities. As he ran short of money, he paused and did as the immortal had instructed him, offering thunderclaps for sale. The procedure worked well, principally because people were curious about thunderclaps and were delighted at the unusual opportunity to buy them, so Tung without difficulty made his way back to Ch'uan-chou.

There, rejoining his parents and a boyhood friend named Kuo, he settled down to a life of affluence as the city's only thunderclap-seller. One day an official of the district heard thunderpeals crashing around the city and, since he could see no clouds in the sky, wondered what was going on. Learning that Tung was selling thunderclaps, he forthwith arrested and imprisoned Tung on charges of sorcery and troublemaking.

This abrupt disenfranchisement perturbed Tung not a whit. His old friend Kuo was a substantial public official and, as it happened, the judgment of Tung's case fell to him.

"There is a warning I must give you, however," Tung said to Kuo. "The official who accused me will soon have an accident."

"Are you sure?" inquired Kuo.

"Yes. You must not accompany him when he leaves his house."

"How can I avoid that?" Kuo asked.

"Take this pill."

"What is it for?"

"Never mind. Swallow it."

Kuo did as he was bidden, and thereupon grew so ill that he could not leave his house. Bandits shortly appeared in the district and the official, left in command of the somewhat dispirited local army, was set upon and killed. Kuo, too sick to fight, had been saved.

On Kuo's recovery, Tung gave him the thunderstone, together with some pictures of wind, thunder, rain, and clouds which he had painted in prison.

After that, Tung turned into a saint and was immortalized in legend; indeed, Kuo's descendants forever after exhibited Tung's paintings on the fifth day of the fifth month, five being a number which the Chinese hold dear.

Now we are left a bit puzzled as to whether Tung, having become an immortal, acquired another stone to replace the one he gave Kuo. There is the probability that he eventually relinquished his monopoly and assigned all rights to the great dragon, for Chinese legend subsequently tells us that this formidable creature, which sleeps all winter deep beneath the ground, breaks through the earth and ascends to heaven on the second day of the second month, producing the year's first thunderstorm.

Whatever the truth of the matter, both Tung and the dragon together would have been hard put to produce the nearly eight and a half million lightning strokes that jab into the earth every twenty-four hours. And if they had succeeded, they would have trespassed the domain of the ubiquitous thunderbird, a mythical creature whose shadow was the cloud, whose flapping wings were thunder, and whose opening and closing eyes were flashes of lightning.

A frightful apparition? Not to Cheyenne, Arapaho, Kiowa, Sioux, Comanche, and other plains Indian tribes. Not to eastern Algonquins, or groups of the northwest coast and Mexico, or Wapishiana and island Caribs, or South American tribes. To them it was sacred and saintly, and it was typical of the super-animals conjured up by primitive peoples to explain superhuman phenomena (as we have seen with the winds, and shall see with floods, earthquakes, and volcanoes). It indicates that men have been watching and listening in awe for as long as they have been lifting their eyes and ears to the sky.

Indeed, Martin Luther said that his decision to become a monk was the result of being struck by lightning—which he regarded as a call from heaven.

For Davy Crockett there was no greater treat in all creation than a peal of thunder. To any who have heard a thunderclap explode above the hickory and sweetgum trees and go reverberating, booming, and banging down into the hollows, this is understandable.

Yet the truth is that thunder takes only second place. Thunder is good, and thunder is impressive, Mark Twain said, but it is lightning that does the work. In all Nature few forces are as instantly explosive as the lightning bolt. It smashes through the sky at sixty thousand miles per second and lasts but a scant few thousandths of a second. During this time it may create as much as 250 thousand amperes of electric current, and rise to a temperature of thirty-six thousand degrees Fahrenheit. This is powerful enough and hot enough to wither nearly anything in the way, and in the United States alone, five hundred persons are cut down each year by this flashing celestial monster.

Thrice as many are wounded, and many more have the daylights scared out of them.

Across the face of the earth occur sixteen million thunderstorms annually, an average of forty-four thousand building up, exploding, and dissipating daily. That in turn is the equivalent of 360,000 lightning streaks every hour, which may seem fantastic to dwellers of temperate climes but is hardly so to residents of Java, where thunder is heard on an average of 223 days out of the year.

With such pervasive distribution, lightning and thunder have been seen and heard by almost every inhabitant on earth—past and present. Lucretius observed how all things quaked from the shock of heavy thunder, and trembled as if the mighty walls of the heavens had been riven and sprung asunder. Clouds became hot by their own velocity, he explained, as did anything heated and fired by motion. "The winds send their growlings through the clouds, and seeking a way out whirl about and roll together seeds of fire . . . and then gather many into a mass and make flame rotate in the hollow furnaces within, until they have burst the cloud and shone forth in forked flashes."

Lucretius knew that nothing could withstand lightning, and reminded Roman citizens that a thunderbolt, like a shout, could pass through the walls of a house; in a moment's time, it could melt down brass and gold, evaporate wine from vessels, break up towers, destroy houses, cast down monuments, and kill all manner of men and cattle.

Despite the superstitious atmosphere of his times, Lucretius insisted that lightning was a completely natural phenomenon. If it were man-made or god-made, he argued, it would strike the sinful only, and not everyone alike. If Jupiter hurled it where he pleased, why then into seas and wastelands, laboring in vain? Why not from clear skies rather than cloudy? Why not as a surprise rather than with thunder? And worst of all, why did the god level holy sanctuaries and temples, desecrating even his own images? No, lightning must be natural, subject to natural laws.

This led to some intriguing explanations of what natural laws were working, and how they worked. Empedocles, the Greek, called lightning the result of sun's rays striking clouds. Anaxagoras claimed that lightning was fire gleaming in the clouds and that thunder was the hissing noise of its extinction. Aristotle disagreed with both. "Exhalations," he explained, were squeezed out of a cloud and sometimes

135

ejected in thin lines of flame. Such was lightning—or the lightning controversy—for centúries.

Back in the days when the Roman Empire flourished from the Rhine to the Euphrates, the laurel bush was presumed to be immune from this heavenly fire; so Emperor Tiberius wore a laurel wreath during thunderstorms. Any Roman house demolished by lightning immediately became consecrated property to be left untouched. Valerius Publicus, never one to shy from daring the gods, once rebuilt his house on the Palatinate after it had been destroyed by a lightning flash. The Roman magistrates were not ones to shy from public welfare either, so they insisted that Publicus' house be promptly and peremptorily pulled down. It was.

From their Etruscan ancestors, the Romans inherited divination by lightning. Their College of Augurs detained the procedures of state until all "signs" in the sky became favorable; if lightning occurred at an unpropitious time, the facts were duly reported and magistrates canceled public meetings for the day. (If Tung had had his thunderclaps *there!* By selling to the opposition he could have altered a goodly segment of history.)

You may still find medieval bells bearing the inscription *Fulgura Frango,* "I break up the lightning-flashes." These bells were once rung feverishly upon the approach of an electric storm but, unhappily, the ringing of such bells in church towers brought death to so many ringers that Charlemagne, so it is said, issued an edict outlawing the practice. The susceptibility of church steeples to lightning has been classically illustrated by no less than the Campanile of St. Mark's in Venice. The bell-tower rises 340 feet in an area of relatively severe thunderstorm intensity. In 1388 the Campanile, then a wooden structure, was blasted by a stroke, and in 1417 lightning set a fire that almost destroyed the tower. In 1489 the tower was burned to embers. Lightning damaged it more or less severely time and time again and in 1745 nearly ruined it. The Venetians must have thought that the Lord had singled out St. Mark's for special attention.

In times of military emergency, gunpowder and other weapons were occasionally stored in the vaults of churches. Such well-dug-in crypts made ideal wartime powder magazines, as was the case at the church of St. Nazaire in Brescia, where one hundred tons of gunpowder were once stored. In 1769 a lightning flash struck the church and detonated the powder, blowing one-sixth of the city to bits and three thousand citizens to kingdom come. A giant powder store was similarly exploded in 1856 in the church of St. Jean on the island of Rhodes, killing more than four thousand persons.

In the passage of men from one milestone of intellectual comprehension to another, there have been numbers untold to whom lightning remained a manifestation of Almighty power. Or of creation. In the beginning, according to some, there was no fire and the world was cold; the Thunders sent their lightning, and fire rose in the bottom of a hollow sycamore tree on an island, and there was life. And there was a world.

To some aboriginal tribes lightning and thunder could be summoned at will by medicine men. The wood of a tree hit by lightning took on mysterious qualities, especially if the tree recovered, for that gave it extraordinary survival capacities. Cherokee tribesmen would not touch it, lest cracks appear in their hands and feet; but their medicine men burned splinters of it and painted charcoal on ballplayers so that they might strike their opponents with the force and speed of a thunderbolt. Hunters prayed to lightning before the hunt, for lightning was a killer, and that was exactly what they wanted to be. Flint, like lightning, gave off flashes, so was held as a lightning stone and worn around the neck to endow the wearer with power.

The ancient Tuscarora figured that the only tree immune from lightning was black gum, for lightning would run around and around the tree trying to get in. Pawnees claimed similar powers for the cedar, and during thunderstorms threw cedar sprigs on fires to turn aside the flash.

Wherever there were reptiles and aquatic animals the train of thought was this: lightning is sinuous, so are snakes; lightning is deadly, so are snakes. The connection was almost universal; and reverence was greatest for that King of Snakes, the rattler. In a Chippewa pictograph a rattlesnake is brandished as a lightning symbol. Micmac legend holds that thunder is produced by seven flying rattlesnakes crying to each other and waving their tails as they clatter across the sky. Cherokees looked upon rattlesnakes as much-prized ornaments of the thunder god, and they meticulously avoided killing any snake, especially a rattler.

In all cultures lightning has been either god or manifestation of god.

Zeus controlled the lightning of historic Greece. Babylonian cylinders depicted Adad, god of wind and storm, with a boomerang (thunderbolt) in one hand and a spear (lightning) in the other.

Many theories were exalted to show how men might flee from lightning or protect themselves. Said an old English rhyme:

> Beware of an oak:
> It draws the stroke;
> Avoid an ash:
> It counts the flash.

In Shropshire, pieces of hawthorn cut on Holy Thursday were presumed to guard any house against lightning because Christ had been born beneath a thorn tree. At Christmastide in Westphalia, a piece of the yule log was withdrawn from the fire as soon as it had scorched; it was safely stored away and later placed on the fire when a thunderstorm began, the theory being simply that no thunderbolt could strike a house in which the yule log smoldered.

If we now know better than all this, it is probably because we have been through the very stages of witchery that set men's minds to thinking. But we are by no means beyond the powers of fable, for even today you may get, with very little difficulty, various sorts of opinions on lightning. It is the devil coming for a man's soul. It curdles milk. It strikes in the North to portend rain, or in the West and South for dry weather.

To escape it you need only jump into water, and hold up a 'coon skin. Or hide the scissors. Or stay away from wet animals.

If you must go on trial (apparently the offense does not make a difference) one sure way to make the decision come out in your favor is to sprinkle ashes from the wood of a lightning-struck tree in the courthouse doorway on the day of the trial.

While man's first serious attempts to depart from these ideas and explain the nature of lightning were clumsy, they were nonetheless increasingly serious and contained the glimmers of rising scientific thought. Jonathan Edwards, in his *Notes on Natural Science*, circa 1718, said: "Lightning seems to be this: An almost infinitely fine, combustible matter, that floats in the air, that takes fire by a sudden and mighty fermentation, that is some way promoted by the cool and moisture, and perhaps attraction, of the clouds. By this sudden agitation, this fine, floating matter is driven forth with a mighty force."

Yet the breakthrough was imminent. For soon began the era of Benjamin Franklin, a man whom Kant would refer to as a modern Prometheus, and whose work would prompt Goethe to say, "The chapter of Electricity is that which in modern times has, according to my judgment, been handled best."

The year was 1752. Franklin had devoted the leisure of six winters to electrical experiments. He had put electricity to every conceivable test. He tried it on magnets. He tried it in vacuum. He tried it on the sick and the well, on animals and men. He used electricity that had been excited by friction, drawn from the clouds, generated in winter, and produced by the electric eel.

He also almost electrocuted himself. He charged two Leyden jars (early types of electrical condensers), each holding six gallons, and was about to kill a turkey by electric shock for the amusement of some friends when, inadvertently, he connected the circuit and took the shock through his own body.

"The flash," he wrote, "was very great, and the crack was loud as a pistol; yet my senses being instantly gone, I neither saw the one nor heard the other; nor did I feel the stroke on my hand, though I afterwards found it raised a round swelling where the fire entered. . . . I then felt what I know not how well to describe, a universal blow throughout my whole body from head to foot, which seemed within as well as without; after which the first thing I took notice of was a violent quick shaking of my body, which gradually remitting, my sense as gradually returned, and then I thought the bottles must be discharged, but could not perceive how, till at last I perceived the chain in my hand, and recollected what I had been about to do. That part of my hand and fingers which held the chain was left white, as though the blood had been driven out, and remained so eight or ten minutes after, feeling like dead flesh; and I had a numbness in my arms and the back of my neck, which continued till the next morning."

It was after this "notorious blunder," as he called it, that Franklin made what his friend Joseph Priestley referred to as "the greatest discovery . . . of the greatest practical use to mankind . . . the perfect similarity between electricity and lightning."

Always before, or at least for as long as electricity had been defined as a substance, nobody had proved that lightning *was* electricity. To many the idea was absurd. Today, of course we ask what else it *could* have been.

The first step would be to prove that lightning was in the hands of Nature what electricity was in the hands of man, that artificial lightning was merely an imitation of the great effects in the sky. Don't be staggered, Franklin warned, by the great difference of the effects. "If two gun barrels electrified will strike at two inches distance," he said, "and make a loud report, at how great a distance will 10,000 acres of electrified cloud strike, and give its fire, and how loud must be that crack!"

The evidence for his theory was impressive. Flashes of lightning were crooked, waving in the air. So were electric sparks. Lightning struck the highest and most pointed objects; in like manner, pointed conductors attracted man-made electricity. Lightning burns, so does electricity; lightning sometimes dissolves metals, so does electricity; lightning rends some bodies, so does electricity.

And yet, Franklin knew that if he went no farther than to argue the matter, *a priori*, he would accomplish nothing. He wanted proof. And the best proof would be to acquire some of the lightning that flitted about from cloud to cloud, or cloud to earth. But how?

The countryside around Philadelphia contained no eminence which he considered high enough for his experiments. His only thought was to get his apparatus, or at least the point of attraction, as close to the clouds and the source of lightning as possible. At that time there was not a steeple in all Philadelphia, and probably none in Pennsylvania. The vestry of Christ Church had contemplated erecting a steeple and had started to build one once before, but had been delayed and had not commenced another. Franklin had been impatiently hoping that they would get on with it so that he could climb to the top of it to test his hypothesis. He must have assumed that the vestry would somehow be amenable to his using the steeple for drawing down lightning from heaven!

At this moment, Priestley says, it occurred to Franklin that "by means of a common kite, he could have a readier and better access to the regions of thunder than by any spire whatever. Preparing, therefore, a large silk handkerchief, and two cross sticks, of a proper length, on which to extend it; he took the opportunity of the first approaching thunder storm to take a walk into a field, in which there was a shed convenient for his purpose. But dreading the ridicule which too commonly attends the unsuccessful attempts in science, he communicated his intended experiment to no body but his son, who assisted him in raising the kite."

It was a sultry day, with the storm approaching. The commons on which the experiment was performed was doubtless not far from his own house, probably near the corner of Race and Eighth streets. (Franklin left no account of this experiment and described the details to only two people, one of them Dr. Priestley.) His son, a robust twenty-two, assisted with the Leyden phials, which were to store some of the lightning brought down.

What a sight it must have presented, however exhilarating to the participants! If anyone had been around to behold, it would have seemed as if two lunatics had decided to fly a kite in the rain—a kite to which, for some odd reason, a key had been fastened at the lower end. Didn't they realize the danger of such an experiment?

"The kite being raised," Priestley says, "a considerable time elapsed before there was any appearance of its being electrified. One very promising cloud had passed over it without any effect; when, at length, just as he was beginning to despair of his contrivance, he observed some loose threads of the hempen string to stand erect, and to avoid one another, just as if they had been suspended on a common conductor. Struck with this promising appearance, he immediately presented his knucle to the key, and (let the reader judge of the exquisite pleasure he must have felt at that moment) the discovery was complete. He perceived a very evident electric spark. Others succeeded, even before the string was wet, so as to put the matter past all dispute, and when the rain had wet the string, he collected electric fire very copiously. This happened in June, 1752, a month after the electricians in France had verified the same theory, but before he heard of anything they had done."

That summer, scientists in every country in Europe were busy repeating the experiment, some with such splendid success that they were struck dead and fell among their apparatus.

Meanwhile, the good doctor kept on experimenting. In September of the same year, 1752, he erected on his rooftop an iron rod "to draw the lightning down into my house, in order to make some experiments on it, with two bells to give notice when the rod should be electrified." He desired now to know whether lightning, which he could experiment with at leisure in his own home, was of positive or negative electricity.

On the twelfth of April the following year, during a test of eight strokes, he succeeded in determining that lightning was negative, and formed a theory to account for it, but two months later he had to adjust his ideas when he found that clouds sometimes changed from positive to negative several times during a storm, and he even observed that the air was strongly electrified during a snowstorm, when there was no thunder at all.

"But the grand practical use which Dr. Franklin made of his discovery of the sameness of electricity and lightning," Priestley wrote, "was to secure buildings from being damaged by lightning, a thing of vast consequence in all parts of the world, but more especially in several parts of North America, where thunder storms are more frequent, and their effects, in that dry air, more dreadful, than they are ever known to be with us."

The lightning rod had arrived. That year, 1753, Franklin announced in *Poor Richard's Almanac*: "It has pleased God in his Goodness to Mankind, at length to discover to them the Means of securing their Habitations and other Buildings from Mischief by Thunder and Lightning. The Method is this: Provide a small Iron Rod (it may be made of the Rod-iron used by Nailers), but of such a length, that one End being three or four Feet in the moist Ground, the other may be six or eight Feet above the highest part of the Building. To the upper End of the Rod fasten about a foot of Brass Wire, the size of a common knitting-needle, Sharpened to a fine Point; the Rod may be secured in the House by a few small Staples. If the House or Barn be long, there may be a Rod and Point at each End, and a middling Wire along the Ridge from one to the other. A House thus furnished will not be damaged by Lightning, it being attracted by the Points, and passing through the Metal into the Ground without hurting any Thing. Vessels also having a sharp pointed Rod fix'd on the top of their Masts, with a Wire from the Foot of the Rod reaching down, round one of the Shrouds, to the Water, will not be hurt by Lightning."

It was to be expected that with such endorsement, lightning rods would come to be highly respected and highly accepted. Installing a "Franklin rod" on the bell tower of St. Mark's in Venice in 1766 halted the perennial damage to that edifice, not to mention the multitude of churches, barns, houses, and office buildings which were later equipped with them.

It was still difficult in some quarters, however, to accept the idea entirely—to understand why the best way of avoiding lightning was to invite it. (Rods were also deplored as impious attempts to thwart God's will.) Someone advised the East India Company that lightning rods were dangerous, so the company ordered them removed from its powder magazines at Fort Malaga in Sumatra. Whereupon lightning promptly struck the right spot at the wrong time and blew four hundred barrels of gunpowder to smithereens.

Equipped with the legacy Franklin left, scientists subsequently began to acquire the knowledge of a natural force that is difficult to photograph, duplicate, store, or even measure.

Today we have tools Franklin didn't have, chiefly aircraft and radar, to probe the thunderstorm, and these probes have discovered that lightning builds up in quite an impressive environment. Where a sheet of cold, dense air overruns a mass of warm, moist air, updrafts begin rising as in a chimney, and reach prodigious velocities. At the same time, high-altitude winds push this thunderstorm "cell" across the countryside, which adds fresh air, fresh moisture, and renewed circulation. Up goes the air: five thousand feet, ten thousand, twenty thousand, thirty thousand, even forty thousand and beyond. And up goes the turbulence, in a condensing, roiling thunderhead.

Warm moisture rises and cools. Ice crystals form. In downdrafts and updrafts the violence increases, like water boiling in a saucepan. When sufficient moisture has condensed, hail or rain may fall. With this, the stage is set for lightning.

The exact origin of electrification in thunderstorms is still a matter of uncertainty. Since so much turbulence is involved and so many things are happening at once, several mechanisms may be at work to charge the cloud. It is known that raindrops, when they freeze, become charged between the water and ice boundary. Hence, water alternately freezing and thawing in updrafts and downdrafts contributes to electrify the cloud. So, likewise, does contact between cold and warm droplets. Electrification of spray driven off by raindrop collisions also helps. There are other factors. Whether these or yet-to-be-discovered mechanisms account for all the charge, or even predominate, is not at present known.

Whatever the case, some parts of the cloud become positive and some parts become negative. Generally speaking, the upper part of the thunderstorm cell becomes positive, the base negative. The small scud cloud at the front of the storm, rolling violently in the throat of the most vigorous updrafts, possesses a positive charge on giant raindrops.

Altogether, the electrical charges accumulating in this complex cell furnish most of the lightning strokes, and it can thus be seen that differences of charge account for different kinds of lightning: cloud-to-cloud, cloud-to-ground, and even within the cloud itself. In fact, most discharges seem to occur inside the cloud or between clouds. Though strokes reaching the ground are less frequent, they may well be more violent.

An active cloud will, during the few hours that it exists, charge and discharge many times. The question is, how from this vast thunderstorm that goes miles into the sky is a slender lightning stroke ten inches in diameter formed?

This, until recently, was a mystery. The triggering of a lightning stroke is thought to be a sparking process in which raindrops play an important role. The necessity of raindrops may explain why snow clouds rarely lead to lightning strokes in arctic and antarctic regions; liquid water is simply not present. Each droplet of rain emits a small positive corona, or envelope, of electric charge, and when the positive droplets of the scud cloud brush the negative base of the thunderstorm cell—wham! It is an instantaneous breakdown in the electrical field—the switch that sets off the lightning stroke.

How the stroke develops and takes the zigzag forms we see is not yet clearly understood in detail, but the process is pretty well known despite the fact that it occurs in a fraction of a second.

An invisible *pilot leader* starts downward in an indecisive, tortuous path to the ground. Depending on the initial electrical push, it advances from three hundred to nine hundred feet and stops. A new charge then advances along this channel to the tip of the pilot leader and pushes it farther. By such stair-steps does the stroke approach the ground.

As this pilot streamer forges downward it begins to "sense" the ground, as if feeling for a point from which to attract a positive charge. If something tall, like a tree or steeple or ship's mast, rises into the sky, the pilot leader will be guided to it.

At this instant the tip of the downfalling leader induces a positive charge in the steeple, which then sends a positive streamer upward. These streamers meet in brilliant display. Terrifically high voltage differences send a shaft of light and heat *upward* at a speed of up to sixty thousand miles per second, nearly a third of the speed of light. This is the brilliant shaft we see.

It drains part or all of the cloud's negative charge in an instantaneous peak current up to 250,000 amperes. The peak endures for one hundred thousandth of a second.

The intense heating builds up a pressure much greater than that of the atmosphere, and this instantly launches a supersonic shock wave in all directions—the crack one hears when close to the lightning stroke. The channel then expands and contracts in violent oscillations of low frequency, sending out intense rumbling at the speed of sound. These low notes reflect from clouds and terrain and reach the ear as thunder, which we shall discuss in a moment.

Meanwhile, the electric current of the lightning stroke declines. The channel becomes cooler and less conductive. But a few hundredths of a second later another stroke may pass along the same channel. Then another. And another. These are dart leaders, and to the unaided eye they appear to be part of a single stroke. But the eye is deceived by the speed at which all this is taking place, and what may sometimes appear as one stroke is in reality several—on rare occasions as many as forty. So rapid-fire are these strokes that they can be observed separately only by cameras with rotating lenses or with film moving at high speed.

Finally the cell is discharged, more or less, and the stroke is complete. After two or three hours the thunderstorm is pretty much drained of its electrification and moves on as a relatively quiet rain cloud, releasing moisture without further fireworks—far cry from the luminosity and violence at the beginning or height of the storm.

Not until relatively recently has thunder received something of the profound study needed for a deduction of its inner nature. In 1957 a young Harvard physicist named Wilfred Remillard began studies that delved into the subject by way of Aristotle, Lucretius, Descartes, Hooke, Arago, and others. Remillard's was a bit of scientific detective work, well worthy of Sherlock Holmes, in which he set up his postulates and confirmed them, one by one.

Remillard's chief contribution was taken from a French astronomer named Joseph-Nicolas de l'Isle, who had, in the early eighteenth century, timed the interval between the lightning flash and the arrival of the first thunderclaps. He also had measured the duration of the thunder. Taking these measurements and setting them in modern perspective, Remillard still could not figure out why thunder rumbled and reverberated as long as it did, why de l'Isle's measurements seemed twice as long as they should.

At length he discovered that each thundercloud's layer of graupel (soft hail) acted like a reflecting shield and not only doubled the apparent length of the lightning stroke—which would account for de l'Isle's seemingly high figures—but also reflected the thunderclap back to the ground and thus set up the noise vibrations. Remillard's investigation of the archives and his persistent examination of the phenomenon under modern conditions had paid off. Such is the mode of man's discoveries.

Inevitably, however, questions remain. Ball lightning, for example, coming down the chimney, rolling across the room, and exploding. Investigators have for centuries been as skeptical as Michael Faraday, the great English scientist, who more than a century ago delivered a considered opinion about ball lightning:

"Such phenomena appear to me to be incompatible with all that we know of electricity and its modes of discharge. As *time* is an element in the effect it is possible perhaps that an electric discharge might really pass as a ball from place to place; but as everything shows that its velocity must be almost infinite, and the time of its duration exceedingly small, it is impossible that the eye should perceive it as anything else than a line of light. That phenomena of balls of fire may appear in the atmosphere, I do not mean to deny; but that they have anything to do with the discharge of ordinary electricity, or are at all related to lightning or atmospheric electricity, is much more than doubtful."

A study of the records of ball lightning discloses much confusion as to the phenomenon itself. The trend of thought during the present era of plasma physics is that some sort of glowing material from the channel of a stroke is detached and stabilized by vortical motion. These "balls of fire" are not illusions in many cases, but they are rare. Competent scientists are studying the phenomenon and may some day discover the truth of the matter. For now, the best procedure is to leave them as a form of that weird manifestation of an electrified atmosphere—St. Elmo's fire.

Since time unknown, St. Elmo's fire has confounded seamen, mountaineers, and many another wayfarer with its crackling, buzzing luminescence. In the days of sailing vessels it seemed to make ships glow. It lighted wire ropes, mastheads, yardarms. It was even said to sound as if thousands of cicadas had taken positions in the rigging, or as if one could hear the crackling of burning grass or twigs.

It was looked upon as beneficial, in spite of the savage conditions in which it occurred. Columbus called it "holy fire" and pointed to it as a good omen. Others termed it *ignes lambentes, corpo santo*, and Castor and Pollux. St. Elmo himself was patron saint of Mediterranean sailors, and his fort and point still guard the Grand Harbor of Malta.

The "saint's fire," as far as we know today, is based on the phenomenon of point discharge. When an electrified cloud floats past a metal tip, or a similar vertical projection such as a mountain top or ship mast, it draws a charge by means of electric induction. If this contact is strong enough, molecules of gas in the air are ignited, causing a bluish or reddish glow. The region about the point is simply ionized, much the same as gas particles in a neon tube light up when electric current is applied.

Yet in places other than neon tubes, St. Elmo's fire presents a dazzling, if mystifying, performance. On mountain peaks one person may reach to touch another and unexpectedly shoot sparks from his fingertips. Halos form around men's heads. Mountain climbers have had their ice axes tipped with flame. Cattle in fields have been decorated with "flaming horns." Captain Ahab, seeking Moby Dick, tempered his fateful harpoon in it. Darwin saw it on the *Beagle*. Shakespeare, in *The Tempest*, drew a clear picture of it:

I boarded the King's ship, now on the beak,
Now in the waist, the deck, in every cabin,
I flamed amazement. Sometime I'd divide,
And burn in many places; on the topmast,
The yards and bowsprit, would I flame distinctly,
Then meet and join.

And could the burning bush observed by Moses on Mount Sinai have been a manifestation of this fiery glow?

As far as can be determined, St. Elmo's fire has never caused severe damage anywhere. (Save possibly on May 6, 1937, when the German airship *Hindenburg,* laden with hydrogen at Lakehurst, New Jersey, exploded and sent thirty-six passengers to their deaths.) It plays about on aircraft and does occasionally interfere with communications, but the tassels trailing from the wingtips (point dischargers) are intended to dissipate such static electricity to the surrounding air. Just the same, St. Elmo's fire represents an electrified atmosphere and the area is *not* safe unless objects within this atmosphere are properly grounded. By that very token, radio and television antennas should very definitely be grounded and equipped with lightning arresters to isolate sets even further from jumping bolts of fire.

There are numerous records of fantastic damage brought about by thunderbolts crashing from the heavens. So unpredictable are the split-second ramblings of lightning that no one can foretell how or where it will strike, and no matter how solid or how sturdily pinioned an object, it can be blown to pieces in less time than you require to blink your eyes. There have been reports of solid rock being reduced to powder when hit by lightning, of holes being blown in stone and brick walls, and of building blocks flying hundreds of yards.

Near the great red pipestone quarries in southwestern Minnesota, immortalized in Longfellow's *Hiawatha,* lies a tangled cluster of rocks about which the Sioux have a moralizing legend. Many moons before white men came to the Land of Sky Blue Waters there was a proud and stubborn young brave who ignored the counsel of his grandmother. He was disrespectful to his mother, deceitful to his playmates, and rude to the maidens of the tribe. He finally became so *waughum ichedo* (snobbish) that he defied Gitche Manitou, the Great, by pitching his tipi at the site of the sacred shrine stone and not permitting other braves to draw near it with their offerings.

Gitche Manitou, angered by this impertinence, summoned a furious thunderstorm and forthwith destroyed the wicked youth—stern warning to other *waughum ichedo* boys and girls who felt they knew more than their elders.

Today the split rocks lie askew in testimony to the banishment of the foolish brave. And beside the quarries, the Legend of Lightning Struck Rock has been engraved for the enlightenment of modern *waughum ichedo*.

The blasting apart of rocks is done simply by lightning striking a moist conducting crack; channels where water, ice, and roots have penetrated deeply can lead the stroke into an explosive shattering of the rock. For this reason it is not a good idea to lean against rocks in a cave during a storm. The cave or overhang itself indicates the presence of moisture paths through rocks.

Something of the same happens when lightning strikes a tree. If the current flows through the moist internal sections of a tree trunk, the high temperatures created by high electrical resistance produce superheated steam that explodes the trunk.

Lightning can rip into and out of a building by tearing holes in a wall; it can knife into a house via a phone line, blast the phone apart, jump to the kitchen sink, twist the chromium stripping into the air like a snake charmer's serpent, pulverize a wood border, and explode chunks of linoleum all over the kitchen. This, though rare, indicates that no matter how effective telephone lightning arresters become, there is still the grandiose possibility of being decapitated at the business end of 250,000 immediate amperes.

Frank Lane, in his book *The Elements Rage*, suggests that lightning at sea might account for the disappearance of some "lost" ships through the ages, that vessels might have vanished without trace because they were exploded or fired by lightning. He supports this with instances of warships exploding in a flash when lightning rammed into their powder magazines.

Because of the spectacle and power, the sudden-burst demeanor, and the expectant interval between flash and clap, lightning perhaps more than any other of Nature's rampages, has lent itself to the fine arts. Mozart, for example, wrote a Kontretanz called "Das Donnerwetter"

(The Thunderstorm). Johann Strauss, Jr., has a "Thunder and Lightning Polka." Beethoven's Sixth Symphony is sparked with thunder. Vivaldi incorporated thunderstorms into two of his "Four Seasons." Passages in *Der Ring des Nibelungen* sound as if Wagner invented lightning and thunder. Music is indeed full of the sound and the fury.

Many of Winslow Homer's oils and watercolors depict a dramatic storm either as a major part of the scene or as an effective backdrop, and John Steuart Curry's "The Line Storm" is grandly streaked with lightning.

Virgil wrote eloquently in the *Aeneid* of a storm at sea:

> Clouds in a moment from the Trojans' eyes
> Snatch heaven and day; black night broods o'er the deep:
> Skies thunder; the air lightens, flash on flash;
> No sign abroad but bodes them instant death.

And Milton, in *Paradise Lost*, wrote

> The Sulphurous Hail
> Shot after us in storm, oerblown hath laid
> The fiery surge, that from the Precipice
> Of Heav'n receiv'd us falling, and the Thunder,
> Wing'd with red Lightning and impetuous rage,
> Perhaps hath spent his shafts, and ceases now
> To bellow through the vast and boundless Deep.

William Bartram, the celebrated American naturalist, encountered lightning and thunder frequently during his sojourns into the southeastern wilderness and in 1773 gave this account as viewed from a farmhouse in Colonial Georgia: "I . . . found secure shelter from a tremendous thunder storm, which came up from the N.W. and soon after my arrival began to discharge its fury all around. Stepping to the door to observe the progress and direction of the tempest, the fulgour and rapidity of the streams of lightning, passing from cloud to cloud, and from the clouds to the earth, exhibited a very awful scene; when instantly the lightning, as it were, opening a fiery chasm in the black cloud, darted with inconceivable rapidity on the trunk of a large pine-tree, that stood thirty or forty yards from me, and set it in a blaze. The flame instantly ascended upwards of ten or twelve feet, and continued flaming about fifteen minutes, when it was gradually extinguished by the deluges of rain that fell upon it."

Mark Twain's story *Political Economy* records the woes of a man composing a complex essay despite interruptions by a workman erecting a lightning rod on his house. "Here the lightning-rod man sent up another call for me," the story goes. "I went down in a state of mind bordering on impatience. He said he would rather have died than interrupt me, but when he was employed to do a job and that job was expected to be done in a clean, workmanlike manner, and when it was finished and fatigue urged him to seek the rest and recreation he stood so much in need of, and he was about to do it, but looked up and saw at a glance that all the calculations had been a little out, and if a thunder-storm were to come up, and that house, which he felt a personal interest in, stood there with nothing on earth to protect it but sixteen lightning-rods—'Let us have peace!' I shrieked. 'Put up a hundred and fifty! Put some in the kitchen! Put a dozen on the barn! Put a couple on the cow!—Put one on the cook!—scatter them all over the persecuted place till it looks like a zinc-plated, spiral-twisted, silver-mounted cane-brake! Move! Use up all the material you can get your hands on, and when you run out of lightning-rods put up ram-rods, cam-rods, stair-rods, piston-rods—*anything* that will pander to your dismal appetite for artificial scenery, and bring respite to my raging brain and healing to my lacerated soul!'"

That men are frightened by lightning goes without saying. Astrapophobia, fear of lightning and thunder, is a mirthless legacy handed down from before the time of the superstitious caveman, and is a phobia common to all animals, particularly dogs. It is a valid fear, for lightning is an outright killer, and no doubt about it.

In the great outdoors, where living things have little means of understanding or avoiding lightning, numerous wild and domesticated beasts have journeyed, suddenly, the way of all flesh. Birds have been killed on the wing, fish in the water. Cattle banding together for protection against rain have been struck and wiped out en masse. A flock of 504 sheep was once abruptly eradicated by a bolt that jabbed into Wasatch National Forest in Utah.

Scissors have been wrenched from the hands of a seamstress, knitting needles from handiworkers, a pitchfork from a farmer's shoulder. There have been reports of human beings completely divested of clothing, of a man having his beard singed, of ladies' jewelry being melted, of a soldier welded into his sleeping bag when lightning fused the zipper.

Yet sometimes lightning serves beneficially, despite its reputation. Without cost to farmers, it enriches the surface of the earth annually by a hundred million tons of fixed nitrogen. The chemicals of air (four parts nitrogen, one part oxygen) are broken down by lightning, and nitrogen is brought to earth with rainfall.

Ever since the days of Publilius Syrus, men have devoted thought to the almost impossible proposition of defending themselves against lightning. Could anything so sudden, so powerful, and so unknown be dodged at all? Syrus took a dim view. Said he: "It is vain to look for a defence against lightning."

Today we disagree, for saving a life (one's own) is usually a matter of keeping one's wits and knowing where to hide. Or where not to hide. For example, darting beneath a tree is an open invitation for an appointment in Samarra; a swinging golf club does a splendid job of attracting lightning on the golf course, as does a flipping steel fly rod on the edge of a trout stream. Avoiding these traps calls only for common sense. Lightning usually, though not always, strikes the highest point in a neighborhood. Why tempt it?

By now the old supposition about lightning never striking twice in the same place should be pretty well demolished. Tall buildings have been hit hundreds of times. Ninety per cent of all lightning casualties occur in rural areas, where people remain outdoors during inclement weather. Surviving is a simple enough matter when you are caught in the open at the approach of an electrical storm—if you follow these rules:

WHAT TO DO IN A LIGHTNING STORM

1. Stay out of small sheds.
2. Get away from isolated trees, fences, tractors, rises in the ground. Take refuge in a cluster of small trees if necessary.
3. Lie flat. Get into a valley or beneath a cliff, or in a cave, or throw yourself in a ditch.
4. Stay out of water; no swimming, boating, bathing, or washing dishes.
5. Get into a car; this is one of the safest places of all, provided it

is metal-top. An automobile resembles a Faraday cage—a metal container with which the British scientist Michael Faraday demonstrated that an electrical charge does not enter a box but is conducted around it. By the same token, an all-metal airplane is equally safe, even though there is now and then an exception to almost any rule laid down about lightning. On February 17, 1959, a P2V Navy patrol bomber was flying at seven thousand feet over the Pacific ocean about a hundred miles northwest of San Francisco when it was struck by a bolt of lightning. The aviation machinist was sitting in the plastic nose cone; the bolt struck below the bubble, entered the aircraft, coursed up the machinist's right leg, and along his backbone to a point near his right shoulderblade where it entered the backrest of the metal seat. The discharge rammed on through the fuselage of the plane, shearing off rivets with one-inch heads and stripping away the plane's stabilizer. The machinist didn't know what hit him. He did not see a flash of any sort, but suddenly his feet hurt and he looked down to see his right shoe burning. With that he straightaway ripped the shoe off and yelled into the intercom for help. Doctors who later examined him expressed belief that the machinist escaped death because his shoulder was resting against the seat.

6. If you are indoors, get to the center of the room, or at least away from walls or from the line of fire between two lightning-attracting objects (fireplace and radiator, for instance).

7. Don't use the phone.

8. Make sure TV and radio antennas are adequately grounded.

9. Avoid stoves and water taps.

10. What can be done if you are actually struck by lightning? About all that can be hoped for is that your insurance premiums were current. However, some persons, apparently killed by a near-flash, suffered only from electric shock and were revived by immediate artificial respiration. You never know. Such treatment should always be applied, at least until a doctor pronounces that it is no longer necessary.

Lightning rods, of course, are excellent protection against property damage, if properly and adequately installed. How much is adequate? It is difficult to calculate what a single rod protects, but scientists think the area best protected is that subtended by a forty-five-degree cone inverted over the tip of the rod. Essentially the total protection depends on the height and location of the tip of the rod; if part of a long building exceeds the area sheltered by one rod, then install another.

There must by all means be a good ground connection, lest the lightning, unable to pass easily into the ground, expend itself on some nearby object, part of the house, for example. The rod needs to be set deep enough to lie in moist ground. Or it can be connected to a neighborhood water pipe, not a gas main! If the ground is dry and no pipes are available, special chemical treatment can be used, or the rod can be hooked to a series of radial copper or galvanized iron strips in trenches around the building. It may be hard work and expense—but so is repairing a burned-out house. Nearby trees do not necessarily offer protection by attracting lightning away from a building; in fact, the root system may be insufficient to carry off the discharge and lightning may leap into the house.

For expanded details, the Bureau of Standards, United States Department of Commerce, issues a handbook called "Code for Protection Against Lightning," which amplifies the mechanics of the problem and answers many a pertinent question.

As time goes on, the theories on which we now depend for our knowledge of lightning and its effects will be revised in the light of continuing observation. One corporation has developed a "trap" that virtually picks lightning from the sky, shuttles it about, and makes it take its own picture on an automatic camera; it also takes "fingerprints" on high-speed and low-speed wheels within an instrument called a fulchronograph, giving engineers such a thoroughly catalogued record that they can forecast, within limits, when and where thunderbolts will strike. Perhaps this will open the way to serious forecasting of lightning. Certainly such researches clear away some of the cobwebs of doubt that have existed ever since the Babylonians worshiped Adad.

Radio observatories have been set up on Unalaska Island and in New Zealand, at the same geomagnetic latitude and longitude in opposite hemispheres. By taking simultaneous tape recordings, scientists have studied how lightning-sent radio waves whistle thousands of miles into space and then return to earth in the opposite hemisphere, bouncing between the poles along invisible tubes of force in the earth's atmosphere.

To the layman whose knowledge of lightning is that it is something to be respected, the ponderings and peregrinations of geophysicists seem wholly abstract. Yet from such abstractions come concrete practical applications that help save uncounted lives through passing generations.

Some scientists are beginning to think that tornadoes are produced in part by the severe lightning in thunderclouds. Perhaps continued research will lead to accurate tornado forecasting.

Lightning-arrester designs have been improved. Lightning research may lead to a better understanding of the upper atmosphere and hence to improved long-distance communications. It may bring us a lightning gun, which could be used as a weapon—preferably in the war against human illness. Ultimately we may learn how to harness natural lightning and put it to work. There is no end to man's skill and imagination when confronted with the challenge of the elements.

10

SNOW

❄❄❄❄❄

Oh, what a blamed uncertain thing
This pesky weather is!
It blew and snew and then it thew,
And now, by jing, it's friz!
   . . . PHILANDER JOHNSON

IN the warm Montana sun, late spring snow lay melting on
the slippery mountain slopes. A fresh fall had brought nearly eight
inches of new snow which piled up lightly at first and then settled with
intermittent freezing and thawing. Steep acres of glistening whiteness
clung at a dizzy angle to a slick underslope of half-melted pack ice.

At the funnel-like base of an "avalanche chute," a crew of four
maintenance men, attendant to a rotary snowplow, seemed to crawl
like sluggish ants along the winding road, opening it for early traffic.

Somewhere on that tense slope above, guided by what whim of destiny no man may know, the snow mass reached a strain beyond its
equilibrium and, with a terrible sigh, gave way.

So suddenly, and at first so silently, did the avalanche enter the
chute that some of the men did not even have time to look up. One, as
if by instinct, leaped against the road bank just as the world closed in
about him. Another had time to shout but the echoes were carried
away in the rumbling, swishing mass that flashed on past, gathered momentum, and crashed down the slope.

It was over almost as suddenly as it began, and silence followed the

156

fading echoes. Or, more correctly, a partial silence, insinuated by little sounds of rocks and balls of snow that continued to roll for a while. Then all was quiet.

Where four men had been, now there were none. Where the snowplow had run, now was no sound. Where the highway had been lay jumbled snow.

Time passed. There was no movement. The snow lay white and still.

After a while came discovery. The air waves crackled with calls for help. The wheels of rescue rolled. Minutes ticked by. There was still no movement on the slope.

The first rescuers braked to a stop and leaped out. Where would they start? And how?

Without a word, without delay, they spread out along the edge of the slide and began to probe. But now they could not hurry. If they did . . . If they probed too rapidly, or too deeply, or too suddenly . . .

Their careful, almost plodding movements had a desperate urgency. In a little while they found the snowplow operator a short distance downslope, dead. Then a laborer, flung near the side of the avalanche and almost pitched out of it into the bushes. He was alive—and mangled for life.

The gang foreman's hat was found below the road; he must therefore have gone over. As the search for him began, across the treacherous snow, the men looked up from time to time. That slope might any moment let go again and carry the searchers to the bottom of the valley.

Minutes ticked into hours. More rescuers arrived. The sky grew cloudy. Leaving nothing to chance, the searchers presumed that someone—possibly the foreman himself—had lunged against the road bank; so the digging began there, gingerly, occasionally with probing rods, always with the fear of injuring the man beneath.

All the time, as they listened and looked up nervously, other slides sounded from near and far across the valley. A lookout stepped away from the scene to watch for dangerous signs on the slopes above.

"Move out!" he shouted once, and then later again, and several more times. The men cleared off the slope each time and waited. But no snow fell, and they returned to the dangerous searching grounds.

What a nadir of absurdity! To risk a dozen lives for two men who almost certainly were dead. But until discovered and determined otherwise, both foremen would be presumed alive.

Fog moved in. Rain fell in cold and drizzling sheets.

A doctor had arrived and was standing by. Yet still the hours wore on.

Then came a shout. "Over here!"

The rescuers dug rapidly but carefully toward the main foreman, back against the roadbank. They brushed the snow away. A hand. An arm. A shoulder . . .

"He's breathing!"

The doctor was already there, edging them aside, crouching to plunge a needle of adrenalin into the foreman's heart.

He was saved. There had been a little melt space around him, a little air. Yet how can human circulation endure unimpaired in such an icy tomb? Can a man be as he was before? The foreman had been buried for eight hours.

Downslope, rescuers found no other sign of the gang foreman, and as darkness and desperation closed in, an order was dispatched for bloodhounds.

With the light of dawn next morning, the dogs were presented with samples of the gang foreman's clothing. Then, followed by rescuers, they began sweeping back and forth across the avalanche.

Half a mile down the mountain the bloodhounds stopped, sniffed, and started digging. The rescuers arrived and quickly dug down to the gang foreman five feet beneath the surface, and beyond all help.

Weeks went by, and when the snow had gone, they found the snowplow. The body was torn from the frame and the battery box ripped to pieces. The cab, wheels, motors, and other twisted parts lay scattered over the rocky slope.

In the endless battle between man and snow, the Montenegrin proverb forever comes true: winter bites with its teeth or lashes with its tail.

Records of extreme snowfall are hard to come by since few measuring devices have been installed in earth's bitterest snow regions. But the measurements that have been taken are shockers indeed.

On March 12 and 13, 1888, New York City fell under the grip of a blizzard which lasted thirty-six hours, lashed the city with winds up to seventy miles per hour, plunged temperatures to fifteen degrees, piled a total of twenty-one inches of snow into drifts twenty feet high, marooned thousands of people, and caused the death of more than four hundred.

That storm was exceeded December 26, 1947, by a single day's snowfall that started at five twenty-five in the morning and by midnight had piled up to 25.8 inches. If there were ever a "snow cloudburst" over New York City, that was it.

Traffic was paralyzed. Even in Times Square, automobiles were stalled by the downfall. State police rescued hundreds of stranded victims from the Merritt Parkway. Stores closed. Patrol cars turned into ambulances. Shipping was suspended. Fire departments sounded the "four sixes," pinning all men to their posts. And while pigeons fled from Battery Park, skiers flocked to Central Park for a glittering extension to their Christmas holiday. One man and his son took to the steep slope on Madison Avenue south of Eighty-eighth Street and enjoyed a few fast runs there.

To remove part of this hundred million tons of snow and unsnarl traffic, the city put thirty thousand workers in action and tallied up a snow-removal cost of over eight million dollars.

Twenty-five inches is a phenomenal amount of snow to a New Yorker; and less than that can paralyze the city, especially when it falls in a single day. But mountaineers and residents of more northern cities might scoff at such a mix-up over a mere twenty-five inches of snow.

Frank Lane, in *The Elements Rage*, lists fifty-two inches of snow on January 21, 1935 at Winthrop, Washington, and sixty inches on January 19, 1933, at Giant Forest, California.

For a single day's snowfall, however, the record belongs to Silver Lake, Colorado, where eighty-seven inches once fell in twenty-seven hours. The greatest seasonal snowfall on record was 1,000.3 inches (more than eighty-three feet) at Paradise Ranger Station in Mount Rainier National Park, Washington. The same station also holds the United States record for highest average annual snowfall: 575 inches.

As to depths of drifts, most records are quelled by the seemingly fabulous report Lane gives that a blizzard in 1891 in Britain filled a ravine on Dartmoor known as Tavy Cleave to a depth of three hundred feet. Perhaps on some wild slope of some wild mountain, even that may be exceeded.

But whether the snowfall is twenty-five inches or twenty-five feet, the common denominator—as far as human beings are concerned—is how well prepared people are to survive. Man is not always ready.

In the winter of 1952 the Southern Pacific's crack streamliner, *City of San Francisco*, plowed to a wintry standstill near Emigrant Gap, California. There thirty crewmen and 196 passengers remained for three days until ski patrols, sleds, tractors, snowplows, helicopters, and a thousand rescuers could bring them aid and dig them out.

A few miles east, and a century earlier, the Donner party—a wagon train of pioneer emigrants—was similarly marooned but met a less happy fate. The plaque on the monument near Donner Lake reads:

> Near this spot stood the Breen Cabin of the party of emigrants who started for California from Springfield, Illinois, in April 1846 under the leadership of Captain George Donner.
>
> Delays occurred and when the party reached this locality, on October 29, the Truckee Pass emigrant road was concealed by snow. The height of the shaft of the monument indicates the depth of the snow, which was 22 feet. After futile efforts to cross the summit the party was compelled to encamp for the winter . . . 90 people were in the party and 42 perished, most of them from starvation and exposure.

Some who starved were eaten by others. Rescuers brought out the rest in early spring.

And it was scarcely a dozen years later that J. W. Watson would write, "Beautiful snow! It can do nothing wrong."

By definition, a snowstorm is a storm—of whatever proportions—in which snow falls more predominantly than rain. If the storm is accompanied by high blowing wind which whips the snow into horizontal fury, that is a blizzard.

Who is not familiar with the geometric patterns of snowflakes? Yet this sheer beauty can merge until the flakes become "aggregates," sometimes mistaken by observers as "giant snowflakes." Some aggregates have been known to measure fifteen inches in width and eight inches thick.

In the geologic past, pile-up of snowflakes big and small has combined with cooling climates to produce advancing continental glaciers that came as far south as the Ohio and Missouri rivers. Mountain and valley glaciers modified scenery farther south than that. These rivers of ice ground and scratched and scoured the earth's surface, rearranging the landscape. Giant boulders were carted down from Canadian mountains and dumped on the Great Plains. Basins were dug, leaving lakes with different outlets or with none at all. And waterfalls like those in California's Yosemite Valley plunged thousands of feet where the glaciers had scooped away deep canyons.

America's record of this sort of thing is not unique. Other places at the same and other times have been similarly covered with ice. But we are led to wonder, now that we have inherited the present-day landscape, why does the United States get so cold? This is a critical question · in the Great Plains, which frequently freeze under the shriveling blast of wintry air from the north.

The truth is that ours is unique among northern continents because in it not a single major mountain barrier runs east and west to damp the winds. Existing north-south mountain chains serve only to enhance the flow of air in a straight chute down from polar regions.

But even though snow has fallen in Death Valley, America does not hold any worldwide low-temperature records. The lowest average annual temperature is minus twenty-two degrees at the South Pole. The lowest recorded temperature in the United States is seventy-six below at Tanana, Alaska, the lowest in Canada is eighty-one below at Snag, Yukon; and the lowest in the Western Hemisphere is eighty-seven below in Greenland. The world's low-temperature record is ninety below, recorded at Oimekon and Verkhoyansk, Russia. Who knows what lower temperatures exist elsewhere? What of the minus 125 degrees noted in Antarctica?

Cold and warm air masses can lead to some strange fluctuations. Cold fronts and warm fronts are sometimes laced with eddy currents that bring on odd temperature shifts. In Rapid City, South Dakota, as an example, the temperature on the morning of January 22, 1943, was four below zero. By nine-twenty it had climbed dizzily to fifty-four degrees. At ten-thirty it was down to twelve, at eleven back up to fifty-five, at eleven-thirty down to ten, at eleven-forty-five up to thirty-five, at twelve-thirty down to sixteen, and then until four in the afternoon it was fifty-six degrees. At five o'clock it was down to eight degrees.

In literature, snow was good. "By abiding of snowe uppon the lande, the lande is fatted." And snow was bad; drinking melted snow would make "the members astonied, and . . . gendereth the stone in the bladder, and feedeth forth cold dropsie."

Painters of rage and storm, such as Maurice de Vlaminck, have turned out compelling canvases devoted to snow on the rampage: Vlaminck's chilly, windswept winter scenes earned him the title "poet of stormy skies."

Of snow on the rampage, the most starkly dramatic action comes when it plunges down a mountain slope in avalanche.

Pearl Buck used an avalanche to excellent advantage in her novel *Other Gods*. Belmore Browne, in his *Conquest of Mount McKinley*, wrote:

"As we reached the open and turned our eyes towards the mountain, we saw that the whole extent of the mountain wall that formed its western flank was avalanching. I have never seen a sight of such overpowering grandeur. The avalanche seemed to stretch along the range for a distance of several miles, like a huge wave, and like a huge wave it seemed to poise for an instant before it plunged downward onto the icefields thousands of feet below. The mountain was about ten miles away and we waited breathlessly until the terrific thunder of the falling mass began to boom and rumble among the mountains. . . .

"A great white cloud began to rise. As it came into view and began to obscure the Brooks range we could almost check off its growth as it billowed upward with startling rapidity, two-three-four thousand feet until it hung like a huge opaque wall against the main range, and then it fell—the range that rimmed our valley was blotted out and the great wave of avalanche debris came rushing down our valley. We were already at work, strengthening our tent in frantic haste.

"We knew that the cloud was advancing at a rate close to sixty miles an hour and that we did not have much time to spare. But with boulders to hold the bottom and tautened guy-ropes, we made the tent as solid as possible and got inside before the cloud struck us. The tent held fast, but after the 'wullies' passed, the ground was spangled with ice-dust that only a few minutes before had formed the icy covering of a peak ten miles away!"

Whether or not it is the most disastrous of Nature's icy rampages, the avalanche, derived from the French *avaler*, which means "to swallow" but originally meant "to descend," is assuredly the quickest, boldest, and most dramatic. The term, strictly speaking, includes the descent of nearly anything from one height to another, but avalanches of rock seem to be more widely known as landslides and are taken up in that sense in Chapter 14.

An avalanche of ice and snow is a deceptively beautiful thing. It seems to break away so leisurely from the lofty slope and pour down the mountain like a liquid sugar frosting. Unknowing observers would scarcely believe that within the avalanche are tons of fury, blinding speed, and the power of infinite destruction. So sudden and so powerfully destructive are avalanches, that man has had little chance to contain them and study them. Consequently, very little is known about them. Serious research commenced in the seventeenth century in Switzerland. Immanuel Kant, in 1817, identified various kinds of avalanches and a little later, Louis Agassiz and others formulated theories of avalanche behavior. The Swiss, acutely aware of the hazards hanging above them, required by law in 1876 that dangerous slopes be reforested and provided with anti-avalanche devices.

One of the world's leading avalanche-research establishments is the Swiss Federal Institute for Snow and Avalanche Research, on Weissfluhjoch, near Davos. Discoveries there have shown that avalanches cascade in different ways. Either a whole mass of snow gives way and tumbles down, or a little snow gets started in one spot and "snowballs" into a full-size run. In some avalanches only part of the snow comes down; in others the entire snow layer is scraped away and spilled downslope. There are other types, but it is pointless (except as a means to an end) to try to confine such unpredictable phenomena within the narrow limits of human definition without more study than has been done.

Like landslides, avalanches do not confine their destruction merely to the path of the fall or flow. The deadly force of the avalanche reaches in all directions. So fast does this mass move, and so violently does it displace the air through which it travels, that it pushes ahead a compressed air column at speeds exceeding a hundred miles an hour—enough to smash houses to kindling. Trees and poles are bent, twisted, and snapped by this wind before the avalanche proper strikes them. Some of the wildest avalanches have killed people from a distance of half a mile, choking and strangling them with fine powdery snow. And just as the plunging mass pushes high pressure ahead, so does it leave low pressure at the sides and behind—resulting in a sucking power strong enough to tear glass out of houses, pull people through windows, and even demolish houses entirely.

Nor do avalanches plunge very often down exceptionally steep slopes, the point being that small snow masses slide down as they accumulate, thus preventing the buildup of large masses. The greatest danger comes from those slopes inclined between twenty-two and sixty degrees, although snow has been known to descend flatter slopes.

The speed of an avalanche depends primarily on the condition of the snow. The wetter it is, the slower the avalanche. The drier, the faster. A skier may scoot out of the path of a wet-snow avalanche, for these do little more than creep down the side of the mountain. But if the snow is dry and powdery, it may hurtle downhill at speeds of three hundred miles per hour.

Escape? Perhaps. If a skier is lucky, the avalanche that closes in on him may be coming down at no more than twenty miles an hour, and can be outrun. Most avalanches mean deadlier business than that. Like landslides, they frequently gain so much momentum that they run clear across a valley and ram into mountains on the opposite side.

How soon a snow mass breaks and rolls is dependent on several things. Water content, for one. Of the snowfield with more than ten per cent water, beware. Its weight is increasing beyond the power of the internal cohesion that holds it together. Wind has an effect, too. Especially a warm wind that starts the thaw. Winds shift masses of snow from place to place, and in so shifting sometimes loosen a poised slope. Temperature changes, too, cause snowfield adjustments and a consequent splitting off of avalanche material. And then you hear stories that a mere yell (or yodel) will precipitate the avalanche. True? Yes. Swiss guides, taking no chances, even prohibit talking when their parties cross a dangerous slope.

The United States Forest Service approaches the subject differently. The *Snow Avalanches* handbook says: "Tradition has long regarded the sound of a human voice as an avalanche trigger. However, it has not been clearly demonstrated that such a weak force as the sound waves from voices can cause an avalanche. The possibility cannot be entirely dismissed because stronger sound waves, such as the concussion from explosions, have been observed to dislodge slides. It is therefore conceivable that much weaker sounds could trigger a slide when extreme instability exists. Evidence, on the other hand, seems to indicate that many cases where the fall of an avalanche has been attributed to sound may actually have occurred because the collapse or fracture of the snow cover was propagated over long distances. It has been observed that such a collapse can travel far, even over level ground. Local mechanical disturbance of unstable snow, instead of sound waves in the air, may thus at times be responsible for distant avalanche releases."

While avalanches roar down mountain ranges all over the world, they are particularly destructive in the Alps and Andes. Peru's 22,205-foot Huascaran massif has yielded great snow and rock slides that wiped out mountain villages—five thousand persons buried under a 1941 slide, four thousand under one in 1962. In the Alps, filled with vacationing skiers, more than ten thousand avalanches fall each year, not counting those beyond sight and hearing of men.

The worst instances of destruction took place on the Austrian-Italian front during World War I (December, 1916) when various avalanches were released on purpose—as weapons of war. Their effectiveness is attested by the fact that some six thousand Austrian soldiers were killed and a comparable number of Italians. One estimate indicates that sixty thousand soldiers died beneath plunging snows during the three winters of the war.

Like other elements of destruction, an avalanche happens so quickly that its victims are dazed. Joseph Wechsberg, in his book *Avalanche!*, gives a scholarly and dramatic account of events in the Austrian village of Blons in 1954:

"Albert called out for his father and mother and Valentin," a few moments after the first avalanche struck. "He knelt down and placed his ear to the snow. No answer. He scratched away at the snow and cried. The fog was gone. He could see the slope, but the sight was more confusing even than the thick fog. Where the houses had stood, there was only snow now. Where snow had been before, broken tree stumps stuck out. The slope was white and quite dead.

"Albert got up from his knees. He tried to find Pirmın Schäfer's house, but no trace was left of it. For a while he didn't know where he was; he'd lost all sense of place and direction. He saw an old pendulum clock lying in the snow. The fragile glass-and-wood case was unbroken. The clock was lying there as if someone had taken it off the wall with great, loving care and placed it in the snow. The dial showed thirty-six minutes past nine—the minute the avalanche had struck.

"Mechanically, without knowing what he was doing, Albert stood the clock up in the snow. He gave the pendulum a playful push. The clock started to run again—exactly where it had stopped. Albert didn't know, of course (and it would hardly have mattered to him), that the clock had been swept down over nine hundred feet, all the way . . . to the bottom of the valley. The living-room was gone and the house was gone and most of the slope was gone, but the clock had arrived safely and was running again.

"The ways of the avalanche are strange and unpredictable."

Of the ninety houses in Blons, thirty-four were destroyed. Says Wechsberg: "No other recorded avalanche in modern history has done so much to so many in so short a time and so small a place."

An 1836 avalanche destroyed a British inn called the Snowdrop. On March 1, 1910, a giant snow mass plowed into the railway station at Wellington, Washington, carrying three locomotives, some cars, a water tank and the station itself over a ledge into a canyon 150 feet below. Ninety people perished.

For centuries the recommended method of avalanche control was planting forests on high slopes. But trees grow only with difficulty at the altitudes involved, and many snow-accumulating slopes lie well above tree line. It takes only one good avalanche, too, to break off a protective forest like a cluster of matchsticks.

Not until recent years have natural controls been supplemented by artificial ones, some of the most effective of which are tunnels and reinforced stone walls. Walls twenty feet high and forty to sixty feet long have been built high on the slopes, and have been equipped with additional twelve-foot racks on top for extra catchment. A series of these five yards apart has so far proved effective in holding the snow back at its dangerous breakoff point, but the technique has to be tested over many years. Engineers need to know what will happen when a *really* heavy snow piles up on them. Perhaps terraces and trenches would be more effective. Or filling in the upslope side of a house so that an avalanche will slide right over the roof without sweeping the house away.

As yet no method is a sure-fire defense against the many types of avalanches that sweep into mountain villages. Reforestation is still considered good avalanche control, wherever the trees will grow, and some projects require tree planting in accordance with specific laws.

The lone skier on the remote mountain slope has little say in the matter when he triggers an avalanche upon himself. Yet despite the enormous speeds and power of sliding snowfields there is a possibility of coming out alive even in the worst conditions.

WHAT TO DO WHEN AN AVALANCHE ROARS

1. Be alert to what is going on. This sounds facetious but it is not. A knowledge of weather conditions is essential to anyone setting out on a ski expedition; you should know what's here now (condition of the snow and potential danger of sliding) and what's coming within the next few hours. Avalanche danger is greatest after ten or more inches of new snow have piled up for twenty-four to forty-eight hours. Sun or rain, causing deep melting, slicks the slopes and sets the stage for disaster.

Good skiers are thus constantly alert for avalanche conditions. Far better to stick to safer slopes, even if wide circuits are required, than not to ski again—ever. Experienced mountaineers know the rules, as, for example, looking back to see whether new snow is sliding into the track cut by their skis; if so, they do not even approach the steeper slopes.

2. Do most of your snowshoeing or skiing in the early morning hours. Before sunup is safest. Avalanches can fall any time, but the colder and more stable the slope, the better your chance.

3. If you must cross a dangerous slope: climb up to a point where an easy downhill traverse will allow you to scoot swiftly and silently across the critical area. Choose good snow on a concave slope where possible. Loosen pack and harness. Get your hands out of wrist loops on ski poles. Fasten your parka across your face. If anyone follows,

have him use your tracks, and for goodness' sake cross one man at a time.

4. If you're caught: get moving! Ski or snowshoe as fast as you possibly can to the edge of the avalanche. Get rid of all your accessories, or as many as you can, and do it at once—ski poles, pack, snowshoes, whatever you have. When the avalanche overtakes you, swim! This sounds ridiculous, but it's the best thing you can do to avoid being sucked under. Swim for your life, lying on your back if possible and with your feet downhill. Of course, you may have no choice, and the avalanche may tumble you whither it wishes, but do what you can to stay on the surface. Cover your mouth and nose—suffocation is easy in dry-snow avalanches. If you do get pulled under, make a supreme effort to widen a little airspace around you just as you come to a stop, and do it instantly! The snow may harden, pack, and freeze almost at once. Then pray for help, and remember that the great magician Houdini made a living proving how long man could survive in tight and nearly airless spaces if he remained calm and confident and didn't panic. How to avoid panic in an avalanche is your problem.

5. Avalanche rescue. Ordinarily there is a trained crew of snow rescue workers within reasonably fast contact, but if a skiing partner of yours goes under, you yourself may have to get to him in a matter of minutes. Most important is to *mark* the spot where he was last *seen*, and mark it quickly. Use a pole, a scarf, anything that will serve as a pivot for searching this suddenly confused and jumbled terrain. Don't trust yourself on this. Mark it! Go along the slide path looking for evidence at or just beneath the snow surface. Probe rapidly but lightly with willow stick, with ski pole minus basket, or with whatever is available. Check the point of main snow pile-up. Check the avalanche fringes where currents or eddies have flung aside clumps of snow.

If you can't find him, go for help as fast as possible. If you do find him, dig him out and apply first aid. Everyone who skis—alone or otherwise—should know first aid.

The annals of exploration are full of hardship, heroism, and privation, and few equal the experiences of British Captain Robert Falcon Scott, who crossed Antarctica to the South Pole in January, 1912. Amundsen, the Norwegian explorer, and his party, had beaten Scott's group to the Pole by some thirty days. It was a bitter blow—the beginning of the end. Scott and his valiant crew mushed on with the worst possible conditions and ill fortune. They had gotten a late start. Gales and head-winds held them back. Soft snow slowed them. Frostbite assailed them. Temperatures plunged to nearly fifty below zero. One man received a brain concussion and died. Jumbled ice and snow made passage nearly impossible. Their food diminished. Fuel for cooking reached the vanishing point. When they had arrived within a day's journey of a supply depot, and were on the verge of survival, a storm struck—a storm so severe that they could not leave their tents or see their way about. Among the final words in Scott's diary * were these:

"For four days we have been unable to leave the tent—the gale howling about us. We are weak, writing is difficult, but for my own sake I do not regret this journey, which has shown that Englishmen can endure hardships, help one another, and meet death with as great a fortitude as ever in the past. We took risks, we knew we took them; things have come out against us, and therefore we have no cause for complaint, but bow to the will of Providence, determined still to do our best to the last. . . .

"Had we lived, I should have had a tale to tell of the hardihood, endurance, and courage of my companions which would have stirred the heart of every Englishman. These rough notes and our dead bodies must tell the tale. . . ."

Scott and his companions were found in their sleeping bags in their tent eight months later.

Snow kills. It kills some people faster than others. Some men have been submerged in just-above-freezing water for fourteen hours—and lived. Others have died within a few minutes after plunging into water no colder. A person in cold water loses body heat faster than in the coldest natural dry cold.

The speed of the wind also makes a vast difference. "Drives it into you," is the familiar saying. Which means that the cold cuts "down to the bone." Experiments prove it. Windchill charts have been drawn up, and the conditions at which exposed flesh freezes vary considerably. For example, if the wind is blowing at forty miles an hour (a sizable gale), your flesh will freeze at about twenty degrees above zero. But if there is little or no wind, your flesh will not freeze until the temperature gets down to forty below.

---

* Reprinted by permission of Dodd, Mead & Company and John Murray (Publishers) Ltd. from *Scott's Last Expedition* by Robert F. Scott. Copyright 1913 by Dodd, Mead & Company, Inc.

Nature on the Rampage

Probably the chief maladies in snow country are snowblindness and frostbite. Snowblindness—technically called niphablepsia—has been reported in deserts (and there termed sunblindness) as well as in snow regions. It is simply the constant impact of prolonged glare against delicate eyes. Pain begins. The eyes start burning and watering. Then the eyes see double.

Snowblindness can occur on an overcast day because the exposure is strictly a product of intensity and time. A cloudy sky may seem to give diminished light, but don't be deceived.

What's to be done about it? Two things: rest and darkness. Apply as light-tight a bandage as possible. Cover the head. Get the victim to a dark room. Don't use eyedrops or ointment; they can cause permanent damage to the eyes.

Snowblindness will usually clear up in a short time. To prevent it in the first place, sun glasses or dark goggles should be worn. One of the best types is the large, soft-rubber-rimmed goggle with polarized green plastic lenses. (Glass lenses may shatter if you fall.) If no glasses or goggles are handy, cut a slit in a piece of wood and tie the wood in front of your eyes.

A somewhat related situation is "whiteout," similar to that condition at sea when you cannot tell where the sea ends and the sky begins. There is no horizon line. On a snowy landscape, with everything white, one has difficulty judging the terrain and hence deciding where to go. Men have walked off cliffs and fallen into crevasses under such conditions. The rule: don't travel during whiteouts.

As for frostbite, many of us recall our parents or grandparents rubbing snow on our frozen feet as first aid for frostbite. That is probably the worst thing they could have done. But they didn't know.

The first necessity in cases of frostbite is warmth. It is as simple as that. Thaw the frozen parts in warm (but not hot) water, or wrap the parts in an abundance of clothing and blankets. Don't rub. Don't exercise the frozen part. Don't apply snow or ice—that makes matters worse and increases the damage. Don't soak in gasoline or kerosene.

Proper clothing is the best preventive measure. Use mittens instead of gloves; they allow the fingers to warm each other. A ski cap with a wool lining and long tie-down ear flap insures against frostbitten ears. (Knitted wool caps are acceptable, but they do collect snow—and snow melts.)

Ski boots are good protection for the feet. So are half-rubber or all-rubber shoe pacs. But remember that it is essential to keep your feet dry as well as warm. Two or three pairs of socks are better than one thick pair, and they should never be pulled on so thickly that the foot must be jammed into the boot. That begins to curtail needed circulation.

Surviving in cold climates is a matter of preparation, and this again involves common sense. The chief protection is clothing. We may be able to survive for short periods in a scanty jacket, but there should always be at hand the proper gear for extra cold. Outer garments should be tightly woven and water-repellent. A parka hood is essential. Beneath that must be several layers of clothing (even if it looks baggy) rather than a few thick pieces. Fish-net underwear is fine insulation. And everything must be dry.

Fire is next in importance. The universal method of making it—flint and steel—is the easiest and most reliable method of getting a spark. Or a convex lens can be used as a burning glass. Fire by friction is reliable, too, if you know how and have practiced. Don't discount the possibility of matches, of course, or electric sparks from a power line somewhere near.

Skin can sunburn even with the air below freezing. The sun's rays reflecting from snow or ice affect areas not normally tanned. Carry a remedy for chapping and sunburning. A little tube at hand all the time is a good rule for snow-country sojourners. *Semper paratus* is a fine motto for all.

"In the range of inorganic nature," said the nineteenth-century English art critic John Ruskin, "I doubt if any object can be found more perfectly beautiful than a fresh, deep, snowdrift, seen under warm light."

Now as to this warm light. The snowdrift is bathed by spring sun and balmy winds. A trickle begins, and then another, and another. They coalesce and form great torrents of water cascading down the mountains to join the mighty rivers that drain the land. The waters rise and keep on rising as melting snowdrifts disintegrate and add to the burden. The rivers burst over their banks, spreading out to the lowlands and the homes of men.

And that is where the battle of the floods begins.

11

FLOODS

There ain't no Yazoo River. It's all
one thing—the Mississippi Ocean—and
the damn thing's got no banks.
                    ... BRIAN HARWIN

A LONG TIME AGO a man had a dog that went down to
the river each day and howled. It seemed to the man very odd that his
dog should go there to howl, instead of to the mountain top or to the
edge of the lake, or perhaps into the valley. Nevertheless, reason or not,
the dog went day after day to the banks of the river and howled.

The man at length became angry and scolded the dog. Whereupon
the dog turned to him and said: "Very soon there is going to be a great
freshet and the water will come so high that everybody will be
drowned."

These seemed strange words from a dog, for dogs are not generally
thought to know a great deal about the weather.

"But if you will make a raft," the dog added, "to get upon when the
rain comes, you can be saved."

At first the man did not believe the dog, but he built a raft just the
same, in case his dog knew more about the weather than other dogs.

Soon the rain came, as the dog had predicted—an unceasing rain that
filled the creeks and rivers and lakes to overflowing. Seeing this the
man loaded his raft with provisions and got his family—presumably in-

cluding the dog—aboard, casting off just as floodwaters reached his house.

The waters rose until the trees were covered, and the rocks, and then the hills, and finally the mountains and the whole world. Of course, everyone on earth was drowned except the man and his family on the raft.

Although this is Cherokee legend, it might, in essence, be part of the creation myth of almost any human tribe in existence. For the deluge concept occurs in virtually every mythology in the world. No scientific evidence of such an enormous inundation exists, geologically, botanically, or zoologically. But scriptures and legends and myths record it, even if symbolically; the belief has persisted in written and unwritten codes and cultures for centuries and will no doubt be pursued for as long as men may think. Or for as long as they may try to explain it.

"And the waters prevailed exceedingly upon the earth," it is related in *Genesis;* "and all the high hills, that were under the whole heaven, were covered. Fifteen cubits upward did the waters prevail; and the mountains were covered. And all flesh died that moved upon the earth, both of fowl, and of cattle, and of beast, and of every creeping thing that creepeth upon the earth, and every man . . . and Noah only remained 'alive, and they that were with him in the ark. And the waters. prevailed upon the earth an hundred and fifty days."

Considering the magnitude some local floods attain, it is little wonder the ancients assumed point-blank that the whole world was being lapped up by floodwaters. Theirs was.

In North America alone floods figure in the creation of the world in hundreds of legends. Down across Latin America, deluge myths are universal. Inca mythology holds that the flood was wrought by the god Viracocha, who was disenchanted with the first men. Other causes for the great flood are known: the killing of a supernatural boa (Jivaro and Murato Indians), a wounded water spirit (Bororo), felling of the Tree of Life (Guiana tribes), broken water gourds (Caraja), overflowing of a kettle (Ipurina), rivalry of two monstrous serpents (Araucanians), violation of a menstrual tabu (Toba).

Some tribes came close to the truth—excessive rains, sudden overflowing of water, swelling of the sea. In more than one mythology the mountains, to which survivors clung, grew higher and higher as the waters rose, and there were variants of the Ark escape concept, perhaps the most quaint of which belongs to the Chiriguano, Guarayu, and Chane: the sole survivors were a little boy and a little girl who had been placed in a calabash.

It was legend based on legend, derived from the fundamentals of the earth's creation. Some tribes divided all their gods into four omnipotent classes: earth, windmakers, fire, and water. Hostility flared between the fire people and the water people, of course, but the water gods were life-givers and therefore preservers of peace.

It takes only a sampling of widely separated, disconnected tribes and beliefs to see that the influence of floods is a great one. And whosoever believes all floods restricted to regions of humid climate and excessive rainfall may forthwith cast the notion off. Deserts and swamps are alike in this respect: they both have floods.

However others may deplore the devastation, Egyptians had a different outlook. Their harvests were wholly dependent upon the floods. Each year by the turn of May the Nile shrinks, and June is a time of worry. Had ample offerings gone to the gods?

Each year the flood came, a renewal of life to the parched valley. And the Egyptians kept right on assuring that the floods would always come. Hâpi was their Nile god, even sometimes king of gods. Cities were named after him. Lavish offerings were made to him. Rameses III paid him great honor. Thousands of figurines of Hâpi were fashioned from gold and silver, copper, lead, turquoise, lapis lazuli, and clay. But what for Isis? Her tears, they said, ran down the Nile and gave the land and its people life.

The floods came and there was rejoicing, and the Nile rose more than twenty feet. Then the praying went on, with a new plea. Would the waters recede in time? Months later they did, and so the peasants waded into the soggy fields and plowed and sowed before the mud hardened. Then followed months of irrigation, then the harvest, then the treading. How many millennia this transpired no one can say; almost certainly it went back to the dawn of civilization.

In the words of Emil Ludwig, author of *The Nile*: "Man's struggle with the Nile is like the struggle for a deeply loved woman; the man who masters the river is never sure of it, and never knows whether he will not himself be overcome. . . ."

Mississippi flood history dates from Spanish explorer Hernando de

Soto, whose progress westward was halted by floods in 1543, at some undetermined site on the lower river. La Salle saw vast regions flooded in 1684, and when the lower Mississippi was settled, the King of France specified that those who received grants of title to their lands must construct levees to prevent overflow. Settlers at Harpers Ferry fled from their cabins in 1748 (and after) when the Potomac River rampaged.

George Washington, on one of his first military maneuvers, is reported to have almost lost his life in 1754 while crossing the flooded Allegheny at what is now Pittsburgh.

Floods troubled George Rogers Clark in Indiana in February, 1779. Marching toward Vincennes, his army came to the icy, flooded Wabash. It and the Little Wabash were no longer rivers but sheets of water. "This would have been enough," Clark wrote, "to have stop'ed any set of men that was not in the same temper we was."

In four days of great distress and peril—from the enemy and from the weather—Clark and his men waded the numbing waters, stumbled and fell, struggled to keep their powder dry, and went on to take Fort Sackville and Vincennes. To Clark the whole operation was, as he put it, too incredible for anyone not connected with it to believe.

No other region in the United States is subject to more tremendous extremes of wetness and dryness than the Missouri Basin, and the French explorers Marquette and Joliet saw "nothing more frightful" than raging floodwaters at the mouth of the Missouri.

Of floods in the canyon and desert region of the American Southwest, Major John Wesley Powell, who negotiated the treacherous Colorado River in 1869, gave eloquent descriptions: "It rains! Rapidly little rills are formed above, and these soon grow into brooks, and the brooks grow into creeks, and tumble over the walls in innumerable cascades, adding their wild music to the roar of the river. When the rain ceases, the rills, and brooks, and creeks run dry. The waters that fall, during the rain, on these steep rocks, are gathered at once into the river; they could scarcely be poured in more suddenly, if some vast spout ran from the clouds to the stream itself. When a storm bursts over the cañon, a side gulch is dangerous, for a sudden flood may come, and the inpouring waters will raise the river, so as to hide the rocks before your eyes."

Ever since pioneer days, the valleys of rivers and streams and creeks that drain away the world's normal floodwaters have become more and more clogged by expanding populations. When George Washington and Père Marquette lived, a flood could go raging down a major stream and result in little damage. No more. When a flood pours down a valley today it rams into advancing civilization—and rips that civilization from its foundations. Basements are flooded, phone and power lines destroyed, subways inundated. Engines, motors, and turbines become short-circuited. Fires break out. Highways and railroads are severed, bridges washed out, airfields flooded. Landslides come slamming down on roads and houses.

Out in the countryside, farms, crops, and harvests lie under water; livestock epidemics begin; topsoil and fertilizer vanish. The farmer is overwhelmed.

And then—the unexpected dangers. Hurricane floodwaters in Louisiana have lifted coiling, maddened diamondback rattlesnakes into the laps of terrified refugees. Floods in India and Pakistan wash great numbers of venomous snakes down from the Himalayas, and thousands of persons are fatally bitten.

The most appalling number of casualties occur on broad river floodplains. Because of the fertile soil there, it is no accident that great hordes of people gather in such places, as in China and India. In the late summer of 1955 one of the worst floods in Asian history swept through India and East Pakistan, wrecking 28,000 villages and forty-five million homes. The Brahmaputra, Ganges, and Indus rivers devastated ten thousand square miles, killing thousands of people. Cattle were drowned by the tens of thousands. Under such overwhelming catastrophe, how can you estimate the total loss? It is staggering. And the suffering afterwards is appalling.

The Corps of Engineers, Department of the Army, has estimated that flood damage in the United States averages nearly a billion dollars a year. The Corps is convinced that current flood-control programs cannot hold this annual loss to its present level because expenditures for control are just about canceled out by development of floodplains. To halt this drain on the national economy, the Corps concludes that the nation must either increase spending for flood control or slow down settlement of floodplains—preferably both.

One of the best ways of avoiding wholesale disaster in time of floods is to forecast the coming of the heavy surge. Merchants, warned ahead of time, carry goods to a second floor; endangered homeowners evacuate valuable possessions; farmers remove livestock from threatened fields.

Flood-predicting became possible with the invention of the telegraph. One of the first instances was in 1854, when telegraphers warned Paris three days in advance that the Seine was on the rise. The residents were thus able to keep an eye on the river and get out of the way in time. Italy and Bohemia organized warning systems shortly afterwards, and by 1871 the United States, through its Army Signal Corps, had gone into the business of flood-forecasting. In 1890, with the birth of the Weather Bureau, the business changed hands.

Today, river forecasting centers in all major river basins of the United States stand guard day and night to warn the public of impending floods. These centers are staffed with hydrologists keeping continuous watch over treacherous weather and river conditions. In 1946, when the Federal Communications Commission set aside specific frequencies for the radio transmission of flood and storm data, radio networks went into operation. As long as flood-forecasting is sharply organized, from the first excessive rain-spattering to the ultimate public announcement, millions of dollars will be saved and countless lives spared.

But that is not enough. As soon as the chaos of a flood and its destruction have passed, citizens from Eastport to Cape Flattery begin talking about "flood control." Few realize the difficulty of harnessing a rampaging river. Can we do an effective job of it? Apparently not. So difficult is the task, and so complex, experts say, that complete flood control may be nearly impossible.

It is easy to assume that dikes, flood walls, levees, dredging, diversion dams, reservoirs, and soil conservation will turn every river perpetually to our will. But there is an economic limit to the effectiveness of these controls, and that limit must be concerned with the price.

So—control the water, or adapt to it? In point of history, control may be as old as adaptation. One of the ancient "tanks" of Ceylon (the Minneriya tank) was a twenty-mile-wide flood-control reservoir built three centuries before Christ. Marco Polo reported in the thirteenth century that beyond the city of Hangchow, China, "there is a ditch about forty miles in length, very wide, and full of water that comes from the river. . . . This was excavated by the ancient kings of the province, in order that when the river should overflow its banks, the superfluous water might be diverted into this channel."

Yesterday or today, the most efficient reservoir is a natural lake, whose outlet may be dammed and whose volume swells with the waters and thereby absorbs the force of maximum flow. Man-made reservoirs, whether more effective or not, are enormously more expensive. Ponds for watering livestock help a great deal. The Cheyenne River basin in Wyoming is dotted with thousands of such ponds. However, only half the drainage area is controlled. And sedimentation must also be taken into account. One authority says that about forty per cent of United States reservoirs have a useful life of less than fifty years, but very likely this figure includes numerous temporary stock ponds.

Still, an ounce of prevention is worth a ton of sandbags. Long-distance control does offer promise, but before man can tackle flood problems intelligently he must probe the secrets behind these unleashed torrents and make sure he knows the causes of flood formation.

It isn't easy. Floods are a normal part of the natural scene. When water from excessive rains or melting snow sinks into porous soil—like the lava plateaus of the Pacific Northwest and northern California, or the sand-hills of the Great Plains—there are few or no floods. But most places are not so fortunate. As extra rain falls, how else can surplus water return to the sea than down stream channels that long ago etched themselves into the landscape? River channels, cut only to handle the norm, are insufficient for super-capacity loads. Hence floods are a routine part of the erosion process, phenomena as old as the hills.

Some rain stops in the trees, swelling the withered leaves. Most of it soaks quickly into the soil, replenishing the ground water table. Some falls into lakes and rivers. Some forms tiny puddles and gathers in catchment basins. The excess keeps moving—whirling, churning, roaring, and plunging with a walloping surge into the rising rivers.

Natural levees fail and the boiling waters break out onto floodplains, driving not only with the force of the water itself but with the momentum gained from mud and silt and stalks of grass, and water-soaked limbs and logs: a battering ram of plunging debris. Everything falls and is swept away.

Water definitely alters the landscape, as witness the incorrigible Colorado River in southern California in 1905. During that year the river turned from its channel and poured westward into the Salton Sink, a broad natural depression two hundred feet below sea level and burgeoning at that time with farmlands. A Mexican diversion canal had been draining away part of the Colorado's waters, but had been scoured and re-scoured so deeply by floods that finally the whole river was flowing down the canal.

Attempts were made time and again to steer the river back on course, and time and again it rose and broke through. For two years the river dumped nearly its entire flow into the depression, lifting the surface of the Salton Sea until it spread out across nearly five hundred square miles. Engineers and workmen of the Southern Pacific Railroad tried repeatedly to stop the gap.

Finally, in 1907, the river was turned for good—at a cost to Southern Pacific of two million dollars. But the Imperial Valley was saved.

Nowhere is the power of raging floods more sorely felt than on the very banks of the stream. And of all the depositional features which Mother Nature spreads on earth, few are more attractive to man than the alluvial flood fans—sloping deposits of debris—at the bases of mountains. Especially in California, the intrinsic values of the window with the view are coveted. Mountain valleys, dry ravines, and washes have for decades brought commanding prices. The land is dry, the builder says. Very well drained.·

And how right he is. In 1934, water sloshed in torrents down Verdugo Creek in California and swept out of the San Gabriel Mountains into La Canada Valley, destroying forty lives and four hundred houses. "For many years," said the United States Geological Survey, "recurring floods have filled La Canada Valley with material eroded from the tributary mountain areas. Until comparatively recent times there has been little human occupancy in this foothill region, and the natural process of erosion and deposition had not particularly affected man's activities. This flood found buildings, citrus groves, vineyards, villages, and several main arteries of motor travel occupying the alluvial cones that are the product of past floods and are subject to periodical future floods."

Floods depend on many things: climate, nature of the collecting basin, nature of the streams, soil, vegetative cover, amount of snowmelt or rainfall. Floods over large river basins usually follow periods of warm weather and dogged rains. A series of colliding weather fronts may become stationary over a watershed, unleashing tons of moisture. If the axis of a rainstorm coincides with the surface of a single watershed, a "gully-buster" gallops down every rill, branch, and channel.

New England floods pour from melting snow, or intensive rains. The humid Southeast, at the mercy of hurricanes, gets lashed with pelting torrents and ocean floods. The Pacific Northwest is drenched by moisture raised from the Pacific Ocean; this, combined with snowmelt, floods the valleys below. Down Texas way occur some of the largest and most frequently flood-producing storms in the nation. There, water is lifted out of the Gulf of Mexico, frequently by hurricanes, and flung over the Balcones escarpment, a range of wooded hills west of San Antonio.

You would hardly think this land choice real estate. But you would reckon without Texas tenacity. To illustrate:

At Lampasas, Texas, a ten-foot wall of water on the night of May 12, 1957, virtually destroyed most business houses and devastated a fifty-block area. "Lampasas *Record* Down But Not Out," headlined a story shortly afterwards in the Austin *American*. It was a story symbolic of people whose love of the land is greater than anything the land may do to them:

Lampasas, May 14. E. M. Pharr is writing a story in his head that will never be published.

The presses of the Lampasas *Record*, owned and published by Pharr, are virtually ruined, and there will be no *Record* this week —the week of the biggest story in Lampasas history.

It is the first story about Lampasas Pharr has missed in 32 years since he bought the pioneer newspaper in 1925.

Sunday night when the wall of flood water from Sulphur Creek swept through Lampasas, the *Record* office was drowned under five and one-half feet of dirty, muddy water. . . .

A newspaper perhaps more than anything else reflects the life of a city. The Lampasas *Record*, through the years since its establishment in 1905, has told the story of the city's growth, of its heartaches, of its triumphs.

Now again, the *Record* is reflecting what has happened at Lampasas.

When Pharr says, "We will be back in business in two or three weeks," he is also reflecting a city's indomitable spirit. Lampasas, also, will be "back in business" soon after the worst blow in its history.

But lest we assume that Texas—with the biggest of everything else—has the biggest of the nation's floods, let us turn to other case histories and examine some of the other causes of floods.

One is *abnormally heavy rainfall*. On the afternoon of June 3, 1921, a series of cloudbursts opened up along the eastern slope of the Colorado Rockies near Pikes Peak. Fourteen inches of precipitation fell, raising the Arkansas River to alarming proportions. Hundreds of people rushed to the levee at Pueblo to watch the flood: when the embankments broke, many were cut off from high ground. Some attempted to swim back. They failed. Inside houses in the lowlands others, who had ignored the warnings, waited, trapped. One hundred and twenty people died, and the damage rose to twenty-five million dollars.

The Columbia River basin was buried under the most damaging flood (in terms of economic loss) in its history during the spring of 1948. Vanport, Oregon, and parts of Portland went under. So did other cities and towns, as well as industrial sites and farmlands. Forty lives were lost and sixty thousand persons made homeless. The property damage amounted to two hundred million dollars. All because of months-long precipitation, deep snow on the mountain slopes, and the sudden arrival of hot weather accompanied by thunderstorms and rain, rain, rain.

But months of rainfall are not essential; floods can move instantly if other conditions are right. On June 14, 1903, a cloudburst, accompanied by hail, struck an area of twenty square miles in the foothills of the Blue Mountains on Oregon's Willow Creek. While the precipitation was only about 1.5 inches at the town of Heppner, it was larger over the rest of the basin. The storm lasted half an hour; the flood lasted less than an hour. Yet a wave of water twenty to twenty-five feet high swept down the creek, taking everything with it. One-third of Heppner washed away and over two hundred persons (one-seventh of the town's population) were drowned.

Snow can melt rapidly and start floods, but not always without additional conditions being present. An extraordinarily heavy snow need not mean disastrous floods to follow. Sudden thaw and persistent rain will do the job, of course, but if the snow melts slowly, through a gradually warming spring, the excess trickles down normal passage-ways in normal volume. Big floods roll when a rainy thaw suddenly ends a snowy winter.

In 1928, for most of March, the western Adirondacks lay under a prolonged icy spell in which the temperature averaged twenty-four degrees. Heavy snow blanketed the mountains and filled the valleys. Then on April 3 the temperature rose into the seventies for five days—five days of clear warm weather and no rain. This sudden thaw pro-duced the highest flood in thirty years on the Black River.

In the colder climates of the world a time of ice-melt comes which brings the annual breakup, or debacle. Stream ice cracks and jams and swells, tearing loose from the banks. The ice run starts. All at once the river is on the move. Ice chunks claw and gouge at the riverbanks, grinding, ripping, shattering, and crushing in a seething chaos of force and energy. Ultimately the ice disintegrates to slush and melts, where-upon the river flows bankfull—and perhaps overflows.

But suppose the ice should not melt rapidly enough. Suppose the river should be choked with collecting ice chunks. Then a jam soon forms which, as effectively as any other kind of a dam, backs up the water into a threatening reservoir. In the winter of 1917-1918 the Mississippi was choked with ice from Memphis north. In the middle of December this ice began to jam on the Ohio River between Warsaw, Kentucky, and Rising Sun, Indiana; ice chunks accumulated, forming a dam that lasted for nearly two months. Ultimately the jam reached dimensions of thirty feet deep and twelve miles long. By the time it broke, backwater extended more than a hundred miles upriver.

Ice jams rarely result in loss of life or extensive damage because they can be dynamited before they grow too big and dangerous. In Alaska, the Knik Glacier, northeast of Anchorage, blocks a tributary each win-ter and spring melting forms a lake called Lake George. When the lake overflows and cuts an outlet through the glacier the waters burst down the Knik River at nearly a million cubic feet per second. The people of Palmer have a gambling pool to select the exact date and time that the flood peak will pass under the bridge on the Anchorage-Palmer high-way.

There are other causes of floods. *Collapse of impoundments*, though chiefly man-made and beyond the scope of our treatment here, cause spectacular floods. *Seismic waves* and *seiches*, the dramatic "tidal" waves, are detailed in the following chapter.

Similar in effect to seismic waves are floods that result from *storm waves* from the sea. Of these, the Dutch are intimately aware.

For days, according to an account published in Amsterdam, high waves had raged in the North Sea and a heavy toll of ships and people had been tallied. Now, on the last day of January, 1953, the storm was moving dangerously close to the coasts of Britain and Holland. As it came closer, it grew worse.

Much about the storm's approach was familiar—people in the low-lying coastlands braced themselves each winter for dire gales from the north. Now something else was happening, a combination of events that might occur only once in five hundred years. The full moon that night would raise the tides to their highest for the year. And on every mind was the same question: would the dikes hold?

The storm might have veered. It might have slowed down. The waves might have abated a trifle. Maybe even the hundred-mile-an-hour winds could have been tempered a bit. But not at all—everything fell into line. The restless seas were drawn above the highest tide lines and funneled by raging winds into the shallow bottleneck of the North Sea.

Calmly the dikes collapsed, and the foaming sea swept down into Holland.

At Stavenisse, volunteers desperately raced to shore up dike defenses —but all too late. A twelve-foot wall of water was on the loose.

The wind increased, roaring and howling across the icy, eerie landscape. A score of villages in Zeeland lay directly in the path of the water, and every available hand who could be rounded up went out to warn the sleeping residents. They rang church bells and set off rusted air-raid sirens. But how could these be heard over the howling wind and roaring waters? A twenty-four-year-old girl named Iny van Nierop, aroused by the flood roar, pulled a cardigan over her pajamas and raced outside into knee-deep water. Struggling from one farmhouse to another she shouted: "The dike is giving way!"

The flood struck. Farmhouses crumbled one by one and by the dozen. Floating furniture turned into battering rams and stove in whole walls. Beams, doors, and railings bobbed in the waters and swirled on to maul the bodies that were whirlpooling in the darkness. Over two hundred people drowned in Stavenisse.

Village after village washed away. People fled for their lives. Some carried children. Some carried ragged bundles—a last few possessions. Most of them stumbled numbly through the mud and rubble and water. The wind blew harder, and grew colder.

Refugees prayed for help. For some, help never came.

A husband and wife in Stavenisse saw water pouring into their bedroom and the husband rushed out to get a suitcase so that they could pack a few belongings before fleeing. He returned in thirty seconds to find that the water had risen three more feet, shutting the door in the process. He pushed from outside. She pulled from inside. The waters held the door closed. The wife then scrambled through a window onto the roof, calling for help. In a moment she saw her husband swept out of the front door to his death.

One woman gave birth to a child as the floodwaters rose around her bed; her desperate husband plunged out into the flood in search of a doctor. But there was no doctor. Three hours later he returned to find that the wife and child were gone forever.

One man at Tholen, helplessly trapped upstairs, watched his wife and twelve children drown. A ten-year-old girl's ordeal was to see her father, mother, and eight brothers and sisters drown before her eyes.

A young engaged couple spent thirty-six hours in the raw wind trapped on a dike. Rescuers found the girl dead from exposure. The young man had gone mad.

Another young couple, married that Saturday, spent their honeymoon holding hands for three days on three square yards of land in a sea of roaring water. Rescuers found them nearly dead from exposure . . . but alive.

Elsewhere, human resistance knew no limit. Many a survivor was pulled from tree or rooftop after being stranded there four days; one man hung on telegraph wires for over forty-eight hours and another, caught under the arms of a radio antenna, was still alive when rescuers got to him seventy-two hours later.

At Spijkenisse a husband and wife clung to the roof of their nearly submerged house, she with one arm around a chimney and the other around her husband. Hour after hour the rippling, swirling rapids dashed his foot against a metal gutter. When they were rescued, his foot was gone.

As the news spread throughout the Netherlands, people rushed to the scene almost by reflex action. Students, clerks, professional people, shopkeepers, pensioners—everybody pitched into the job of rescue, relief, and rehabilitation.

"All at once," the Queen said, "the perfect unity in which our people worked together during the war was there again. It suddenly removed all barriers and compromise in our society. We all feel the goodness of working together for one great cause, and in our enthusiasm we work on without noting that we are getting tired, and we give without realizing that we are denying ourselves."

Ships arrived on the scene, despite still-stormy seas. An airlift began. Calls went out for more food, more medical supplies, more rubber boats. And from the Zuyder Zee to Zierikzee the people came, in every kind of craft, and with every kind of daring. It was as if an armada of mercy had arrived, and soon the 133 villages and towns that had been severely flooded were brought back within the sheltering fold of civilization.

Said Prince Bernhard, breaking off a United States tour and arriving back in Holland: "The struggle against the seas has always been a continuous fight for the Netherlands people whose historical task has been, and still is, to wrest large areas of fertile land from the waters. The present catastrophe reminds us of the fact that Holland's fight against the sea is still continuing."

Some 1,500 people died in the floods. Also lost were close to fifty thousand cattle, pigs, sheep, and horses.

It was not the first time the Netherlands had been hit by floods, and probably would not be the last. Wherever the raging waters flowed again, the entire nation would bear Zeeland's motto: *Luctor et Emergo* —I struggle and rise again.

It is a Dutch legend how a little boy named Hans plunged his arm into a leak in a dike, stayed there all night, saved the city of Haarlem— and became immortal.

Like every other rampage, floods have influenced literature. "Waters ascend up, and turn into clouds," wrote Pliny; "they congeale . . . and downe they hasten headlong into brookes and land flouds."

Shakespeare's Northumberland, rebelling against King Henry IV, says: "Let not Nature's hand/Keep the wild flood confined! let order die!"

Berry Fleming's *The Fortune Tellers* is a tense human drama set against the background of a raging flood, and it points up the action of the human mind when the world is overwhelmed with water: "All afternoon she had written down the stages of the river as McLeod phoned them in, up and up, inch by inch, foot by foot. She plotted them on the graph like a nurse plotting a fever. Once she had been tempted to take the graph down when nobody was looking; she liked graphs but there was no use in torturing yourself. About four o'clock, when the trucks had come roaring in with the hundred and fifty convicts, she felt so good about it that it occurred to her to counter the graph of the river stages by devising a graph to show the rise in manpower. Except for the convicts, however, such a graph would certainly not have been impressive, and besides, almost immediately McLeod had phoned in that the river, during the last hour, had risen a foot and a half. She went out bareheaded and drove about the town for twenty minutes, trying to forget it."

In real life, countless flood situations yield countless human reactions to wholesale inundation. A survivor of a Japanese storm that dumped twenty-nine inches of rain on Kyushu said, "It seemed like someone had dumped the contents of a lake on us from a giant barrel."

Citizens of the southern United States are well aware of flood hazards, and they, too, react in predictable and unpredictable ways. Major floods used to sweep into Savannah every fifteen or twenty years. The Mississippi, since De Soto's time, has had at least fifty outstanding floods. In the winter of 1961, heavy rains in the Deep South swelled many a river, particularly the Leaf and Bouie. At the confluence of these two sits the town of Hattiesburg, Mississippi, where, in the raging silt-laden waters, children were drowned, homes swept away, and businesses ruined.

But it was the *spirit* of the people, their reaction to disaster, their unity, that seemed most impressive to Hattiesburg citizens and rescuers. A Red Cross official wished afterwards that there were some way to recapture that spirit. It was something he could not describe.

Everyone within miles plunged in to assist. The Red Cross came; the National Guard organized an evacuation team; a boat pool of Coast

FLOODS

Guard auxiliary personnel and volunteers was made up; schools, churches, and motels were filled with refugees; and businessmen, Boy Scouts, Girl Scouts, Salvation Army volunteers, and many another helper pitched in.

Side by side they worked, and side by side they crowded into temporary shelters. Everything led to a demonstration of "the true soul of our people," as a high school principal stated it. There was no color line whatsoever, the mayor said; Negroes and whites "sweated it out together," as one woman described the work; "it's something I won't forget."

Neither would the survivors forget how, in the aftermath, they would be given a new start in life by the rescue agencies that had come to help them.

"The most important help I can get," said one old man to a Red Cross case worker, "is a home for my mule, Ella. Ella had a real nice home in a shed next to my house, but I haven't seen that since the water came through. . . . It just plain floated away.

"Now, old Ella is getting on in years and can't stand the night cold like she used to."

The request was approved.

Like Ella's master and the other citizens of Hattiesburg, seven per cent of the United States population lives on land subject to inundation. Politics being what they are, the flood policy of the United States has constantly undergone change, and legislative history is full of authorizations and appropriations for surveys, examinations, and enormous construction projects.

Since passage of the Federal Reclamation Act in 1902 the Interior Department's Bureau of Reclamation has constructed more than a hundred dams and reservoirs for purposes of storage, irrigation, and flood control. The Tennessee Valley Authority built nineteen reservoirs for power, navigation, and flood control. The Department of Agriculture operates runoff and erosion control programs. The Army Corps of Engineers oversees a vast system of flood-control works, including well over four hundred projects that may in time add up to a twelve-billion-dollar program.

We have to face it—flooding of floodplains is a natural process, and imprudent occupancy of these areas must be discouraged. It has been, by some cities. Milwaukee County has a program of buying stream frontage for public park purposes. Duval County, Florida, specifies that "no building intended for residential purposes shall be moved into or constructed on land subject to periodic or frequent flooding, nor shall any existing building so located be enlarged, repaired, or altered." New York, New Jersey, and Pennsylvania have authority to regulate encroachment upon stream channels.

Another answer is wise conservation—the planting of watershed trees, the care and control of farmlands, the attention to destruction or obstruction of natural floodplains. Heavy rainfall trickles down root systems wherever there is good vegetative cover, and the soil is not packed into an impervious layer that blocks absorption. The Watershed Protection and Flood Prevention Act authorized federal assistance in developing projects for flood prevention, water management, and the like. By 1961 there had been nearly 1,500 applications for various conservation works.

If man should not, for his own sake, live on the valuable floodplains, what use should be made of them? The best and most feasible uses are agricultural (crops and grazing) in the country, and recreational (parks and parkways) in the city.

It is indeed a familiar problem, this coping with the floods of Nature, and it has been a problem for a long, long time. The pharaohs of Egypt were plagued by them; De Soto was stopped by them; Marco Polo was fascinated by their control. And the future? We can only guess. Perhaps the crushing spread of mankind will, in a century or two, become so critical that floods will *have* to be controlled.

Or is it possible that, with a headlong rush into space, we shall pick up some fresh ideas from those master canal-builders of the solar system, the men of Mars?

So far the rampages we have examined are manifestations of that element the ancients called air—and we call weather. Now we turn to another of their elements—water, meaning the sea—which can be measured and controlled. Not much, perhaps; not much more than wind can be measured or controlled. But conquest of the sea and waves, such as it is, becomes a measure of man that gives us hope for the conquest of floods and snow and rain and everything else that has gone before. There is a glimmering of possibility that all the violent forms of all the elements may one day be at the service of man.

12

WAVES

Oh pilot, 'tis a fearful night!
There's danger in the deep.
... THOMAS BAYLY

In the celebration of *Sannō-Sai*, one of the three great Shinto festivals of Japan, happiness pervades the streets like a breeze from the slopes of Bandai-san. Banners flourish, and paraders in brightly colored kimonos and huge lion-head masks angle down the streets in happy processions. In few places, perhaps, is the revelry as great as in the tri-province coastal Sanriku district, three hundred miles north of Tokyo.

On the evening of Monday, June 15, 1896, great crowds thronged in gaiety for the festivities. At seven P.M., as the sound of laughter drifted across Miyako Bay, a violent earthquake rocked the sea floor of the Tuscarora Deep, seven hundred miles to the northeast.

No one in the Sanriku prefectures seemed to notice. The sake and the celebration gave this night's twilight a dreamlike texture, unpervaded by the curtain of care. At seven-fifty the sea slowly receded from shore, far beyond the limit of low tide. With the surf hushed, the seashore became strangely and ominously silent.

Suddenly a tremendous roar reached the ears of the merrymakers and they looked in terror toward the sea. By then it was too late to escape.

The sea returned to Sanriku as a swelling surge almost a hundred feet high, crashing inland, sweeping a mingled mass of homes, towns and mankind into a raging, deafening torrent. Over thirteen thousand houses were destroyed; 27,122 lives lost.

Even for Japan, to which have come more than two thousand major earth shocks, disturbances, and catastrophes in the last thousand years, it was a disaster of enormous amplitude.

At two A.M. on the morning of April 1, 1946, another violent subterranean earth shock jolted the ocean floor of the Aleutian Trench, seventy miles southeast of Alaska's Unimak Island. Soon a series of waves more than a hundred miles long was spreading outward like ripples in a pool. Almost identical to the waves that struck Sanriku, they headed south at speeds up to six hundred miles an hour.

At six o'clock gray storm clouds scudded across the Pacific off Kilauea Point, in the Hawaiian Islands. In small shore houses on Haena Bay some of the women were cooking breakfast. Sampans prepared to put off from the wharf at Pakala. Most of Honolulu lay sleeping, and the tide gauge in the harbor was making, as usual, its small, indefinite squiggles on the depth graph. Hilo's Kamehameha Avenue lay quiet under leaden skies. In Hilo Bay, the palm trees on Coconut Island bent with the wind.

At six-nineteen the initial assault wave struck the northern coast of Kauai. At the head of Haena Bay, two women, one of them carrying a baby, were standing in front of their houses when the water suddenly rose up around them. They swam to safety in nearby trees while their houses floated off and disappeared in the swirling waters. Not far away, beach sand was dumped four feet deep across a highway. Coral blocks were carried five hundred feet inland, and ten-ton blocks of limestone tossed up on the reef.

In less than an hour, the wave swept around all eight of the islands, leaving in its path the first wake of disaster. Yet no sooner had the force of that wave subsided, when a new and bigger one roared onto the beaches, then another, and another, and still another. The Hawaiian Islands, caught by surprise, were being pounded by the worst seismic sea wave in their history. "Tidal wave!" the people would shout. But the tides had nothing to do with it.

Powerful swells rammed into coastal settlements, demolished houses by the dozens, and knocked over dense groves of pandanus trees. Boats put out, as best they could, to rescue victims washed into the bay. The naval air service dropped lifeboats to survivors adrift in the turbulent waters.

At Hilo, destruction was rampant. Wave force, converging on the mouth of the Wailuku River, ripped out the railroad bridge there and carried one of its steel spans 750 feet upstream. Most of the buildings along Kamehameha Avenue were either destroyed, damaged, or shifted, leaving the street wrecked and rubbish-littered.

On Maui, waves plunged over the breakwaters and roared into rail tracks, cars, and warehouses in Kahului Harbor. Even Marine Corps amphibious tanks were floated away. Lawns and tennis court pavement were stripped off, and thousands of fish swept up onto airfields and golf courses. Where reefs protected the shore, much of the force of the waves was broken, but in open unreefed shoreways the waves bore down upon the beach and plunged inland in a hissing, roaring, clattering pandemonium.

A rolling sea wave of these magnitudes is not just a surge of hip-deep water; it is backed by a terrific sea-borne force that packs a wallop wherever it hits. And sometimes a freak wallop. At Kawela Bay, on Oahu, the wave's gentle lift carried a house two hundred feet inland, floating it into a cane field and setting it down with breakfast still cooking on the stove and dishes still in place on the shelves. Near Limaloa Gulch, waves carried one house along a shore ridge, dumped it, picked up another on the return and deposited it at the brink of high tide.

Fortunately, the heaviest concentration of population on the islands —located on the south side of Oahu—lay protected from the direct frontal attack. In Honolulu Harbor, the tide-gauge went wild with sudden fluctuations, but the water rose only four feet, and in Pearl Harbor even less than that. Few inhabitants in either place realized that a wave had struck.

But in the Kolekole Valley a railroad trestle was collapsing with the surge, leaving its bridge deck hanging by the rails. On Molokai the waves rose gently, pushing inland to an elevation of more than fifty feet, then flowed back to the beach with astonishing turbulence, undermining roadways, stranding launches, dashing tugboats against breakwaters, shifting buoys, washing away buildings, and sucking debris of all sorts into the deep.

Wave and sea oscillations lasted all day—on what will probably be

Hawaii's longest-remembered April Fool's day—but by mid-morning the violence had diminished.

Hawaiians fearfully surveyed the damage. Railroad tracks had been wrapped around trees. Eighty-eight hundred tons of sugar had "dissolved" from the Hilo docks. Bridges lay collapsed, concrete piers and abutments undermined, sugar mills ruined, plum and hau trees uprooted, taro patches destroyed. Total property damage was on the order of twenty-five million dollars. Casualties: 159 dead, 163 hospitalized.

Since oceanographers and other scientists were assembling in the Pacific at the time (for the Bikini atom tests) this seismic sea wave was well documented.

To the seismologists, who also call these waves *tsunamis* (Japanese for "cove waves"), this one followed the pattern of tsunamis down through history. But now the question was: could anything be done to prevent loss of life and property from these oceanic deluges?

Everybody knew that six prominent locations produce the majority of Pacific Ocean tsunamis. In order of importance they lie off the coasts of the Aleutians, Japan, Chile, Kamchatka, Mexico, and the Solomon Islands. Generated by violent sea-floor movements, seismic waves travel at terrific speeds for thousands of miles. The vigor of the attack depends considerably on whether the coast in question is facing the direction of the earth shock from which the waves are coming. Moreover, the submarine landscape helps either to spread and dissipate, or to channel and ramrod the wave's force. If coral reefs are present, they break up the violence of the catastrophe. If there happen to be storm waves at the time, as in Hawaii's case, then the devastation is increased.

The shape of the shoreline can mean relative safety or sudden death. Headlands are not always badly hit. Bays often are, as are river valleys, which funnel the approaching waves into a small space, confining and magnifying the turbulence. Once inside a bay, cross-motions are set up so that the wave force bounces around in a crazy pattern of violence and destruction.

Hawaii did not receive the only damage from the tsunami of April 1, 1946. The waves reached 115 feet up the rocky shore of Unimak Island, in the Aleutians, to wreck Scotch Cap lighthouse and its radio masts. Actually, small and inconspicuous waves from this earthquake were recorded all the way from Yakutat Bay, Alaska, to Valparaiso, Chile.

Nor was it the first time Hawaii had been visited by these sea-borne disasters. Hilo had been deluged before—in 1837, 1868, and 1877. Yet it has taken time for the islanders to learn to recognize the symptoms of approaching tsunamis. In most cases, the onrush of waves is preceded by a slow and quiet withdrawal of water from the shoreline. On the evening of November 7, 1837, the sea retreated 120 feet from Maui's Kahului Bay and the residents followed it gleefully down—delighted to catch the stranded fish and explore a newly exposed beach.

But then the sea came back—engulfing the people, their houses, their effects, canoes, and animals, and flinging them into an inland lake. And all this after the wave had already traveled six thousand miles from Chile.

Not all earthquakes at sea result in disastrous tsunamis—one in the Aleutian deep in 1929 nudged Hawaiian beaches with seismic waves only half a foot high. Of these the public rarely hears.

Nor are all destructive waves caused by earthquakes. The greatest life toll in the history of giant waves has come from other causes: hurricane waves in the Bay of Bengal in 1737 drowned three hundred thousand persons; Krakatoa, a volcanic island between Sumatra and Java, exploded in 1883 and sent eighteen cubic miles of debris into the air, creating hundred-foot waves which swept onto nearby islands killing more than thirty-six thousand persons and obliterating more than a thousand villages.

Earthquakes are rare in the Atlantic Ocean, and so are tsunamis, but one of each struck Lisbon, Portugal, in 1755, and pounded the coast with giant waves.

In point of fact, tsunamis are relatively uncommon even in the Pacific. Last century the average was one damaging seismic wave every twelve years. Yet that—and the havoc wrought upon Hawaii in 1946— set seismologists thinking. How could this wholesale damage be avoided?

Stay away from the seashore? No. Ports at the water's edge constitute the commercial *raison d'être* of island and coastal provinces. Build bigger breakwaters? They help. Build stronger houses? Yes; concrete-reinforced structures at Hilo withstood severe wave pressure admirably.

Locate residential areas on high ground? Yes, again; that saves human life and reduces loss of personal property.

How about warnings? When the 1946 earthquake occurred on the floor of the Aleutian Trench, it took five minutes for the sudden slumping of the sea floor to jiggle seismographs in Hawaii and nearly five hours for the deadly waves to strike the island shores. That would have been plenty of time for a warning. Should distress alerts be transmitted after each such undersea earthquake? Hardly; if Pacific residents were alerted every time a submarine earthquake rocked the Aleutian or Tuscorora or any other deep they would too often move out of danger needlessly, for very few undersea shocks stir up destructive tsunamis. Of the numerous subterranean tremors that occur, the need is to differentiate between the dangerous and the harmless.

Thanks to researches like those of the Hawaiian Volcano Observatory, special seismographic warning systems have been set up, and are being facilitated by radio networks of the Federal services. The United States Coast and Geodetic Survey, according to its chief seismologist, Dr. Dean S. Carder, has developed an efficient warning service to protect coastal areas from seismic sea waves resulting from certain strong earthquakes in the Pacific Basin.

"A seismic sea wave generated by a shock off the Aleutian Islands or Kamchatka," says Dr. Carder, "will reach the Hawaiian Islands in four hours. However, seismic waves through the earth will reach strategic seismograph stations within a few minutes, and if the shock is strong, a bell will ring, awakening or alerting an observer. The arrival times of the seismic waves are read from the records and forwarded by telegraph to a central station at Honolulu. The earthquake will be located within a half hour or so after its occurrence, and tide stations alerted. If a developing sea wave becomes apparent, Civil Defense and military agencies are alerted.

"The whole procedure thus far requires two or three hours, with time to spare to alert coastal areas of the United States mainland and Hawaii. Cooperative programs with Japan and other countries are under way. Eventually it is hoped that the time interval between the generation of a sea wave and the alert may be an hour or less. The seismic sea waves generated by the May, 1960, Chilean earthquakes were detected in ample time to alert most of the coastal areas, not including Chile. Any resulting loss of life was not because of a failure in the service, but because of the failure of persons to heed the alert."

Warnings of a tidal wave were posted and shoreline residents were evacuated in Hawaii on Election Day, 1952. The resulting tsunami, although comparatively not a severe one, caused tens of thousands of dollars in property damage. And the casualties? Six cows.

"There has been a storm for the last twenty-four hours," said John Millington Synge in *The Aran Islands*, "and I have been wandering on the cliffs till my hair is stiff with salt. Immense masses of spray were flying up from the base of the cliff, and were caught at times by the wind and whirled away to fall at some distance from the shore. . . . The suggestion from this world of inarticulate power was immense, and now at midnight, when the wind is abating, I am still trembling and flushed with exultation."

To know the sea and to love it is to share this exultation. And what greater exultation than living alone with the sea, for endless days? How better to understand its power—or man's frailties? Man and his ships are puny and ill-prepared for the monstrous powers of the deep, for the seething force of the waves.

Joshua Slocum, in his small sailing vessel, the *Spray*, embarked upon a lone journey around the world when he was fifty-one years of age. His narrative, *Sailing Alone Around the World*, published in 1900, is studded with superlative descriptions of the might and power of the overwhelming elements. And as might be expected, his greatest adventures were experienced in that ocean of greatest peril—off the southern tip of South America.

"The sea was confused and treacherous," he wrote. "In such a time as this the old fisherman prayed, 'Remember, Lord, my ship is so small and thy sea is so wide!' I saw now only the gleaming crests of waves. They showed white teeth while the sloop balanced over them. . . . The waves rose and fell and bellowed their never-ending story of the sea; but the Hand that held these held also the *Spray*. . . .

"Night closed in before the sloop reached the land, leaving her feeling the way in pitchy darkness. I saw breakers ahead before long. At this I wore ship and stood offshore, but was immediately startled by the tremendous roaring of breakers again ahead and on the lee bow. This puzzled me, for there should have been no broken water where I supposed myself to be. I kept off a good bit, then wore round, but finding broken water also there, threw her head again offshore. In this way, among dangers, I spent the rest of the night. Hail and sleet in the fierce squalls cut my flesh till the blood trickled over my face; but what of that? It was daylight, and the sloop was in the midst of the Milky Way of the sea, which is northwest of Cape Horn, and it was the white breakers of a huge sea over sunken rocks which had threatened to engulf her through the night. It was Fury Island I had sighted and steered for, and what a panorama was before me now and all around! It was not the time to complain of a broken skin. What could I do but fill away among the breakers and find a channel between them, now that it was day? Since she had escaped the rocks through the night, surely she would find her way by daylight. This was the greatest sea adventure of my life. God knows how my vessel escaped."

What is this mighty perturbation we call a wave? What does it do?

Few could answer better than Jack London: "A wave is a communicated agitation," he wrote in *The Cruise of the Snark*. "The water that composes the body of a wave does not move. If it did, when a stone is thrown into a pond and the ripples spread away in an ever widening circle, there would appear·in the centre an ever increasing hole. No, the water that composes the body of a wave is stationary. Thus, you may watch a particular portion of the ocean's surface and you will see the same water rise and fall a thousand times to the agitation communicated by a thousand successive waves. Now imagine this communicated agitation moving shoreward. As the bottom shoals, the lower portion of the wave strikes land first and is stopped. But water is fluid, and the upper portion has not struck anything, wherefore it keeps on communicating its agitation, keeps on going. And when the top of the wave keeps on going, while the bottom of it lags behind, something is bound to happen. The bottom of the wave drops out from under and the top of the wave falls over, forward, and down, curling and cresting and roaring as it does so. It is the bottom of a wave striking against the top of the land that is the cause of all surfs."

If the water moved, navigation would be impossible—it is difficult enough when waves are high. The fact is that water rotates vertically to varying heights and slightly forward and back, so that each particle of the wave describes a circle in deep water and an ellipse in shallow water.

On leaving a storm, the waves spread out. Their surface manifestations become less pronounced, and the waves become swells. Moving at great speed these swells may travel thousands of miles. Ships pass over them without difficulty. It is only when the swell arrives at a distant shore that the violence begins.

For it is then that the wave, on encountering the ocean floor, is cramped, confined, and compressed. The accumulated energy of the faraway storm and the leagues of distance are deflected from the sands and rocks to the surface. With this the wave erupts skyward, exploding into foam, and either curling over in a thundering cascade, or shattering itself to spray against a cliff.

Unless, of course, the original swell has been influenced in its passage across the sea. It may have met a tide and been slowed; it may have coincided with tides going the same way and been accelerated. And, as we have seen in the case of the Hawaiian tsunami, the configuration of the coast on which the wave finally dissipates can reinforce or diminish the final effect.

The motion is generated, as we know, from the power of the wind. Water is fluid; it is subject to pressure and friction. The winds are also fluid. They exert pressure and pulling forces in varying amounts. Thus from a storm at sea come forces from several directions, imparting energy to the fluid ocean. This energy, absorbed by the moving water, starts out from the storm in the form of waves—precisely as pond ripples move out when you blow your breath upon still water.

It is a simple concept, and Bartholomaeus guessed it early. In his *De proprietatibus rerum* (ca. 1472) he said: "In his subtilnesse and violence, winde perceth and commeth into the inner partes of the sea, and reareth up great tempests and great waves in the sea, and stretcheth them, and maketh them spred into contrary countries and parts."

Winds of hurricane intensity along the Antarctic Circle combine to force and reinforce the waves of that region into monstrous cliffs of powerful, surging water. These, legendary among seafarers, are called Cape Horn rollers, or graybeards. Hissing and foaming, they approach an unsuspecting vessel at a considerable overwater speed (variously estimated up to fifty-five miles an hour) and rise like an ominous mountain of water. How high they reach is unknown. Reports from terrified mariners call them two hundred feet high—very likely an exaggeration doubling their actual height, but one hundred feet is amply high when you are in the low end of the trough. The ship is lifted rapidly up the slope of the wave and soon is hurtling forward on the bubbling, foamy crest, only to be let down again until the next arrives. This goes on a thousand times a day, day after day, their crests a mile apart. Said Charles Darwin of them, "The sight . . . is enough to make a landsman dream for a week about death, peril and shipwreck."

Sir Ernest Shackleton, adrift with his exploring crew in the South Atlantic ice pack, once heard a strange, hoarse roaring that seemed to be getting louder. Looking off to starboard he was stunned to see a wave of tumbling ice bearing down upon them. It was a tide rip, two feet high, coming on at about three knots.

They stared in disbelief, then spun the boats around and pulled with all their might. The strange rumbling ice wave gained on them. They kept rowing for their lives. One of the boats was almost overtaken. This went on for fifteen minutes, and the strength of the men began to fail. But luckily the tide rip began to fail, too, and a few minutes later it flattened and disappeared.

Whoever goes to the sea may expect other hazards as well—among them, whirlpools. As in a seething river, the run of tides through tricky terrain yields dangerous eddies and undertows. As anyone who had read Edgar Allan Poe's "Descent into the Maelstrom" can avow, these whirlpools may reach sizable proportions. Even though Poe's story was fiction, it gave a stirring and apparently accurate account of the Norwegian *Malström*, which is not fictitious. Irregularity of parts of the Norway coast makes certain tideways exceptionally dangerous. The strength of the tide increases, and eddies and whirlpools form with the coming of the irregular current. These whirlpools, say the directions for sailing the north and northwest coasts of Norway, are shaped like an inverted bell—wide and round at the mouth, narrow at the bottom. Largest when first formed, they slowly dissipate as they ride the tide, and as others form. Boats and men have been drawn into these whirling vortices, and much loss of life has resulted.

Just as deadly are tidal bores, incoming flood tides which enter the mouth of a river and roar upstream. They consist of one or more waves with a high, foaming, churning front that advances upriver. Amazon bores travel upstream as much as two hundred miles.

The power and distance of a bore is dependent on the continuing power (and hence the height) of the incoming tide. So long as that power remains, the bore goes farther and faster, and wreaks more damage. The configuration of the mouth of the river and the stream channel also help guide the force. As a result, there are some impressive bores along a few of the world's seacoasts. One of the most spectacular is on the Tsientang River, China, where a twenty-five-foot wave may advance as rapidly as thirteen knots.

While it is true that destructive waves are spectacular, we need always to bear in mind that the *constructive* effects are equally impressive. Were it not for the work of waves, including their longshore movements, the materials brought down by rivers might be lost. Instead, this land debris is deposited along the coasts in bars, spits, barrier islands, and other depositional forms. These protect the coast. In many places they assist in trapping sediments. As a result, marshes and other deposits are increased, actually adding land areas. The British Royal Commission on Coastal Erosion (1911) concluded that the British Isles, over a long period of years, have had a net gain of land.

Nevertheless, as sea waves batter the land by day and by night, year after year, it becomes abundantly clear that the shape of the land is by no means fixed. For the power of running water is the greatest erosive force on earth—and always has been.

The force exerted by waves is tremendous. During the construction of the Dubh Artach lighthouse in Scotland, completed in 1872, fourteen stones of two tons each, which had been fixed into the tower by joggles and cement at the level of thirty-seven feet above high water, were torn out and carried into the sea.

At Ymuiden, the harbor entrance of the Amsterdam Canal, the breakwaters rise vertically, or nearly so, with mounds of concrete blocks on the seaward side. During a gale a twenty-ton block was lifted by a wave to a height of twelve feet and set upon the pier, which was four feet ten inches above high water.

In 1857 a storm in the harbor of Sète, France, moved a block of concrete weighing about 125 tons for a distance of more than three feet.

A breakwater at Wick, Scotland, was damaged in 1872 when an enormous mass of stone blocks set in cement and reinforced with 3½-inch iron rods—the whole weighing more than 1,350 tons—was removed en masse and settled to the side of the pier. Another chunk of concrete, nearly twice as heavy, was substituted, this time the whole business weighing about 2,600 tons. And in 1877 *that* was carried away.

Taking all things into mathematical consideration, scientists calculate that the maximum possible pressure of the wave that struck the Wick breakwater in 1872 and did so much damage was 6,340 pounds per square foot.

Such being the force of the waves at their worst, it is no wonder that they accomplish some tremendous feats, leaving landsmen and seafarers struck with awe. William Dampier, an articulate seventeenth-century buccaneer and explorer, met a storm near Hong Kong in 1687 and wrote: "It thundered and lightened prodigiously, and the Sea seemed all of a Fire about us; for every Sea that broke sparkled like lightning. The violent Wind raised the Sea presently to a great height, and it ran very short, and began to break in on our Deck. One Sea struck away the Rails of our Head, and our Sheet-Anchor, which was stowed with one Flook or bending of the Iron, over the Ships Gunal, and lasht very well down to the side, was violently washt off, and had like to have struck a hole in our Bow, as it lay beating against it. . . . I was never in such a violent Storm in all my Life; so said all the Company. . . . This Storm had deadned the Hearts of our Men so much, that . . . they thought of going somewhere to shelter before the Full Moon, for fear of another such Storm at that time."

Ringing testimonials to the majesty and power of the waves have come down to us at every side. The first great sea adventure in Western literature was, of course, the *Odyssey*. Homer gives glimpses of the sea in every phase, though dangers and distinctiveness are far more prominent than beauty and benignity. Two things are striking: the hazards of navigation in ancient Greece, and the vast amount of it that went on. Evidently, the prosperity of the Aegean people at the time was owing in no small measure to trade. The Phaeacians, Homer claimed, were the best sailors in the world.

This extent of their overseas trade seems all the more surprising in view of the primitive stage of the art of navigation. The compass, astrolabe, tables of the sun's declination, and calculations of the altitude of the pole star were still to be discovered. Under these circumstances navigation depended on the judgment of experienced navigators and must have been precarious in the extreme.

The *Iliad* likewise gives us many references to the majesty and terror of the sea. So great were the dangers of ocean travel that none of the Greeks would ever think of setting sail if there were any other way to reach his destination. Constantly they feared that the Trojans would succeed in burning their black ships, in which case they would be stranded on foreign shores and probably never reach their homes again.

Although the Greeks had a healthy dread of the ocean, they remained a seafaring people *par excellence*, and in their homeland many cities were so near it that the people constantly heard its loud-sounding surge. The lure of the sea, of course, was trade as well as plunder. According to one theory, it was not the wealth of Troy which incited the plunder-loving Greeks to set sail across the Aegean, so much as their desire to open up trade routes to the Black Sea wheatlands, which were being blocked at the Dardanelles by the Trojans.

In the *Aeneid* one is never far from the splendors and vicissitudes of the sea. The French author Rabelais dramatized some sidelights on the ocean and its whims in his *Gargantua and Pantagruel*:

"Alas, the mizen sail is split, the gallery is washed away, the masts are sprung, the main-top-masthead dives into the sea; the keel is up to the sun; our shrouds are almost all broke, and blown away. Alas! Alas! where is our main course? *Al is verlooren, by Godt;* our topmast is run adrift. Alas! who shall have this wreck? . . . Alas! do not let go the main track nor the bowlin. I hear the block crack; is it broke? For the Lord's sake, let us have the hull, and let all the rigging be damned."

Shakespeare's plays abound in shipwreck and disaster at sea. In *The Merchant of Venice* it is the delay in the return of Antonio's ships that all but costs him his life. *The Tempest* begins with a shipwreck, and it was another shipwreck that brought Prospero and Miranda to the island in the first place.

The sea is pictured throughout as the arbiter of fate and the disposer of human fortunes. Shipwreck and calamity at sea play important parts in *The Comedy of Errors* and in *Twelfth Night*, where Viola is cast up by the sea in one wreck and Antonio and Sebastian in another. Besides these examples, many passages throughout the plays bear testimony to Shakespeare's sense of the violence and anonymity of the sea which impressed him always, but never favorably.

Nature on the Rampage

Joseph Conrad incorporated in his works fascination for the sea. In *Mirror of the Sea* he wrote: "If you would know the age of the earth, look upon the sea in a storm. The greyness of the whole immense surface, the wind furrows upon the faces of the waves, the great masses of foam, tossing about and waving, like matted white locks, give to the sea in a gale an appearance of hoary age, lustreless, dull, without gleams, as though it had been created before light itself."

When Charles Darwin, on the *Beagle*, was rounding the southern tip of South America, a violent squall compelled the crew to shorten sail and stand out to sea. "The surf was breaking fearfully on the coast," he wrote, "and the spray was carried over a cliff estimated to 200 feet in height. . . . A great sea broke over us, and filled one of the whale boats, which was obliged to be instantly cut away. The poor *Beagle* trembled at the shock, and for a few minutes would not obey her helm; but soon, like a good ship that she was, she righted and came up to the wind again. Had another sea followed the first, our fate would have been decided soon, and for ever."

Samuel Taylor Coleridge's *The Rime of the Ancient Mariner* is a moody and masterful piece of sea literature, tuned to the power of the sea:

> But tell me, tell me! speak again,
> Thy soft response renewing,—
> What makes that ship drive on so fast?
> What is the Ocean doing?

Of the early exploring parties that probed the unknown North Pacific, one of the most nearly disastrous yet successful was Vitus Bering's second voyage. It was in 1741 and 1742; scurvy ransacked the crew, and Bering himself succumbed to the disease. A storm smashed the vessel into the Commander Islands and the naturalist of the expedition, Georg Wilhelm Steller, nursed what was left of the crew back to health. Steller's description of the height of one of the Aleutian storms that plagued their trip is a classic of nautical literature:

"About five o'clock in the morning, we encountered a storm from the southwest of such redoubled violence as we never have experienced before or since; we could not imagine that it could be greater or that we should be able to stand it out. Every moment we expected the destruction of our vessel, and no one could lie down, sit up, or stand.

Nobody was able to remain at his post; we were drifting under the might of God whither the angry heavens willed to send us. Half of our crew lay sick and weak, the other half were of necessity ablebodied but quite crazed and maddened from the terrifying motion of the sea and ship. There was much praying, to be sure, but the curses piled up during ten years in Siberia prevented any response. Beyond the ship we could not see a fathom out into the ocean because we continuously lay buried among the cruel waves. . . . Let no one imagine that our situation is here represented as too dangerous, let him rather believe that the most eloquent pen would have found itself too weak to describe our misery."

Herman Melville's was an eloquent pen, and from it flowed profound assessments of the power and beauty of the sea. "When gliding by the Bashee Isles," he wrote in *Moby Dick*, "we emerged at last upon the great South sea; were it not for other things, I could have greeted my dear Pacific with uncounted thanks, for now the long supplication of my youth was answered; that serene ocean rolled eastwards from me a thousand leagues of blue.

"There is one knows not what sweet mystery about this sea, whose gently awful stirrings seem to speak of some hidden soul beneath; like those fabled undulations of the Ephesian sod over the buried evangelist, St. John. And meet it is, that over these sea-pastures, wide-rolling, watery prairies and Potters' Fields of all four continents, the waves should rise and fall, and ebb and flow unceasingly; for here, millions of mixed shades and shadows, drowned dreams, somnambulisms, reveries; all that we call lives and souls, lie dreaming, dreaming, still; tossing like slumberers in their beds; the ever-rolling waves but made so by their restlessness."

Nearly every chronicle of a ship in a storm on the open sea bears reference to "mountainous waves." Dr. Vaughan Cornish, the celebrated British geographer, made a long and close study of sea waves—including personal observation and sifting of information from competent sources—and decided that the maximum height of waves in the open Atlantic is probably forty feet, and in the Antarctic fifty feet. Subsequent measurements by a shipborne wave recorder developed at the National Institution of Oceanography (Great Britain) showed that waves frequently exceed forty feet in the North Atlantic, especially in winter.

A report from the U.S.S. *Ramapo*, proceeding eastward across the Pacific in 1933, says that at the height of a storm one of the officers standing watch on the bridge sighted a giant wave astern. For a fleeting moment, as the ship lay in the trough, he was able to sight along a point on the mainmast to the crest of a wave, and later calculate the height of the wave to be 112 feet.

At the strand line, where the irresistible waves meet the nearly immovable land, the greatest collisions take place and the greatest wave heights occur. Stones are torn from cliffs and slammed into buildings. Water may rise so high and weigh so many tons that when it comes back down it can break twelve-inch timbers as if they were pipestems.

Douglas Wilson Johnson, in his *Shore Processes and Shoreline Development*, lists some fabulous wave heights, especially at such splendid observation posts as lighthouses. The keeper of the Trinidad Head light on the Pacific Coast reported in a 1913 storm that waves repeatedly washed over Pilot Rock, 103 feet high. One wave struck the cliff below the light and water flew up to 196 feet, with the spray leaping twenty-five or more feet higher.

Johnson goes on to report that at Unst, in the Shetland Islands, a door was broken at 195 feet above the sea. Tillamook Rock lighthouse, on the Oregon coast, has had a particularly rough time of it. Waves have risen as much as two hundred feet, breaking panes of plate glass in the lantern. In one case a rock fragment weighing 135 pounds sailed clear above the lightkeeper's house, one hundred feet from sea level. And the windows of the Dunnet Head lighthouse on the north coast of Scotland, more than three hundred feet above high water, are occasionally broken by stones swept up the cliffs by waves.

The highest known wave occurred on July 9, 1958, in one of the world's strikingly picturesque locations—Lituya Bay, a T-shaped inlet cutting the flank of the Fairweather Range of the St. Elias Mountains on the coast of southern Alaska.

The time: ten o'clock in the evening—about sunset in that latitude. A few scattered clouds seemed to indicate rain in the offing, but on this pleasant evening the air was crisp and clear.

Lituya Bay is a wild and lonely place and you would never think of it as a place of violence. On this evening two trolling boats, the *Edrie* and *Badger*, lay peacefully at anchor in the outer part of the bay, and another, the *Sunmore*, was under way near the entrance, presumably coming in to anchor for the night. Each had two persons aboard. None of the occupants had any premonition of what was about to happen.

Howard G. Ulrich, a thirty-two-year-old commercial fisherman from Pelican, Alaska, had entered Lituya Bay two hours before. With his seven-year-old son aboard, he had swung the *Edrie*, a forty-foot trolling boat, around the long, narrow sandspit that almost closes the bay and protects it from the wild Pacific. Danger lay even in entering that small opening, for there, four times a day, great tidal bores gush past. There in 1786 the French explorer La Pérouse had also entered— discovering Lituya Bay—and when three small boats surveying the entrance were swept into the vicious tide, two were wrecked and twenty-one men drowned. Today the United States Coast and Geodetic Survey's *Coast Pilot* warns: "Enter Lituya Bay only at slack water after careful inspection of the entrance."

Ulrich had entered the bay safely. Once there, he was in a wildlife sanctuary of extraordinary beauty. Ahead stretched the bay for seven miles, cutting fiord-like into the foothills that lay beneath jagged, snow-capped peaks of the coast mountains.

It is a narrow bay, two miles wide at the most. At the upper end it opens to the right and to the left—the cross-arms of the "T"—and into these spurs pour glistening white glaciers. But the glaciers were invisible to Ulrich from the point where he anchored. He could see only the nearly sheer-walled head of the bay and the high, steep, forested spurs that swing down and drop into the water on either side of the bay.

Part of this scene was obscured by a forested island lying squarely in the center of the bay, an island named cryptically—and aptly as it turned out—Cenotaph Island.

The water lay calm, reflecting the distant snow peaks that were reddening in the sunset. Ulrich anchored in about five fathoms of water in a small cove on the south shore of the bay. He turned in shortly and was soon asleep.

After Ulrich, in the *Edrie*, entered Lituya Bay, another boat came in and anchored just inside the spit near the entrance. This was the *Badger*, a forty-foot craft steered by a man named Bill Swanson, who was accompanied by his wife. They, too, turned in promptly and were asleep soon after ten o'clock.

So far as history knows, the only other boat there at the time was another forty-foot fishing vessel, the *Sunmore*, under way near the entrance with two persons, Mickey and Orville Wagner, aboard.

Thus at the moment in time when Nature struck Lituya Bay, six human beings were there to see and to hear what happened. At ten-sixteen P.M. the quiet of Lituya Bay was shattered. The bay, and the boats on it, began to rock violently.

Ulrich, on the *Edrie*, leaped out of bed and went on deck. Steadying himself against the vibrations of the boat he squinted toward the head of the bay. There he could see great avalanches of earth and trees and ice cascading almost vertically into the waters. Dust rose eerily in the twilight. It must have seemed as if the mountains themselves were coming apart and disintegrating into the bay.

Then came the crash, a deafening, earth-shaking crash that issued from the head of the bay.

What the commotion was up there Ulrich could not see at all. He did, however, see the wave. It started in Gilbert Inlet—the north arm of the "T"—and with a mighty roar splashed up a cliff on the opposite side of the inlet. Veering off, it plunged into the main bay, and then in one swelling surge extended from shore to shore, advancing toward the mouth of the bay and the ships that floated there.

Ulrich leaped for the anchor and pulled. It would not come loose. He looked back. The wave was now midway between the head of the bay and Cenotaph Island, thundering relentlessly toward the ships.

Still stretching from shore to shore, the wave was rolling in at a height of nearly a hundred feet. Ulrich pulled on the anchor again. Still no luck. Quickly he paid out all the chain—forty fathoms of it—and started the engines.

The wave was beginning to break in a foaming cascade as it came around the north end of Cenotaph Island.

The *Edrie* lay waiting; there was nothing Ulrich could do. Earthquake vibrations still rocked the boat.

The wave came closer and closer, and then in one momentous surge it struck. The *Edrie* rose, up, up into the cold night air. The anchor chain snapped. The boat was lifted toward the south shore—probably moving over land—then caught in the backwash and returned in a melee of turbulent waters back toward the center of the bay.

The water splashed about violently. Floating logs appeared everywhere. Somehow Ulrich managed to keep the boat under control and steered out of the bay.

Meanwhile, on the *Badger*, the Swansons were faring less well. As the wave plunged under their boat, it lifted them across the sandspit at the bay entrance. The *Badger* rode precariously just below the crest of the wave, stern first, like a surfboard on a tropical wave.

Swanson, hanging on for dear life, looked down. There, an estimated eighty feet below, he could see the treetops on the spit.

With a roar, the wave crest broke, and the *Badger* fell, striking bottom and floundering. Miraculously, a small lifeboat on board was undamaged. As water, laden with logs and other debris, poured over the spit and then subsided, Swanson and Mrs. Swanson abandoned their vessel and made away in the skiff. They were picked up by a fishing boat that arrived at the scene two hours later—by which time they were nearly unconscious with shock and cold.

As for the *Sunmore*, under way near the mouth of the bay, no one knows what happened except that the vessel was swamped and went down with her occupants. No trace was ever found.

On the following day Don J. Miller, a geologist with the United States Geological Survey, chartered a small pontoon-equipped aircraft and flew over the bay at low altitude. Miller had studied Lituya Bay before. He knew what to look for. And what he saw, despite a low ceiling with rain and fog, was something indeed.

"Gilbert and Crillon Inlets," he wrote, "and the upper part of the main trunk of Lituya Bay for a distance of 2½ miles from the head were covered by an almost solid sheet of floating ice blocks. . . . Nearly all of the larger blocks had flat upper surfaces and were heavily debris-laden, and many had scattered, loose, large rounded boulders on their exposed surfaces. . . . As much as 1,300 feet of ice had been sheared off of the glacier front. . . . The delta on the northeast side of Gilbert Inlet had completely disappeared. . . .

"The most striking change at the head of Lituya Bay, aside from the new trimline, was the fresh scar on the northeast wall of Gilbert Inlet, marking the recent position of a large mass of rock that had plunged down the steep slope into the water. Loose rock debris on the fresh scar was still moving at some places, and small masses of rock still were falling from the nearly vertical rock cliff at the heads of the scar. . . .

"Floating logs and other vegetation formed a nearly continuous raft as much as 1,200 feet wide along the outer 3 miles of the north shore of the bay."

Such widespread chaos spelled a familiar pattern of action to Miller, but this had been bigger than anything before. After additional visits to the area, piecing together what fragments of information remained, he re-created the events of the night of July 9, 1958. Beginning at about ten-sixteen P.M. a sharp earthquake displaced portions of the upper end of the bay, astride the Fairweather fault. Slides and avalanches plunged all over the place, but from the northeast wall of Gilbert Inlet dropped a rock mass weighing an estimated ninety million tons. It fell with a deafening crash, forcing a huge sheet of water up over the spur on the opposite side of the inlet. This wave reached destructively to a height of 1,800 feet. Every tree, every pebble, every blade of grass, was removed from the spur to 1,720 feet, and the water reached higher to upset other trees and wash their roots clean.

The wave surged on into the main bay at up to 130 miles an hour. All along shore the deadly waves roared inland and twisted off the trees to sweep them away. In one place the waves reached inland a distance of 3,600 feet horizontally.

So powerful was the wave that at another point a living spruce tree four feet in diameter was broken off cleanly. Four million cubic yards of soil were removed in one swoop. Where barnacles and mussels had almost completely covered the rocks in the intertidal zone, not one living shellfish was seen after the wave. No one can assess how many crabs and bottom-dwelling creatures were destroyed by the settling of wave-borne sediment.

This was not the first time an earthquake had set off a slide that caused a giant wave. On the Shimabara Peninsula of Japan a series of slides and waves in 1792 killed more than fifteen thousand people. Falling earth in the steep-walled fiords of Norway is a commonplace happening, and some giant waves have been generated thereby.

But the surge of water in Lituya Bay to a height of 1,800 feet will very likely remain for a long, long time as the world's record of water propelled aloft by a giant wave.

So picturesque is the action of waves against land that man has always insisted on building villages and homes on delightful promontories.

Many a town and village has plunged into the sea with collapse of the coast, particularly in heavily populated islands. Great Britain, for example. Some coasts erode at the astonishing rate of forty-five feet a year. It thus takes only a few years to deliver to the depths a choice bit of seaside real estate, and the records are full of towns and villages whose epitaph is simple: "Washed away by the sea."

To stop this destruction and fight back against the sea is not as absurd as it sounds. Apart from the very successful work of corals against the sea, man himself has actually been able to hold the ocean in place. The initial objective was to find some way of stabilizing seaside sand dunes. If that could be done, then grasses could grow on them and the ocean's advance would be checked.

In early experiments a Frenchman named Bremontier sowed large plantations of pines on the coasts of Gascony. After that, similar methods were used to fix moving dunes in the Benelux lowlands, Denmark, Spain, along Germany's Baltic Coast, and in New Zealand. One of the most successful of all such pioneering methods was carried out on North Carolina's Outer Banks in the vicinity of Cape Hatteras. Conditions had deteriorated so severely that North Carolina was in danger of losing not only some extensive territory but a number of valuable industries as well.

A century ago the Outer Banks were covered in part by lush forests. On the elongated sandbanks water oak and live oak thrived. So did dogwood, pine, sycamore, pellitory, holly, persimmon, and mulberry —so thickly that you could have traveled half a mile, it is said, without stepping on the ground. Fennel, sweet flag, and cattails burgeoned in the marshes. Industry thrived. Acorns were used to fatten hogs. Tea was made from yaupon cured and marketed by the hundreds of bushels. Fishing meant food for all. Ponies, cattle, sheep, and hogs grazed everywhere.

But the Banks were a thin and sandy lifeline that could not bear overpopulation—or overexploitation by industry. Slowly but surely the horses and cattle mowed down stabilizing grasses. Hogs rooted out everything they could, destroying a vast amount of native vegetation. More and more the winds began to pick up sand and move it inland. Dunes encroached on grasses, then on shrubs, then on forests, engulfing entire tracts of timber, or whatever timber remained after shipbuilding long ago had taken toll.

Soon a chain reaction started. With sands on the move, the inlets practically closed. The Banks turned into wasteland, subject to oceanic fury. Salt water overflowed into the once-fresh Currituck Sound, killing wild celery and other foods needed by waterfowl. Destruction of holly and dogwood trees wiped out some of the greatest concentrations of robins in the country. Field larks and doves virtually disappeared. The greatest haven for waterfowl on the Atlantic coast all but vanished. Fresh-water fishing declined. Clams and oysters died by the millions of bushels under sand blown from the dunes.

By the early 1930's, the sportsmen, gun clubs, and other groups went to work on beach fixation, and built sand hills to protect the inland ponds from sand and tide. It was a quixotic venture, and an expensive one, but it was a start.

However, no major project could be successfully undertaken by private clubs whose interest lay in luxury sport. Conditions continued to grow worse. Fishing villages deteriorated. Between Salvo and Avon, on Hatteras Island, the beach became so low that normal tides ran clear across the island. Travel up and down the banks almost stopped. Half of Ocracoke Island disappeared under water at high tides. The fish and shellfish industry almost collapsed. Said A. Clark Stratton, supervisor of the initial government project which set out to do something about the situation: "All of these facts combined brought the State and Federal Governments to realize that, unless certain steps were taken towards the control of drifting sands, a vast area would be lost physically, causing inestimable damage to our coast line which would result in an economic crisis for thousands of people. Thus it was decided to set up a large Federal project to be supported by emergency funds with the State of North Carolina as sponsor. Some 1,500 workers were recruited and work was started over more than a hundred and twenty-five miles of coast line."

A sand laboratory was set up, data collected and evaluated, weather

conditions studied, field experiments tried out, and a whole new concept of erosion control established over the vanishing banks.

Piles of brush, of all things, turned out to be the key to success.
Winds passed right through them, but not without leaving a few grains
of sand. Then a few more grains. And a few more. The brush did not
offer enough resistance to allow scooping, instead permitted the sand
to build up evenly on both sides. The result was a brand new dune.

Thus was the so-called barrier dune begun, for miles along the coast,
usually following the contour of the beach, and periodically with spurs
to trap any adverse winds. One fence after another was built on the
crest of each succeeding dune until the desired height had been reached.
Then, to pin the dune for good, the planting of grass began.

Months passed and the grasses grew and thrived. After that, shrubs
could be planted, for now the roots of larger plants would settle into
firmer sand—their chances for survival vastly increased.

By the time the job was completed in 1940, a barrier dune stretched
from the Virginia line to Hatteras Inlet. The dune was from ten to
twenty-five feet high and seventy-five to three hundred feet thick at
its base, an enormous construction job in which man's ingenuity was
aided by the work of the wind and the sea. The workers had set in
six hundred miles of fencing, and planted more than two and a half
million seedlings of trees and shrubs.

And then, as if by a miracle, the Outer Bankers saw their world
come back to life. Songbirds and waterfowl returned. Fresh-water fish
swam into Currituck Sound. Oyster beds were planted again. And historic Hatteras lighthouse, symbol of the Banks, had been saved from
crumbling into the sea.

From Hatteras to Hawaii the violence of the wild waves is slowly
being tempered—convincing and heartening evidence that one day the
raging elements may be contained.

13

EARTHQUAKES

And thirty cities' shattered remnants fly,
With ruin and combustion through the sky.
... VOLTAIRE

Oᴎ the night of August 17, 1959, there were eighteen thousand people in Yellowstone National Park. The night was fairly warm, the moon was shining, and the brisk clear air of the plateau country—with the scent of pine in it—lured many a camper and hotel guest to bed early. Rangers patrolled the roads, campgrounds, and hotel areas, and at Old Faithful Recreation Hall some eight hundred employees were attending an evening program. In the wilderness beyond, there was only the murmur of breeze through pine and water past rock.

It would have been like almost any other night in the wilderness had not, somewhere below this serene and restful surface, a network of rock structures shuddered and shattered and shifted. At 11:37:13 P.M. the peace of the wild was broken.

The master of ceremonies at Old Faithful Recreation Hall leaped to the microphone. "Hold your seats, everybody!" he said. "Hold your seats! We have these quakes every once in a while. Nothing's going to happen. You're all right. Just sit tight."

Without prompting, rangers in attendance went quietly to the doors, and opened them wide. Then people began moving. Slowly and with a quiet orderliness, the crowd filtered out.

The rangers spread smoothly throughout the village, checking on the state of readiness of the hospital, the first-aid stations, the fire department. Everything was in order. These places were always ready. The rangers knew that. But . . . well, it wouldn't hurt to check. Just in case.

Everybody in authority had been alerted automatically by the tremor. The fire chief himself was on the job.

Water systems were checked. In fact, a sprinkler system in Old Faithful Inn had already gone off. But not from fire. A chimney fell through the roof of the Inn and plunged into the dining room. The crash knocked a sprinkler head off, and the cascade began.

The rangers moved on, inspecting buildings, checking for injuries. One lady leaped from bed in alarm, caught a sheet around her ankle, fell and sprained the ankle. How many others were hurt? And where?

In every official mind was one fear—the fear of panic. Rangers, cruising through the campgrounds with portable megaphones, advised that there was no cause for alarm, that the roads were open, and that anyone who wished could leave the park. "But wait for daylight, please," they added. "And check with us before going anywhere."

The concession operators immediately opened the kitchens and provided coffee and doughnuts for anyone who wanted them—and that went on all night.

Patrol cars moved out in all directions. Outside the West Yellowstone entrance they found trouble. The road had broken up badly and three sections had dropped into Hebgen Lake. Several miles below the lake some forty-four million cubic yards of mountainside had given way, plunging to the floor of the Madison River valley and into a United States Forest Service campground.

Midnight came, and with it another shock of major proportions. Some campers slept right through it. Others thought bears had been trying to turn over their trailers. Everywhere people were waking and wandering—and wondering.

For some people, it was a long night. For nineteen campers buried under the Madison River Canyon slide, it would never end.

Next morning the sun rose on a Yellowstone whose landscape had been permanently altered. Much, of course, was the same: the primeval forests still stretch for miles in all directions, the streams still flowed pure and cold through the grassland, and the wild animals went on with their work as if nothing whatever had happened. But there was change, and the events of the night were punctuated when early that morning another shock of major proportions lifted and jarred the land.

Clouds of dust rose into the sky as cliffs and hillsides collapsed. Great boulders rammed into the highways. At celebrated Obsidian Cliff the dawn revealed new shine and glisten from the freshly cracked and exposed piles of volcanic glass.

In the Firehole Canyon three rock slides rumbled down the slopes. In one of them, workers clearing the road nine days later found a trapped bear. Evidently it had been sleeping in a depression near the cliffs when slide debris rolled down and blocked escape. Workmen loosened the rocks and opened a side channel that would have required the bear to swim the river. This, for some ursine reason, it would not do.

The only other possibility was to escape vertically through an opening among the rocks, but this was too steep for the bear to climb. So the workmen lowered a lodgepole pine trunk down as a ladder, and that was better! Out went the bear, at a rate of departure calculated to put it halfway to the North Pole by sundown.

Meanwhile, communications had been partially disrupted and in many cases the rangers were on their own. They'd had to close the Park's west entrance; cars could not get through rock falls along the Madison River. Soon there was a flood of people at the entrance—each with cogent reasons why he had to come in there and no other way. Calmly and patiently, the rangers explained that it would be necessary, in the interests of safety for all concerned, to drive to another park entrance.

Superintendent Lon Garrison, immediate master of the park's 3,472 square miles, and an ebullient and efficient administrator, moved his headquarters staff from a 1910 unreinforced stone building into a tent for safety. To him the greatest danger was handling the thousands of people "caught" inside the park. No one knew how near hysteria the people were. Some didn't even know about the earthquake till they read it in the papers. But the situation was critical on the west side of the park and Garrison knew it.

If all the people in the park had tried to leave at once, there wouldn't have been enough gasoline in the stations to handle them; the gasoline came in from the west, and that road was closed. (Within ten minutes phone calls went out to dispersing points to send trucks via other routes.)

"One goof on our part," said Garrison, "and the people would have fled in terror. There would have been more fatalities, more casualties, and more damage from our panicking them than had ever happened at Hebgen."

His decision: announce to the world that the park was open. It took two men two days at telephones to furnish information to clamoring news services, organizations, and individuals. The Office of Civilian Defense offered to take charge. Instead, Garrison and his staff, after shoring up their own defenses, called the United States Forest Service to offer their aid in that agency's stricken Hebgen Lake area.

Buildings had cracked and become dangerous. Roads had ruptured. Repair crews went out immediately to clear away what debris they could. Sometimes they had to work at the foot of freshly disturbed slopes where a breath of wind could start new avalanches. The workmen wore hard hats, but what good would they do beneath cascading tons of giant boulders? At the edge of the slide zone they posted lookouts whose duty was to warn when something started to fall. And to assure alertness, lookout duty was rotated among the workers.

Park visitors departed by droves, leaving the park concessioner with tons of meats and vegetables on hand.

Out in the shock zone, park naturalists were already recording observations. A United States Geological Survey field party, camped near Hebgen Lake, was making spot checks, and members of the Coast and Geodetic Survey were arriving to study the effects at first hand. The Atomic Energy Commission dispatched a party of specialists to check on the possibility of an earthquake in or near Arco, Idaho, where radioactive materials might be disturbed.

With all this hectic coming and going, it is a wonder the disaster wasn't increased. Says Superintendent Garrison with the air of a man taking pride in his outfit: "The visitors in the park kept their heads and all of them got out safely. The only automobile accident that occurred later was to one of the rangers who went too long without sleep and cracked up his car down in the Firehole Canyon."

Inevitably all eyes turned to the park's major features: what had happened to the geysers? It was a simple question, and a critical one. The Yellowstone area has some ten thousand thermal features and about two hundred known geysers. Even the term "geyser" denotes deep-down mechanisms that go off and on, controlled by subterranean circumstances. Had the earth tremors disrupted the subterranean channels that fed the geysers? Was Old Faithful still faithful?

The morning after the earthquake it became startlingly evident that there was change, and a lot of it. In the Lower Geyser basin a number of new crevices had opened and steam was issuing from them. A new geyser spurted into being, and was promptly named Earthquake Geyser. (It erupted regularly for about a week—and then quit.)

The fountain paint pots, normally plopping in colorful, slow-motion bubbles in a vat of mud, had exploded all over creation and ripped up part of a parking lot.

Morning Geyser, nearby, used to erupt occasionally—three or four times a week. Immediately following the earthquake it erupted violently every hour, and kept going each time for about thirty minutes. (That went on for a week; then the geyser stopped. It may take years and perhaps decades to get a new timetable on each geyser.)

Clepsydra Geyser erupted occasionally and faithfully before. With the earthquake it went into a violent steam phase, roaring so loudly that it could be heard for a quarter of a mile.

Steady Geyser—which spouted constantly—ceased.

Some picked up, some slowed. Hot pools cooled off; cold pools got hot. Many remained the same.

Sapphire Pool showed dramatic change. Formerly it had been a brilliantly clear and quiet pool, with great bubbles of gas welling up so that the pool would erupt to a height of four or five feet. No more. Sapphire Pool became a true geyser. The first eruption, fifteen days after the earthquake, scalded and warped a portion of the visitor's boardwalk, and made direct approach unsafe. It erupted every two hours for nine days. Then came another strong tremor—one of many which followed the initial three major shocks—and the geyser ceased. Two weeks later, after another tremor, it started in again, blowing water as far as 150 feet high and two hundred feet horizontally.

Who knows where this activity will end, Garrison inquires. "People ask, 'Did the geysers get damaged?' and we have to say no, that you don't damage these things. Whatever Mother Nature wants to do, that's what she does. We can't stop it, we can't change it. So when people ask if there was any damage to the thermal features of the park, I have to say no. No damage. Was there change? Yes. A great deal of change. And the changes are still going on. There are a lot of things we don't know. We're just finding out. All we can do is to record everything that happens. Ranger-naturalists have remarkably complete records of it all."

And Old Faithful? As far as could be told, Old Faithful continued to erupt on schedule—an average of every sixty-three minutes, with a minimum of thirty-three minutes, and a maximum of ninety-three. Still, happily, it was a symbol of faithfulness, yet subject perhaps to the whims of some future action of the gods of earthquakes.

In essence, the Hebgen Lake earthquake of 1959 was a golden opportunity for a real contribution to knowledge. Says Garrison: "We were fortunate enough to be there on the day when Mother Nature turned a page in the geology textbook, that exact instant when one of the great cataclysmic events of time took place. We saw it. We had the chance from these thermal things that showed above the ground to get more information about what goes on under the ground. That is the chance of a lifetime, a chance of centuries. Yellowstone gained a new look, yet still retains the charm it always had."

In summary, Garrison looks back on the event with mixed feelings of awe and relief. As the man responsible for the eighteen thousand lives in the Park that night, he is fully aware of what might have happened had the shocks struck at eleven-thirty-seven in the morning instead. The parking lot destroyed by the paint pots might have been jammed. The boardwalks that disintegrated might have been full of visitors. The dining room at Old Faithful, where the chimney crashed, might have been filled with diners.

"The Lord had his arms around us all the way," says Garrison, "because it could have been a terrible catastrophe."

It was a miracle of good fortune. Except for the nineteen campers beneath Madison Canyon slide.

The Hebgen Lake earthquake was only one of a millenniums-long series of adjustments this antique earth has been making as its "solid" crust shrinks and cracks and expands and disrupts. The Hebgen campers joined a fraternity of victims which goes back farther than men can remember, and to earthquakes much more deadly.

One of the earliest records comes down to us from Pausanias, the

Greek geographer, who wrote, in a kind of early-day pocket guide, "Going on you come to the river Selinus, and forty furlongs from Aegium is a place Helice on the coast. Here there used to be a city Helice, and here the Ionians had a most holy sanctuary of Heliconian Poseidon. . . . But in after times the Achaeans of Helice forced some suppliants from the sanctuary, and put them to death. The wrath of Poseidon did not tarry. The land was instantly visited by an earthquake, which swallowed up not only the buildings, but the very ground on which the city had stood. . . . The sea advanced far over the land and submerged the whole of Helice. . . ."

According to the testimony of a contemporary, the historian Heraclides Ponticus, Helice was destroyed on a winter night in 373 B.C. The city had been a mile and a half from the sea, but all this buffer space, as well as the city itself, vanished beneath the waves. Two thousand Achaeans went to bury the dead, but found none. Eratosthenes, visiting the site years later, was told by sailors that the bronze statue of Poseidon still stood under water and formed a dangerous shoal. Strabo cites the same event, and Pliny and Ovid asserted that the ruins of Helice were visible under the sea.

Most of China is more or less immune from earthquakes, but some have caused appalling loss of life. Biggest of all was the earthquake of February 2, 1556, which devastated the three large provinces of Shensi, Shansi, and Honan, killing 830,000 people.

"If this appalling figure is trustworthy," says Akitune Imamura, who reports it in his book *Theoretical and Applied Seismology*, "then in the matter of human destruction it stands unrivalled in the annals of the world's earthquakes. So much so that its verity may be questioned. However, by tracing on a map the recorded area of fallen dwellings, it will be found that it follows the valley of the river Wei-ho, a tributary of the Hoang-ho, and involves an immense territory. . . . The figure may not be exaggerated."

All Europe was earthquake-conscious in the eighteenth century. And for good reason. There had been a spate of them. Popular speculation was that earthquakes, representing the voice of God, were pointing out that we humans should attend to our sins. Repeated moralizing and pamphleteering enforced the theme. Occasional tremors left the people jittery, ripe for prophets who used past shocks to predict future ones and, as happened at London, cause the temporary evacuation of a hundred thousand persons from the city.

Then came the calamity of the century. It was All Saints' Day in Lisbon, Portugal—Saturday, November 1, 1755—and the people were crowded into temples and cathedrals. At nine-thirty A.M. rose a rumbling noise that sounded like heavy traffic on an adjacent street. Buildings trembled, and fear was struck in the hearts of the people.

Then there was quiet. But only for a moment.

A second shock came, lasting two full minutes. This brought down roofs, walls, façades, churches, homes, and shops in a roar of destruction and death. Then a third tremor quickly followed, after which a suffocating cloud of dust settled like fog over the city.

Day turned into night. Fires broke out. Aftershocks kept slamming again and again into the stricken city, and marble churches swayed like ships on the sea. Within an hour the fires had grown into an all-consuming conflagration and then, down at the waterfront, the waters of the Tagus poured into town in three great towering waves, breaking with mighty impact on the shore between the Alcântara docks and the Terreiro do Paço.

The whole southwest corner of Portugal had been jolted. So had part of Spain. North Africa experienced violent shocks and much loss of life. Reverberations from the seismic wave raised waters along the European coastline and as far away as the West Indies.

Many a magnificent and monumental building might have survived had not the fire that followed the earthquake reduced them to ruin. This fire burned for a week, gutting the low parts of the city and much along the neighboring slopes. The great cultural treasures of Lisbon were consumed by flames: tapestries, libraries, textiles, paintings, furniture. One author lists the loss in the palace of the Marquês de Louriçal at two hundred pictures (including works of Titian, Correggio, and Rubens), eighteen thousand printed books and a thousand manuscripts, including a history written by Emperor Charles V in his own hand, a herbal once owned by King Hunyadi of Hungary, plus priceless archives, maps, and charts, some relating to Portuguese discovery and colonization in the New World.

There had been an old saying: *Qui n'a pas vu Lisbonne, n'a rien vu de bon.*

But now there was no Lisbon. And no beauty. In the Hospital Real, hundreds of inmates burned to death. Six hundred persons were wiped out in one church, four hundred in another, three hundred in another. The total number killed may have reached sixty thousand.

And month after month the smaller shocks continued. "Will your Earth never be quiet?" asked a diplomat in Madrid of an envoy in Lisbon.

The Lisbon earthquake, one of the greatest seismic events of which we have scientific descriptions gave rise to a vast amount of comment by the literary men of the time. The most vociferous was Voltaire, who tells how Candide and his tutor, Dr. Pangloss, arrived in Lisbon after a severe storm and shipwreck at sea.

"They had scarcely set foot in the town when they felt the earth tremble under their feet; the sea rose in foaming masses in the port and smashed the ships which rode at anchor. Whirlwinds of flame and ashes covered the streets and squares; the houses collapsed, the roofs were thrown upon the foundations, and the foundations were scattered; thirty thousand inhabitants of every age and both sexes were crushed under the ruins. Whistling and swearing, the sailor said: 'There'll be something to pick up here.'

* * *

". . . Candide had been hurt by falling stones; he lay in the street covered with debris. He said to Pangloss: 'Alas! Get me a little wine and oil; I am dying.'

"'This earthquake is not a new thing,' replied Pangloss. 'The town of Lima felt the same shocks in America last year; similar causes produce similar effects; there must certainly be a train of sulphur underground from Lima to Lisbon.'

"'Nothing is more probable,' replied Candide; 'but, for God's sake, a little oil and wine.'

"'What do you mean probable?' replied the philosopher; 'I maintain that it is proved.'

"Candide lost consciousness, and Pangloss brought him a little water from a neighboring fountain. Next day they found a little food as they wandered among the ruins. . . .

"After the earthquake which destroyed three-quarters of Lisbon, the wise men of that country could discover no more efficacious way of preventing a total ruin than by giving the people a splendid *auto-da-fé*. It was decided by the university of Coimbre that the sight of several persons being slowly burned in great ceremony is an infallible secret for preventing earthquakes."

As if that were not enough, Voltaire proceeded to immortalize the Lisbon earthquake with a slashing bit of poesy titled "An Inquiry into the Maxim, 'Whatever is, is Right,'" a maxim that had been propounded by Alexander Pope. Cried Voltaire:

> Meditate awhile
> Yon shattered walls, and view each ruined pile,
> Women and children heaped up mountain high,
> Limbs crushed which under ponderous marble lie;
> Wretches unnumbered in the pangs of death,
> Who mangled, torn, and panting for their breath,
> Buried beneath their sinking roofs expire,
> And end their wretched lives in torments dire.
> Say, when you hear their piteous, half-formed cries,
> Or from their ashes see the smoke arise,
> Say, will you then eternal laws maintain,
> Which God to cruelties like these constrain? *

There was an interesting booklet called *Commentary*, published in 1756, written by António de Figueiredo, a young priest who later became one of the most famous theologians of eighteenth-century Portugal. It was the first sensible piece of reporting by a Portuguese writer on the earthquake.

Immanuel Kant published three short papers on the same subject in 1756, speaking more in scientific terms, concluding by noting the beneficial effects of such tremors. Death? he would ask, and then answer— all men must die. Destruction? No property is everlasting. After all, earthquakes are part of Nature, something to which man must accommodate himself. Earthquakes spring from subterranean fires, and don't these fires also give us hot springs and baths? Don't they form minerals in the rocks? Help vegetables in the ground? Give us all warmth?

This seems like specious reasoning today—and not really to the point—but Kant was young then, and a part of the eighteenth century.

* John Morley, *Works of Voltaire*, Vol. XXXVI, 1901.

The roots of his philosophy were embedded in the science of the times.

Years later, across the Atlantic, Oliver Wendell Holmes would write:

> —there stood the stout old one-hoss-shay
> As fresh as on Lisbon-earthquake day . . .
>
> First a shiver, and then a thrill
> Then something decidedly like a spill,—
> And the parson was sitting upon a rock,
> At half-past nine by the meet'n'-house clock—
> Just the hour of the Earthquake shock!

All this attention and publicity should have come as no surprise in 1755. Herodotus, centuries earlier, had handed down the first earthquake accounts, for he spoke of an oracle in ancient Greece which said: "Delos' self will I shake, which never yet has been shaken." And when Delos, an island in the Aegean Sea, was shaken by an earthquake, the event was taken as a prodigy whereby the gods warned men of evils to come. During the three succeeding generations—fifth century B.C.—more woes befell Greece, so Herodotus said, than in the twenty generations preceding.

In the Bible are twenty-one references to earthquakes. How better or more majestically to introduce God's works than with the awesome rages of Nature? For instance, St. John the Divine wrote: "And I beheld when he had opened the sixth seal, and, lo, there was a great earthquake; and the sun became black as sackcloth of hair, and the moon became as blood; and the stars of heaven fell onto the earth. . . ."

To early peoples, it seemed impossible that the earth should float in space. Obviously, it had to be held up by something. From this came the concept of Atlas, a muscular giant who supported the world and set off earthquakes when he shifted the earth from one shoulder to another.

Democritus said that the earth was full of water and when rain fell and forced its way in, an earthquake resulted. Or, conversely, as the earth dried, it drew water "from the fuller to the emptier parts, and the inrush of the water as it changes its place causes the earthquake."

Anaximenes avowed that the earth, on growing wet or dry, broke into pieces and that earthquakes were due to the falling of the broken masses. But Aristotle demolished these and other suggestions by stating bluntly that "not water nor earth is the cause of earthquakes but wind."

This was the beginning of a theory that would last for centuries and be taken as scientific gospel by generations to come. "We must suppose the action of the wind in the earth," Aristotle explained, "to be analogous to the tremors and throbbings caused in us by the force of the wind contained in our bodies. Thus some earthquakes are a sort of tremor, others a sort of throbbing."

It seemed sensible enough at the time. He also deftly tied together earthquakes and volcanoes.

In Renaissance times, one of the horrors imagined was that the airs imprisoned beneath the earth were "diseased," that when the earth ruptured and these were released, dire pestilence would ravage the world.

Shakespeare dramatized the notion in *Henry IV:* "Diseased nature oftentimes breaks forth / In strange eruptions; oft the teeming earth / Is with a kind of colic pinch'd and vex'd / By the imprisoning of unruly wind / Within her womb. . . ."

Donne referred to earthquakes as the world having fits. Other writers saw them as "gapinge, rendyng, or cleaving" the land.

The change in scientific thought from darkness to enlightenment came with men like Gabriel Harvey, who could doubt that earthquakes were supernatural, or even an action of God. "There may be sufficient naturall, eyther necessarie or contingent cause in the very earth it selfe."

It was left to Robert Mallet, an Irish geologist and civil engineer, to draw order from the chaos of early observations and suggestions, and he published in 1846 the first general study of earthquakes. Mallet suggested that the only way cliffs could be sheared off and landscape features displaced was with the passage of a "wave of elastic compression, or of a succession of these, in parallel or in intersecting lines, through the solid substance and surface of the disturbed country."

This was a novel notion—an earthquake wave passing through the crust of the earth. Mallet believed that earthquakes were primarily volcanic in origin, and that some subterranean explosion such as might result from superheated steam or lava entering a fissure would cause the jarring of the earth. He supported this contention by pointing out that earthquakes frequently occurred in volcanic areas.

By the middle of the nineteenth century, scientists began to realize that earthquakes occurred most often in mountainous regions adjacent to breaks in the earth's crust. Montessus de Ballore reminded his colleagues that high relief, wherever it might be—on land or in the ocean—could be counted a sure sign of earthquake activity. It might even be possible for earthquakes to arise from underground disturbances that were not volcanic at all.

Edward Suess, a Viennese professor of geology, was one of the strongest advocates of this approach, and his *The Face of the Earth* became a classic of early geology. All geological processes, he said, may be accounted for by gravity in the crust of a shrinking earth.

While these and other scientists developed theories which could be helpfully used in solving the riddles of earthquakes, Mother Nature faithfully kept supplying the searchers with fresh and authentic source material.

Nearly three score years after the Lisbon ruckus, the town of Caracas, Venezuela, was destroyed by an earthquake in 1812, an event described in detail by the celebrated Prussian natural scientist and world traveler, Alexander von Humboldt, who happened to be on the scene.

Another alert observer a few years later witnessed the great earthquake of 1835 in Chile. H.M.S. *Beagle* was there, and of the events Charles Darwin said: "In my opinion, we have scarcely beheld, since leaving England, any sight so deeply interesting."

Not a house in Concepción remained upright. Seventy villages were reported destroyed, and the coast was beset with a giant wave. "The first shock was very sudden," Darwin went on. "The mayor-domo at Quiriquina told me, that the first notice he received of it, was finding both the horse he rode and himself, rolling together on the ground. Rising up, he was again thrown down. He also told me that some cows which were standing on the steep side of the island were rolled into the sea. . . .

"After viewing Concepción, I cannot understand how the greater number of inhabitants escaped unhurt. The houses in many parts fell outwards; thus forming in the middle of the streets little hillocks of brickwork and rubbish. Mr. Rouse, the English consul, told us that he was at breakfast when the first movement warned him to run out. He had scarcely reached the middle of the court-yard, when one side of his house came thundering down. He retained presence of mind to remember, that if he once got on the top of that part which had already fallen, he would be safe. Not being able from the motion of the ground to stand, he crawled up on his hands and knees; and no sooner had he ascended this little eminence, than the other side of the house fell in, the great beams sweeping close in front of his head. With his eyes blinded, and his mouth choked with the cloud of dust which darkened the sky, at last he gained the street. As shock succeeded shock, at the interval of a few minutes, no one dared approach the shattered ruins; and no one knew whether his dearest friends and relations were not perishing from the want of help. . . .

"Shortly after the shock, a great wave . . . broke in a fearful line of white breakers, which rushed up to a height of 23 vertical feet above the highest spring-tides. Their force must have been prodigious; for at the Fort a cannon with its carriage, estimated at four tons in weight, was moved 15 feet inwards. A schooner was left in the midst of the ruins, 200 yards from the beach. The first wave was followed by two others, which in their retreat carried away a vast wreck of floating objects. In one part of the bay, a ship was pitched high and dry on shore, was carried off, again driven on shore, and again carried off. In another part, two large vessels anchored near together were whirled about, and their cables were thrice wound round each other; though anchored at a depth of 36 feet, they were for some minutes aground."

Robert Mallet once estimated that for the earth as a whole, over a period of four thousand years there have been at least thirteen million lives lost through earthquakes. And no wonder, for the earth trembles constantly. Seismograph needles jiggle unceasingly with minor vibrations, most of them unfelt by man. Some tremors travel to all parts of the earth's surface. Vibrations leaving the Yellowstone earthquake were strong enough at a seismograph station near Lassen Peak, California, to knock the stylus off a rotating drum.

Hence, an earthquake of consequence is never an isolated event. Preliminary tremors may occur for years beforehand, and there almost certainly will be aftershocks echoing the force of the disturbance. These rules are often breached in part, and it is frequently difficult to tell whether a good ground-shaking was (1) a foreshock, (2) the main shock, (3) an aftershock, or (4) part of a swarm of smaller shocks.

It is a rare earthquake that is not preceded by motion at the surface.

And time is not necessarily a determining factor, as in the case of the Long Beach earthquaké of 1933. Its foreshocks began in 1920, when a minor shaking at Inglewood heralded activity along a fault. Small tremors jolted the vicinity from 1927 on, and then the land quieted. One might have thought that the action was over.

Then early in March, 1933, came some small shocks, followed by a foreshock of substantial magnitude at Huntington Beach. On the following day came the big earthquake, culminating a long train of events. The shaking was especially destructive of school buildings, but fortunately classes had just gone home for the day. Even so, 120 lives were lost and property damage was estimated at fifty million dollars.

At any given moment in time and space we are not always sure whether a series of earthquakes is culminating or continuing. In any case, the subsequent years at Long Beach were much less active.

But beware! After a strong earthquake, there is no reason to assume that quiet has returned; the movement may merely have been a strong and destructive foreshock.

After a big tremor does come, the natural follow-up is a series of aftershocks decreasing in magnitude, but these may originate close to a center of population and cause more damage than was caused by the main shock (as happened at Bakersfield, California, in 1952). At some localities, a strong shake is frequently followed by one of equal or greater intensity. You never know.

Other places experience so-called earthquake swarms, a series of small and large shocks, sometimes as many as a hundred a day. This is especially true in volcanic regions and especially preceding an eruption, but is not limited to either.

In the beginning a tremor may start simply enough: by breakage of the rocks of the earth's crust. This crust is a relatively thin cap that has hardened over the earth's molten and considerably plastic interior. Over long periods of time the outer rocks are distorted by pressure from beneath. At any given place the rocks are subject to intense strain that may accrue until the rocks, especially along zones of weakness such as fractures, give way.

The land is then ruptured or, as the geologist says, faulted. The blocks which had been strained and distorted snap back as far as they can toward a position of equilibrium. This snapping produces the vibrations we call earthquakes. Geologists know this as the "elastic-rebound" theory, developed in the aftermath of the 1906 San Francisco earthquake by Harry Fielding Reid, professor of geology at Johns Hopkins University, and based on field work by the United States Coast and Geodetic Survey.

When the fractures occur at the surface, we see cracks in the ground. These may be inconspicuous breaks. They may be substantial ruptures in which one side has been raised or lowered with respect to the other. A Yakutat Bay, Alaska, earthquake in 1899 produced a vertical displacement of nearly fifty feet.

The initial rupture, however, is often invisible and very deep. Most earthquakes appear to originate within a depth of forty miles, but some are known to occur as deep as 450 miles. Deeper disturbances result also from releases of strain, but how is unclear. The composition and activity of the earth's core remain maddeningly enigmatic.

However deep an earthquake may originate, seismologists speak of the spot on the land surface directly over it as the epicenter. This location is established most accurately by means of triangulation from several reporting stations, hence the point of origin of an earthquake is difficult to determine precisely until several stations report.

Damage may not be excessive at the epicenter, for the tremor is merely the starting point for a succession of seismic waves sent out through the earth. And these may cause trouble, far from the point of origin. If we could see how the underground structure is sheared, shattered, and shot through with cracks we might comprehend more clearly how earthquakes work.

The motion of an earthquake is highly irregular, although the effects may indicate otherwise. After a substantial shock in which all houses are shifted northward off their foundations, the dazed residents may be convinced that the tremor "came" from the north. Or the south. Or from somewhere. During the Yellowstone earthquake, in the town of West Yellowstone, everything on shelves facing east and west fell off. Everything on shelves facing north and south slid to the end. (Someone remarked later that it was the only day in the history of West Yellowstone when you couldn't buy a bottle of whiskey; they had all fallen off the shelves.) The jolting, under those circumstances, appears decidedly directional. But it is local and not characteristic of the whole event.

Nature on the Rampage

To get the big picture of an earthquake and what it does, we need to know the point of origin and how far we are from it, and by these two criteria are earthquakes and their effects judged: the power of the rupture itself (magnitude), and the extent of damage caused (intensity).

Intensity describes not the earthquake itself, but the *effects* of that earthquake on human beings and habitations. As noted in the Modified Mercalli Scale which follows, intensity is computed according to how many chimneys are shattered, how many walls are demolished, etc. Thus one earthquake may be observed as intensity III (weak) in one city and intensity VI (strong) in another, depending on the nature of the destruction. In a sense, intensity describes the whiplash end of the earthquake.

Various people have various ways, however, of reporting the severity of damage. As the station agent at Cisco, California, said, on August 30, 1912: "Had a hell of an earthquake."

The Modified Mercalli Scale, developed originally by H. O. Wood and F. Neumann in 1931, is a little more selective, and is widely used in news reports. It is not to be confused with the Richter Scale, named after the American seismologist Charles F. Richter, which measures the *magnitude* at the point of origin or focus of the shock. The Modified Mercalli Scale of Intensity judges an earthquake by how severely its outgoing seismic waves shake up the landscape and the works of men. Its measurements, on a scale of one to twelve, are written in Roman numerals to distinguish them from measurements of magnitude, which are given in Arabic numerals.

MODIFIED MERCALLI
SCALE OF EARTHQUAKE INTENSITY *

I. Not felt.
II. Felt by persons at rest or on upper floors.
III. Felt indoors. Hanging objects swing. Vibrations similar to the passing of light trucks. May not be recognized as an earthquake.
IV. Hanging objects swing. Vibrations similar to passing of heavy trucks or a jolt like a heavy ball striking the walls. Standing motor cars rock. Windows, dishes, doors rattle. Glasses clink. Crockery clashes. Wooden walls and frames creak.

---

* After *Elementary Seismology* by Charles F. Richter. San Francisco: W. H. Freeman and Company, 1958.

V. Felt outdoors; direction estimated. Sleepers wakened. Liquids disturbed, some spilled. Small unstable objects displaced or upset. Doors swing, close, open. Shutters, pictures move. Pendulum clocks stop, start, change rate.

VI. Felt by all. Many frightened and run outdoors. Persons walk unsteadily. Windows, dishes, glassware broken. Knickknacks and books off shelves. Pictures off walls. Furniture moved or overturned. Weak plaster and masonry cracked. Small bells ring in schools and churches. Trees, bushes shaken.

VII. Difficult to stand. Felt by drivers of automobiles. Hanging objects quiver. Furniture broken. Damage to masonry. Weak chimneys broken at roof line. Fall of plaster, loose bricks, stones, tiles, cornices. Waves on ponds; water turbid with mud. Small slides and caving along sand or gravel banks. Large bells ring. Concrete irrigation ditches damaged.

VIII. Steering of automobiles affected. Fall of stucco and some masonry walls. Twisting, fall of chimneys, factory stacks, monuments, towers, elevated tanks. Unbolted frame houses moved on foundations; loose panel walls thrown out. Decayed piling broken off. Branches broken from trees. Changes in flow or temperature of springs and wells. Cracks in wet ground and on steep slopes.

IX. General panic. Masonry destroyed or damaged. Unbolted frame structures shifted off foundations. Frames racked. Serious damage to reservoirs. Underground pipes broken. Conspicuous cracks in ground. In alluviated areas sand and mud ejected, earthquake fountains thrown up, sand craters formed.

X. Most masonry and frame structures destroyed with their foundations. Some well-built wooden structures and bridges destroyed. Serious damage to dams, dikes, and lakes. Sand and mud shifted horizontally on beaches and flat land. Rails bent slightly.

XI. Rails bent greatly. Underground pipelines completely out of service.

XII. Damage nearly total. Large rock masses displaced. Lines of sight and level distorted. Objects thrown into the air.

Using this scale with on-the-spot reports, the intensity can be readily derived. For example, the 1959 Hebgen Lake earthquake reached a maximum of X in the epicentral area. If accurate eyewitness descriptions are available, we can also determine the intensities of earthquakes that occurred centuries ago.

But regardless of what it does to buildings, trees, and men, what of the earthquake itself? Speaking objectively, every shock has only one initial burst of energy. The moment in which rock masses break and snap is the moment of maximum force of the earthquake—its magnitude —measured independently of other factors.

Therefore, by referring to magnitude we talk not of the damage caused but of the movement itself, i.e., its original strength. But that strength varies widely—from slight earthquakes detected only by delicate instruments to great bursts of force from the shifting of thousands of cubic miles of solid rock. How to record these extremes on one scale? You could hardly compress such a range of force into a scale as simple as the I to XII used for intensity. A linear scale, reaching from one to infinity, would be too broad, too cumbersome to use; if one earthquake was a million times stronger than another, comparisons would involve long figures and time-consuming computations.

Charles Richter solved the problem by making use of a logarithmic scale which, by reducing large numbers to powers of ten, would simplify calculations. By an adroit scale arrangement, as well as by establishing certain other criteria, Richter fashioned a scale on which the smallest earthquakes identifiable by instruments would have magnitudes of just above zero; the smallest earthquakes felt by man would have magnitudes of about three, and for the largest earthquakes there would theoretically be no upper limit.

So far, the largest earthquakes measured on this scale have had magnitudes of 8.9, and chances are that that is about as high as they will go. If there is ever an earthquake of magnitude 10, the whole world will know it at once.

Of course, it frequently follows that earthquakes with the greatest magnitudes stir up the greatest damage—but only if they are near enough to human habitation to do so. Some are six miles under water and their damage is not direct. Tremors of high magnitude may have high intensity ratings if there are observers around to assess the effects. Intensity of an earthquake differs from place to place. It is a means of comparing damage. Magnitude does not change. It rates a tremor independent of its locality, and is useful in comparing earthquakes (Yellowstone 7.1; Chilean 8.5).

To determine earthquake magnitude just by reading instruments at a single seismological station is difficult or impossible unless the epicenter is nearby. This is because complex computations from other stations at other distances have to be completed. When all the information is received and analyzed, a magnitude may be assigned to an earthquake. Since this may take days, beware of early press reports stating anything but intensity (which, of course, can be observed as soon as the dust clears).

Magnitude scales have come into use only within the past three decades but reliable measurements since the turn of the century allow us to assign magnitudes to earthquakes that occurred prior to the development of scales. Only two earthquakes have reached a magnitude of 8.9, highest of all. These were the Colombia-Ecuador earthquake of January 31, 1906, and the Sanriku, Japan, earthquake of March 2, 1933.

Each year, besides the countless number of small tremors, some good-sized shakes occur. Seismologists consider any shock having a magnitude of 7.0 or above a major shock. How many major shocks occur annually? Richter indicates about twenty-five.

How strong can an earthquake get? Richter says: "It is evident that there must be some upper limit to earthquake magnitude. . . . A physical upper limit must be set by the strength of the crustal rocks, in terms of the maximum strain which they are competent to support without yielding. . . . There is no historical seismic event to which we are inclined to assign magnitude above that (8.9) assigned to the largest shocks of the past fifty years."

If that is true, then those of Helice and Lisbon, which proved so devastating, were no more powerful than some in recent years. The cities were simply too close to the epicenters.

Even the most celebrated United States earthquake—San Francisco, 1906—does not rank at the top. Its magnitude is estimated at 8.3. But this was powerful enough, and near enough, to shake the city to its foundations.

San Franciscans had not been deeply concerned about earthquakes, although there had been destructive tremors before. "There's nothing we can do about them," they would say. "And besides, a good stiff shake is not half as bad as a twister or hurricane coming at you!"

The stiff shake came a few seconds after five-twelve on the morning of April 18, 1906.

"The whole street was undulating," said one man looking up Washington Street. "It was as if the waves of the ocean were coming toward me, and billowing as they came."

In a single minute, towers and chimneys and walls and buildings toppled, frame houses crumbled into kindling, rails twisted, bridges collapsed, pipelines broke, church bells clanged. Then a pause. Then another tremor of mounting intensity.

"It was like a terrier shaking a rat!" said another observer, in a statement more graphic than original.

Then silence. All up and down the coast, hundreds lay dead or dying, and buildings were bursting into flame.

The final damage was estimated at four hundred million dollars. Some seven hundred lives were lost, mostly by fire, but in truth no one will ever know how many people died. Bodies were buried hurriedly, without official record. No count could be made of persons trapped in buildings completely consumed by fire. There was no current census of the city, or any way of knowing the number of transient residents.

The extent of action on the fault was the longest ever measured for a single earthquake: about 270 miles. Displacements of one side of the fault in relation to the other were chiefly horizontal, and approached twenty-one feet. Vertical displacement amounted to no more than three feet. Giant coast redwoods were split and divested of branches. Concrete bridge piers were damaged. So were frame houses along the fault trace.

Could the San Andreas fault move again? It could indeed, and San Francisco, not anxious to get caught, has an emergency water system utilizing sea water for fire fighting if all other sources are cut off. Building regulations are improving, too, but not fast enough. As Richter says (1958): "Few of the larger buildings have been designed to be earthquake-resistant."

However disastrous this event was, it came as no surprise to Californians. Ever since Gaspar de Portola and his expedition were shaken by a 1769 shock near Los Angeles, the residents of California have been rocked repeatedly. Earthquakes troubled the builders of the early Franciscan missions. In 1812, the church at San Juan Capistrano was shaken down with a resultant forty deaths. Other missions have been damaged periodically since the time of their construction. From 1906 to 1956, approximately eighty-four earthquakes of magnitude 6 or above struck the California-Nevada region.

Any place is fair game for earthquakes, and they occur where such things are "unheard of." South Carolina, for example, in 1886. The

North Atlantic in 1929. Brazil's Mato Grosso in 1746 and 1955. Quiet New England has had at least one perceptible tremor a year since the settlement of the United States.

While they occur all over the world, earthquakes are especially abundant in well-defined tracts called seismic belts. One of these is the so-called Circle of Fire bordering the Pacific Ocean on the north, east, and west. Another stretches from the Mediterranean through the Alps, Caucasus, and Himalayas to the East Indies.

The same is generally true of volcanic belts, perhaps because in these regions new mountain ranges are abuilding. And in the building of such new ranges, earthquakes and volcanoes are the spectacular but superficial effects of vast underground activity.

Scientists divide these effects into primary and secondary categories. Primary effects are those accomplished directly by the rock slippage, such as warping the earth's crust, forming cliff scarps, diverting waterfalls, offsetting highways, and crushing such structures as buildings and bridges. Secondary effects are those that result from the shaking, that is, from pressure waves sent out by the vibrations of the shock. Such effects include landslides, damming of streams, and collapse of distant buildings.

After an earthquake strikes, destruction can be quick and complete. Railroad tracks are bent and shifted out of line. Bridges are weakened. Tunnels collapse. Irrigation is disrupted, in part by power lines being downed and pumping curtailed. Dams are broken and their waters sent cascading downstream. Submarine cables are cut directly, or indirectly, or both, in the same earthquake.

Seismic disturbances may shake water as well as land, and if at sea the phenomenon is called a seaquake. This term was first used to describe seismic disturbances of the ocean, including seismic sea waves. In present usage it denotes a tremor caused by an earthquake but felt aboard ships at sea. There are hundreds of accounts of seaquakes. Richter quotes a British seaman's report from the equatorial Atlantic in 1855:

"While standing near the wheel I heard a sound as of distant thunder; on walking over to port side to look to the southward, experienced a tremendous and grating motion of ship, as if grazing over a coral reef; it caused everything to shake for about a minute after the sound had ceased. The whole lasted two minutes. I tried for soundings, but had no bottom with 120 fathoms line. There was not the least ripple on the surface of the water, but the sound seemed to come from ship's bottom, and the motion was not unlike letting go the anchor in deep water when the chain runs out quickly."

Often these seaquakes kill fishes, in great numbers, by the transmission of shock waves.

Back on land, some rare and freakish things take place. If there is sufficient ground water, an earthquake may disrupt the crust enough to bring it spurting out in fountains and "geysers." These are sometimes called sand spouts. Richter reports how one man got caught in an Indian earthquake in 1934:

"My car suddenly began to rock. . . . As the rocking ceased, mud huts in the village, on either side of the road, began to fall. To my right a lone dried palm trunk without a top was vigorously shaken, as an irate man might shake his stick, then water spouts, hundreds of them throwing up water and sand, were to be observed on the whole face of the country, the sand forming miniature volcanoes, whilst the water spouted out of the craters; some of the spouts were quite six feet high.

"In a few minutes, on both sides of the road as far as the eye could see, was vast expanse of sand and water, water and sand. The road spouted water and wide openings were to be seen across it ahead of me, then under me, and my car sank, while the water and sand bubbled, and spat, and sucked, till my axles were covered. 'Abandon ship' was quickly obeyed, and my man and I stepped into knee-deep hot water and sand and made for shore. It was a particularly cold afternoon, and to step into water of such temperature was surprising.

"It was distressing to see the villagers, running some east some west, others to, others from their fallen houses, wailing and beating their chests.

"In less than half an hour I should say, the water spouts ceased to play. . . ."

Of all the manifestations of earthquakes, none seems to be more dreaded than the opening and closing of fissures in the ground, even though such events are extremely rare. In a 1797 earthquake at Riobamba, Ecuador, fissures opened, men fell in, and the fissures closed again, pinning the hapless citizens by their legs. The British geologist Sir Charles Lyell tells of an earthquake in Jamaica in 1692 in which the ground heaved like a rolling sea, opening and closing rapidly again.

Many people were swallowed in the cracks, some caught by the middle and squeezed to death, some pinned with their heads protruding, others engulfed and then cast up with great quantities of water. History records other instances, such as the Calabrian earthquake of 1783 in which houses, trees, cattle, and men were engulfed completely, never to be seen again.

Another dramatic issue is whether an island can be drawn beneath the waves. The legendary Atlantis, mentioned by Plato, Pliny, and other ancient writers, was a mythical land that lay far to the westward in the Atlantic, and was presumed to have been sunk beneath the waves by an earthquake. The real-life island of Uryû-jima, a short distance off the coast of Japan, at one time measured four by 2.3 kilometers and had a population of five thousand. On September 4, 1596, it was struck by a single sharp tremor. Fissures opened and a few buildings were damaged, but then quiet returned. Soon a seismic sea wave rolled in, drowning over seven hundred people. On the following morning the sea covered fully three-fourths of the island. Later subsidences, apparently slow enough to permit escape by the residents, dropped the island to a depth of more than thirty fathoms. Exit Uryû-jima.

There is also the question of what an earthquake sounds like. Indoors one may have difficulty telling, because of the rattling of dishes and the thumping of furniture. But outside, the characteristic sound seems to be unmistakable: an extremely low-pitched rumble, like thunder, or like distant gunfire, or like the roar of traffic at an intersection some blocks away. Sometimes the sound resembles explosions coming apparently from high in the air, or from deep within the earth.

Whence the noise? A grinding together of massive blocks of rock beneath the surface? Perhaps. It is more likely the transfer of shock waves from earth to air, creating audible compression waves.

Those who have heard it seem deeply impressed. In his *Conquest of Mount McKinley*, Belmore Browne says: "Strangely enough most of the shocks were preceded by a deep detonation. The sound resembled the noise made by exploding steam, and it came always from the same place—Mount McKinley. . . . We would be sitting in our tent, when suddenly the deep, explosive noise would reach our ears. One of us would say, 'Here comes another,' and if the explosion was of sufficient power we would take the precaution of seeing that our teapot was in a safe place. And then, after a few seconds had elapsed, the quake would reach us. . . ."

Had we had ability to foresee earthquakes in the past, some awful calamities could have been avoided. We could have eliminated much of what happened, for example, in the heart of Japan on September 1, 1923.

The day had dawned with a strong wind accompanied by rain, and when the shower ended, the wind abated a little, the sky cleared, and the brilliant morning sun came out with great intensity. Tokyo and Yokohama, together with other communities in the seven surrounding prefectures, sweltered in the heat.

Midsummer was past, but the lingering heat seemed almost unbearable, especially on this morning. At popular summer resorts facing Sagami Bay and the Pacific Ocean thousands of visitors had come to pass the hot season.

Shortly before noon * a red motor-bus with eighteen tourists aboard pulled out of a hotel grounds and headed for Miyanoshita. "Say!" one of the passengers shouted. "All we need are streams of colored paper to be a departing liner."

They laughed, and the bus began the steep ascent of Ashinoyu.

"Be careful, driver, we don't want to go sliding back to the hotel."

The bus made a few slips backward at curves where it had to change gears.

"My goodness," said one of the girls, "this is dangerous, isn't it?"

"Of course it is," giggled another. "Isn't it exciting?"

"But suppose the brakes fail."

"Silly!"

At precisely two minutes before noon, all hell broke loose.

The bus began rocking and lurching as if in a bog, swaying, swinging, bumping. Passengers were flung helter-skelter in their seats and pitched into the aisle.

"Hey, driver—" someone yelled, but didn't finish. The bus bounded up and down and side to side in the road.

"Stop her, stop her," came shouts from the startled riders. They could see the earth careening in front of them and at the sides.

* As later reported to the *Japan Chronicle* by a member of the Yokosuka Naval College and adapted slightly here.

"We're floundering in a ditch," said one.

"The chauffeur's lost control," said another.

"Get down, get down!" someone else shouted. "Let us down! We'll go off the road."

The bus came to a halt. Passengers spilled out through windows and doors like fireworks from a flaming fountain.

"Look!" came a shout, and they turned to see the mountain sliding on all sides of them.

"Earthquake!"

The road bore scarcely any resemblance to a highway. Huddling, the people watched with unspeakable strain as shock followed shock for thirty minutes.

When the frequency of the tremors diminished, they stepped away from the bus and started cautiously down the road, only to find it overhung with precariously balanced boulders, some of which were crashing to the road and blocking it.

They turned and plunged through steep thickets at the side of the road. Coming out from time to time on the highway they were stupefied to see fallen houses and bridges, and demolished walls and gateways everywhere. Furthermore, the shaking and cracking ground was accompanied by shock reverberations that sounded as distinct and ominous as the booming of guns.

The closer they approached Miyanoshita, the worse everything grew. Thick clouds of smoke rose ominously above the land, obscuring the city in a murky pall. . . .

The same black pall was spreading rapidly over Tokyo and Yokohama. Everywhere buildings had come down and both cities had been turned into heaps of rubble. The wind rose, picking up flames and spreading them.

The disaster had struck at lunchtime, when coal, charcoal, and gas fires had been lighted in preparing the midday meal. Down went the houses and up went the fires, hundreds of them, from places beyond the bluff all the way around the bay to the great dockyards northeast of Yokohama. Thick smoke columns swirled up to join clouds of yellow dust that had billowed skyward with the collapse of buildings. The air turned from yellow to brown to black.

Sampans in the bay caught fire and broke loose, floating unattended, driven by the mounting gale. Like traveling furnaces, they aimed straight for other vessels in the harbor.

At that moment, a terrifying seismic sea wave rose out of the bay and swept into the shoreline, floating bodies and flaming debris into the city.

On the southern part of the Bo-So peninsula thousands of landslides fell. One of them rolled over the entire village of Nebukawa and crushed into oblivion all of its seven hundred inhabitants.

In Tokyo, a special correspondent wrote to the *Japan Chronicle*, "Some had gained the street and escaped the direct flames. Their bodies lay almost entire, but with cruel blisters. Theirs must have been a far greater agony than that of others whose remains are but charred fragments—perhaps just a bit of blackened skull visible amid piled-up bricks and twisted wire and shop goods. How many are buried in that tangled mass? No one will ever know. But already the stench is high, especially around the canal to which scores had run in vain hope of safety."

The wind shifted and the fire burned on. Roiling gales from the typhoon coupled with intense heat from the fires stirred the atmosphere into devastating violence. A tornado appeared on the upper reaches of the Sumida River about four in the afternoon, and swept downstream, lifting small boats out of the water. It roared into the flaming Higher Polytechnic School at Kuramaye, and scooped up a huge mass of burning debris, transferring it to the opposite shores where the buildings immediately caught fire. Flames promptly spread to the open grounds of the Military Clothing Depot, in Honjo Ward, to which an estimated forty thousand persons had fled from falling and burning buildings.

Smoke and fire quickly enveloped the whole scene. Refugees and their belongings burst into flame. Immediately the place became a veritable sea of fire, spinning and roaring as the tornado swept down upon the luckless refugees. In all the annals of human tragedy it was one of the closest to hell on earth.

Only a handful of the forty thousand survived.

For three days, conflagrations raged through Tokyo. To stave off destruction, buildings were blown up in the path of the fire. Earth shocks kept on, relentless, terrifying. On the day of the earthquake there were 222 aftershocks. The next day there were 323, the next 181, the next 184, and so on in decreasing numbers.

Tokyo was almost totally destroyed. So was Yokohama. The number of citizens killed and missing: 311,564.

Later there were heavy rains and floods, and what had not slid during the major shocks slid then. A precipice overhanging a mountain stream collapsed and blocked the stream, subsequently creating a flood that carried houses down the mountain. A hamlet containing some sixty families was buried under a layer of earth more than a hundred feet deep. A train bound for Manazuru with over two hundred passengers was carried away by floodwaters and sent to the bottom of Sagami Bay with every soul on board.

It was perhaps the only time in history when a single area was visited at one time by so many elements on the rampage, with such an enormous loss of life and property. In a short span of time, the people of Tokyo and the vicinity had been struck by earthquake, tsunami, fire, tornado, typhoon, landslide, flood, and torrential rain. It was one of Nature's most diversified and disastrous visitations upon the lives and homes of men.

If the victims needed an epitaph, a newspaper reporter provided it: "What is to be said? A boy kicks an ant hill and leaves only a few meaningless and shapeless pillars of earth standing above the levelled mass. Such is Yokohama. The ants get busy and build again, there or elsewhere. Men build in the same place, because Nature bids them use the opportunities she gives, whatever the risk."

Today's and tomorrow's engineers, considering the risks of our expanding cities, have an enormous problem on their hands—how to build safe buildings. Darwin recalls a group of men playing cards in South America "when a German, one of the party, got up, and said he would never sit in a room in these countries with the door shut, as owing to his having done so, he had nearly lost his life at Copiapó. Accordingly he opened the door; and no sooner had he done this, than he cried out, 'Here it comes again!' and the famous shock commenced. The whole party escaped. The danger in an earthquake is not from the time lost in opening the door, but from the chance of its becoming jammed by the movement of the walls."

Duration of shaking is one of the more important factors in causing damage. It takes time for a building to be rattled to pieces, and the more time the more damage.

Fireplaces and chimneys need steel reinforcing rods running through them to add strength and rigidity so that they will hold together when vibrating like a vertical pendulum. A chimney should also be attached to the adjacent structure so that chimney and building move as a unit. A strong chimney can come through a shock unscathed, but do serious "pounding" damage if it breaks its bonds to the building.

Experience has shown that properly reinforced masonry when well laid is as safe as many other types of construction. Most total failures of masonry structures have been attributable to complete lack of reinforcement, poor workmanship, poor materials, or all three. Steel frame and concrete hold up well under severe shocks but, like masonry walls, must be well-built.

Flexibility of movement may also be considered, that is, let the edifice sway with the tremor. When nearly all the buildings in Tokyo came down in the 1923 disaster, the Imperial Hotel stood. It had been designed by Architect Frank Lloyd Wright with earthquake hazard in mind. There were diagonal supports to strengthen the building against lateral motion. The building had been constructed in units, connected by corridors but joined so as to permit expansion and contraction. Hence one unit shaking might rub against another but could not pull down the whole building. Each unit was anchored to bedrock, but part of its weight rested on looser sediment so that, in a sense, it "floated" on the trembling ground.

This *seemed* to be successful in the 1923 earthquake. But only repeated testing and experiments would confirm the suitability of all these construction techniques. And how do you test a building to see whether it will come down in a violent shock?

Homeowners should check their ceiling plaster and chandeliers. It's a good idea to check building codes in your community, too. Richter allows that official standards in many localities still permit erection of structures that would hardly stand in a strong wind, let alone an earthquake.

But as Thomas Jefferson said, it takes time to persuade men to do even what is for their own good.

And sure enough, in 1960 Phoebus came again to Chile. Concepción was destroyed for the sixth time in history. In the first two days came five major earthquakes, and then a stream of jolts that seemed as though it would go on forever.

A six-year-old boy grabbed his baby brothers and tucked one under each arm. Down came crumbled masonry all around, burying him to the neck. When he was dug out, his brothers were dead.

To placate the gods, Mapuche Indians reportedly beat a six-year-old boy to death with sticks, tore out his heart and offered it to the sea. Their explanation: asking for calm in the sea and on earth.

That this might happen as late as 1960 may come as a surprise to the civilized world, but it is rooted as deeply as anything else in our civilization. It is rooted in fear of the elements.

The mind takes a long time to understand. Some day San Francisco or Tokyo will be struck again. Perhaps they are overdue now. Only Atlas knows, and he is disturbingly mute as to when and where he will next shake his shoulders.

While we have emphasized the direful consequences of earthquakes, it is true that they have their uses. As John Milne, the father of modern seismology, put it, "Earthquakes are the eye through which one may view the innards of the earth." From a study of the elastic waves sent out from earthquakes to all parts of the earth, seismologists have learned much of the nature of the earth's interior. Oilfields and other underground structures are determined from a study of shock waves artificially created. And in time to come, man may well be further enlightened by the shifts and shudders of terra firma.

Meanwhile the earth goes on pitching and yawing on its course through space and time. "Nothing," Darwin said, "not even the wind that blows, is so unstable as the level of the crust of this earth."

And the experience will continue to be one of the most fearful on earth: "A bad earthquake," Darwin continued, "at once destroys our oldest associations: the earth, the very emblem of solidity, has moved beneath our feet like a thin crust over a fluid;—one second of time has created in the mind a strange idea of insecurity, which hours of reflection would not have produced."

Yet it is left to Robert Mallet, who first brought order into the science of seismology, to sum up the subject in words with as much impact today as when he wrote them in 1862. Uniting our knowledge, he said, we will ultimately "form a clear conception of what is the function of the earthquake in the Cosmos, and to recognize the connection, fitness, order, and beauty, even of the volcano and the earth-quake, as parts of the machinery of a wondrous and perfect creation. Like every aspect of nature, that we obtain with the more enlarged and undimmed eye of truth, it will prove to us that even here the great Author of all, is a God of order, not of confusion."

14

LANDSLIDES

If thou hearest that a mountain
has moved, believe it.
. . . *Mohammedan proverb*

On the night of December 16, 1920, a cold and bitter wind swept across the bleak, treeless hills of China's remote Kansu province. Over an area of thirty thousand square miles, night settled with icy suddenness into the valleys and along the cliffs. Peasants bundled together for warmth and sleep in mud huts and in hundreds of cave homes carved in the high bluffs.

Suddenly, under an earthquake of shattering proportions, the ground cracked, and immense landslides of rock and sand gushed from yawning crevasses above the valleys. Mountains slid sickeningly into lowlands. Roadways dropped out of sight. Trees toppled. Gullies opened. City walls collapsed. Village after village lay buried or in ruins.

Seven slides crashed simultaneously into a three-mile gap in the hills, obliterating every living thing except three men and two dogs. These five living creatures, along with a house and orchard, were miraculously carried across the valley on the crest of one slide. The grotesque island was caught in the cross flow of two other slides, whirled in a giant vortex, and catapulted to the slope of a nearby hill.

After the movement subsided, seven thousand rescuers began releasing dammed rivers to forestall disastrous floods. The few surviving inhabitants remained so frightened by recurrent shocks that they dared not build substantial houses for the duration of the winter, and many froze to death under Kansu's bleak and icy winds. The final toll: two hundred thousand persons.

The Kansu earthquake, as such, might not have been so disastrous had it not started so many slides. For years the ground kept shifting, flowing, faulting, and traveling, inch by inch, until no road or path remained safe for passage. No camel driver crossed the fissured plains lest his beasts break through the uncertain crusts.

Did a legendary dragon lash its tail beneath the earth? Nothing in Chinese vocabulary fitted this kind of catastrophe. They called it simply "a time when the mountains walked."

Alpine valleys in Europe have also been devastated. On September 4, 1618, a landslide in Italy's valley of Chiavenna buried two small towns, and out of the population of 2,430 only three escaped. In 1772 three villages in the Treviso area were buried and their entire population wiped out.

On September 2, 1806, an eyewitness watched Switzerland's Rossberg Peak crack and split, saw the forest on the mountainside wave to and fro, and then watched the whole gigantic rock mass move down the slope, gathering velocity and sweeping away everything in its path. It was said that so much friction was generated that moisture turned to steam and flames shot out from the slide. But observations of this sort are usually based on misidentifying clouds of dust. The entire avalanche rammed into the Goldau Valley, burying four villages. Estimates of the lives lost range from 457 to eight hundred.

What causes these catastrophic rock deluges? How do they get started?

Elm is the highest village, 3,162 feet, in Switzerland's Sernf Valley, and for years its inhabitants had been digging slate from a quarry at the base of the Plattenbergkopf, a towering peak that rose directly above the town. From time to time, rock fell into the quarry and from the mountain. Even fatal accidents occurred. But no one seemed to sense what was happening.

The villagers continued, as the years went by, to work the quarry in spare time, removing the mountain's delicate underpinnings. Even after a great crack split the summit, blasting was continued.

Finally, on September 11, 1881, after a month of rain, part of the mountain broke and splattered into the valley, its debris reaching to within a hundred yards of the inn. The people ran for their lives. Seventeen minutes later another landfall crashed down upon the village, overwhelming the inn and several houses and killing a score of the villagers.

Four minutes after that there was a third fall, and it seemed as if the whole mountain had come loose. Witnesses said that as the great mass roared into the valley with terrific velocity, it pushed before it a tornadolike wind that overthrew houses like haystacks and blew down trees like so many matches. Within a few minutes, over ten million cubic yards of rock had buried the village beneath fifty feet of twisted, jumbled earth. The landslide obliterated 115 townspeople.

In the Canadian Rockies, peaceful Turtle Mountain rises 3,100 feet above the village of Frank, Alberta. Frank is a mining town and always has been. Its coal seams lie squarely at the base of the mountain.

At dawn on April 29, 1903, after heavy rain had sopped the mountainside, a mass of rock nearly half a mile square and five hundred feet thick broke loose from the east face of Turtle Mountain and plunged thousands of feet. It plowed through the village, blocked the mine entrance, destroyed seven thousand feet of track along the Crow's Nest Railway, and rumbled on at express-train speed for 2½ miles to the far side of the valley. Between sixty and seventy persons were killed. The scene today is still marked by a wicked and naked scar that spans the valley, an effective reminder that when old terra firma gets up and moves, nothing can stop her.

As we have seen, man himself is occasionally the culprit. But even though coal mines and quarries sometimes encourage slides, Nature's unaided forces often combine to make a cliff collapse. Streams undercut slopes. Weak rock strata crumble. Earthquakes generate subterranean forces that tear loose unstable mountainsides; and other deep-seated stresses and strains rattle precarious slopes beyond their equilibrium. Even the Rock of Gibraltar, that symbol of stability itself, lost six hundred tons of slab rock off its northeast corner in 1935.

By far the greatest cause of landslides is saturation by water which contributed to the Swiss and Turtle Mountain slides. Every rock mass or jumble of boulders holds itself in place by friction—at a position known as the angle of repose. When heavy rains douse these slopes, each piece of rock is "lubricated" by ground water. The whole slope is slicked just as surely as if it had been greased. If the bedrock on which it rests is nothing more than slippery clay—look out below!

In 1950, the Swedish town of Goteborg, built on a clay meadow and stream bank, rode along on a horizontal landslide that jumbled houses, swallowed up the railroad station, and pitched furniture, autos and inhabitants into the wavy, lurching streets.

When landslides plunge into and block well-watered mountain valleys, they often create huge reservoirs. Probably the best-known one was formed in Wyoming's Gros Ventre Mountains, just south of Yellowstone National Park, on June 23, 1925. For days, the Gros Ventre valley lay under pelting rains combined with the downwash of melting snows. Suddenly an enormous rock mass, estimated at fifty million cubic yards (enough to cover Manhattan to a depth of two feet), pulled loose from the north spur of Sheep Mountain and slid across the valley, ramming against the opposite side of the valley to a height of 350 feet.

This heap of rock, soil, forest, and debris jammed so tightly that it blocked the rampaging Gros Ventre River and formed a dam behind which a lake began ominously to rise.

For two years the dam held, discharging the lake's surplus waters by seepage. But on the morning of May 18, 1927, after heavy snows had begun melting in the mountains, the slide-blocked lake overtopped its dam and broke through.

At that moment, four miles downstream, the village of Kelly was anxiously eying the swollen river. Suddenly the appearance of ranch utensils in the water warned Forest Ranger C. E. Dibble that something was wrong at the dam.

Jumping into his automobile, he rushed up the road leading to the dam. On a hill above Woodward's ranch, about a mile below the dam, he saw the flood crest. While he watched, it wiped out the remaining ranch buildings.

There was no time to lose.

Dibble turned around and sped back to the village, shouting the alarm. He dispatched messages down the Gros Ventre and Snake River valleys to warn the inhabitants of impending flood.

At eleven A.M. a wave fifteen feet high burst from the mouth of the gorge above Kelly and swept through the village, carrying away every building in sight except the school, the church, and one high-level cottage. It continued on down the Snake River, to be felt as far away as Idaho Falls, Idaho.

Mudflows have wiped out forests on Lassen Peak in California and Mount Rainier in Washington. Even New England's Green and White Mountains have been scarred by avalanches in centuries past. John Muir, in *Our National Parks*, describes one that fell in California's Yosemite Valley:

"One morning about two o'clock, I was aroused by an earthquake; and though I had never before enjoyed a storm of this sort, the strange, wild thrilling motion and rumbling could not be mistaken, and I ran out of my cabin near the Sentinel Rock, both glad and frightened, shouting, 'A noble earthquake!' feeling sure I was going to learn something. The shocks were so violent and varied, and succeeded one another so closely one had to balance in walking as if on the deck of a ship among the waves, and it seemed impossible the high cliffs should escape being shattered. . . . The Eagle Rock, a short distance up the valley, had given way, and I saw it falling in thousands of the great boulders I had been studying so long, pouring to the valley floor in a free curve luminous from friction, making a terribly sublime and beautiful spectacle—an arc of fire fifteen hundred feet span, as true in form and as steady as a rainbow, in the midst of the stupendous roaring rock-storm."

It is the rare eyewitness who gets *caught* in a landslide and comes down with it—to live again. And we are fortunate that the observer from whom we have a record was an articulate and eloquent writer. Arnold Lunn, an accomplished skier and mountaineer as well, was climbing in Wales in 1909 when "suddenly the mountain seemed to sway, and a quiver ran through the rocks. I clung for one brief moment of agony to the face of the cliff. And then suddenly a vast block, which must have been about ten feet high and several feet thick, separated itself from the face, heeled over on top of me and carried me with it into space. I turned a somersault, struck the cliff some distance below, bounded off once again and, after crashing against the ridge two or three times, landed on a sloping ledge about seven feet broad. The thunder of the rocks falling through the hundred and fifty feet below my resting-point showed how narrow had been my escape.

"I had fallen a distance which Lindsay estimated at a hundred feet. It was not a sliding fall, for except when I struck and rebounded I was not in contact with the ridge. The fall was long enough for me to retain a very vivid memory of the thoughts which chased each other through my brain during those few crowded seconds. I can still feel the clammy horror of the moment when the solid mountain face trembled below me, but the fall, once I was fairly off, blunted the edge of fear. My emotions were subdued, as if I had been partially anaesthetized. I remember vividly seeing the mountains upside down after my first somersault and that I was still falling. I remember making despairing movements with my hands in a futile attempt to check my downward progress.

"The chief impression was a queer feeling that the stable order of nature had been overturned. The tranquil and immobile hills had been startled into a mood of furious and malignant activity, like a dangerous dog roused from a peaceful nap by some inattentive passer-by who has trodden on him unawares. And every time I struck the cliff only to be hurled downwards once again, I felt like a small boy who is being knocked about by a persistent bully—'Will he never stop? . . . surely he can't hit me again . . . surely he's hurt me enough.'

"When at last I landed, I tried to sit up, but fell back hurriedly on seeing my leg. The lower part was bent almost at right angles. It was not merely broken, it was shattered and crushed."

Canoemen in the upper Amazon's untamed jungle country live in dread of riverbank slides, which sometimes stir up violent waves that overwhelm good-sized boats.

The U.S.S.R. has had landslip catastrophes, especially in its Transcaucasus and Volga regions. In Scandinavia, slides are most common in clay banks along streams and fiords. An Allied bombing raid near Norway's Kjeller Aerodrome in April, 1944, started landslides that lasted all summer.

And in Japan, the great Zenkozi (Nagano) earthquake of May 8, 1847, cut loose an estimated total of forty-three thousand landslides.

On a flight over Central and South America, scars, slides, and slump terraces give airline passengers the impression that the Andes are falling apart.

In truth, all mountains are. But they do not always collapse with violence and destruction. Some landslides move so slowly that their movement is perceptible only by measurement or by the visible displacement of trees and telephone lines.

Switzerland's creeping Monte Arbino remained harmless and virtually unmoving until the beginning of the twentieth century. Then its summit slowly began to move at a rate of about six inches a year. Nobody in the valleys below was alarmed. But Monte Arbino's annual rate of movement kept increasing.

Cracks appeared in the mountain, and boulders started sliding downhill. At length, the menace became so great that government authorities ordered the valley evacuated. And just in time. On October 2, 1928, over thirty million cubic meters of rock rumbled into the valley, burying forests, fields, houses, and roads.

Whether they move fast or slowly, landslides are costly wreckers. Slides closed the Panama Canal seven times after it was opened in 1914 and caused the loss of millions of dollars in tolls. Before that, slides had disrupted excavation of the canal for weeks at a time, destroying steam shovels, locomotives, and other equipment, as well as miles of track. Said Lieutenant Colonel D. D. Gaillard, who had charge of the Central Division where most slides occurred: "So far as my own experience . . . is concerned . . . I know of no single thing which has done so much to complicate the engineering problems of our work, or to hinder and lessen the yardage output, as the slides. . . . I do not think it any exaggeration to say that nearly 200 miles of track work . . . has been necessitated since the commencement of the work, solely on account of slides."

What do landslides cost? It's hard to estimate. There are such indirect costs as traffic delays, damage claims, and interruptions of public services. Engineers calculate that the total runs into hundreds of millions of dollars a year.

One state alone (California) reports yearly slide damage of over a million dollars, three states just under a million, and six over a hundred thousand dollars. Water backing up behind Grand Coulee Dam has caused slides costing upwards of twenty million dollars. An oil company in California spent more than a million dollars to control slides in a single field. One railroad company shells out between 500,000 and a million dollars a year to control and clean up after slides.

Of even more concern is the hazard to public safety. With America's growing road network designed for high-speed, high-density traffic, one rockfall in the middle of one lane could bring multiple collisions with an appalling loss of life.

Yet highway engineers cannot remove every dangerous mountain. They cannot stop rainfall. They cannot abolish earthquakes. They cannot halt vibration. Only with great difficulty can they retard erosion or alter the courses of rivers.

One thing the engineers have learned is that sudden slides are not quite so sudden as they seem. Intensive study in recent years has shown that a coming landslide gives itself away by such telltale clues as slumps or depressions appearing suddenly in a roadbed, cracks in the earth, displaced paving, and crooked fences.

But these are only surface signs. The basic trouble lies deeper. By a careful study of neighborhood rocks, soil, terrain, and climate, engineers can secure an enlightening picture of the slide danger and do what once seemed impossible—stop the slide before it starts.

The National Research Council has issued a compilation of landslide information which includes results of investigations on the control and prevention of slides. Many measures today are proving effective in holding dangerous slopes.

Steps often have to be taken to hold back the slide itself, a seemingly gargantuan task. In some places, however, crib walls, pilings, and bulkheads are proving remarkably useful. Buttresses at the foot of some potential slides help prevent them from moving farther. Dowels, or rock bolts, can pin a slope directly to a mountainside.

One of the most effective methods, especially on turnpikes, is the bench—a protective shelf dug back into the embankment at the side of a road. This trough catches incidental debris before it falls on the road or passing cars.

If even these do not work, the engineer may remove the slide completely, remove part of it, or build a bridge over it as over a river and let it slide. In the latter case, provision for realigning the superstructure should be made in case the slide causes the bridge to shift. This was done with a bridge over the Squaw Rock Slide, an active slide near Hopland, California. Another case of a highway bridge crossing a slide can be seen near Santa Cruz, California.

Japanese engineers have even rigged landslides to set off a warning before breaking loose. Strain gauges indicate when a slope is nearing the breaking point. And United States railroads have devices that warn when slides have occurred or are in progress. These connect to automatic block signals to slow a speeding train in time. Perhaps these two schemes will some day be combined to reduce still further the danger of a mountain crashing down on passing motorists.

Highway engineers are a long way from knowing fully about slides and how to control them. So far, corrective and preventive techniques are inadequate, and geologists are constantly searching for new remedial measures. When more is learned about these catastrophes, it may be possible to stop landslides before they start, thus avoiding the kind of doom that befell Kansu, Frank, Goldau, Elm, and other valleys where the mountains walked.

15

VOLCANOES

And out of that hill breaketh fire
with brimstone, as it were in hell.
. . . BARTHOLOMAEUS

L̲AFCADIO HEARN called it "the quaintest, queerest, and
the prettiest withal, among West Indian cities; all stone-built and stone-
flagged, with very narrow streets, wooden or zinc awnings, and peaked
roofs of red tile, pierced by gable dormers."

So lay the peaceful city of St. Pierre, on the Caribbean isle of Martinique, at the turn of the twentieth century. St. Pierre was an old city.
It had been founded by the French privateer Esnambuc in 1635 and,
because of its favorable position, soon became the most important commercial town on the island, fed by rich cane and cacao agricultural
districts.

St. Pierre had always been an idyllic resort, with an attractive tropical setting. Bankers lived there, and merchants, and shippers. Many of
the large planters had homes there. Some had exquisite villas along the
height of Morne d'Orange, the Reduits, and Trois Ponts, and these
villas were embellished with charming and luxuriant gardens.

"Most of the buildings," Lafcadio Hearn added, "are painted in a
clear yellow tone, which contrasts delightfully with the burning blue
ribbon of tropical sky above; and no street is absolutely level; nearly
all of them climb hills, descend into hollows, curve, twist, describe sudden angles. There is everywhere a loud murmur of running water,

pouring through the deep gutters contrived between the paved thoroughfare and the absurd little sidewalks, varying in width from one to three feet. The architecture is that of the seventeenth century, and reminds one of the antiquated quarter of New Orleans. All the tints, the forms, the vistas, would seem to have been especially elected or designed for aquarelle studies. The windows are frameless openings without glass; some have iron bars; all have heavy wooden shutters with movable slats, through which light and air can enter."

Others agreed that St. Pierre was the most beautiful city in the West Indies; and some felt that this was counterbalanced by its wickedness.

St. Pierre's population approached thirty thousand. There was a cathedral, town hall, hospital, theatre, Lycée (which made it the educational center of the island), and promenades and squares. It also boasted a botanical garden that was the delight of the Antilles.

Beyond the city, caressed by tropic zephyrs, rose the tumbled heights of the island itself. Bold and rugged prominences leaped from the sea, their slopes clad with a rich, green woodland mixed with fields of sugar cane. From misty clouds wreathed around the island summits, rain and fog condensed into tumbling waters that cascaded through the forests to the sea. Here and there along the way, in the shade of coconut, mango, and breadfruit trees, lay cottages adorned with bright red hibiscus and bougainvillaea.

Though not large (Martinique covers less than four hundred square miles) the tranquil island glittered like a gem in the Caribbean. Practically speaking, it was a good land. Sugar and rum were produced from it. So were banana, cassava, and Carib cabbage, in garden patches that sustained the almost two hundred thousand people on the island. Most of the roads that threaded through the dense and matted vegetation were primitive, and on them could be seen the heavy, lumbering ox carts, with double-yoked teams.

Dominating the island, and especially the town of St. Pierre, was the highest point—a rugged, jungle-clad mountain called Mont Pelée, soaring 4,429 feet above the sea. Mont Pelée commanded the northern part of the island. Along its flanks some twenty-five streams leaped down to the Caribbean. Palms adorned the summit, and along the gentle slopes and steep ravines grew clumps of fern and lobelia. The summit proper afforded a handsome view of the island, and of the bright blue sea. Inside the crater lay a small lake basin bounded by ridges on the north and west, and containing a shallow pan of water.

Toward the southeast a long ridge ran from Pelée to the Pitons de Carbet, second highest land on Martinique. All this expanded into a mountain relief that made up most of the island. Pelée itself covered about fifty square miles, a fourth of the island.

Pelée was a volcano, though when it had last erupted, nobody knew. They called it a "closed mountain." Never had it disturbed the tranquil peace of Martinique within historic times, save for an occasional feeble emission of steam. Erupt? Oh no, said the citizens of St. Pierre. Not Pelée. It never had.

On the twenty-third of March, 1902, some travelers made their way to the summit of Pelée. It was an easy and pleasant hike, and indeed Pelée's crest was a popular vantage point (when the mists did not surround it) from which to view all Martinique. But the travelers on this day found that something had changed. They saw vapors coming from the ground at several points, and they detected a strange odor of sulphur in the air.

How gay! How exciting! "La cratère," wrote one of the travelers in his notebook, "est en éruption." Could it be at last?

Or was this really an eruption? Could one refer to sulphur and vapors as a true eruption? Reluctantly, the travelers had to admit that nothing else unusual was evident. Martinique, crowned by Pelée, still lay as it always had, in the peace and quiet of the blue Caribbean.

A month passed. On April 23 the citizens of St. Pierre noticed something strange floating down out of the sky. Ashes! From far away came the scarcely audible sound of rumbling and reverberations. The ground seemed to be rocking a little now and then. Not much. Nothing to be concerned about, not in this serene and lazy climate—where nothing happened.

As soon as they saw cinders drifting through the air, the people of St. Pierre looked up at sprawling Pelée. And there, sure enough, was smoke issuing from the vent at the summit. *Ma foi!* After all these years!

Even as they watched, a storm of rock and ashes sailed into the air.

Well, at last Pelée was showing some vitality. The next day it showed more, and cinders began to accumulate in the city.

Curious persons who went to the summit had news for the people of the city below. Pelée was not the mountain of old. Inside the summit the lake now boiled. At one side, a new cinder cone had formed, and from it were being thrown out trains of steaming vapor.

All this at first did not seem to disturb the people of Martinique. But ashes continued to fall, and soon the streets and houses took on a wintry aspect. The peaceful streams flowing through and adjacent to the town had risen to wild torrents.

Then came the first week of May. "The rain of ashes never ceases," said the town newspaper *Les Colonies*. By now everything was covered. The palms and hibiscus of the botanical garden lay under a mantle of gray and white. Ashes swirled in the streets. Puffs of wind blew clouds of stifling dust from roofs and awnings into the eyes of the people. Birds fell from the sky. Horses refused to work. Cattle were asphyxiated.

"The smell of sulphur is so strong," the wife of the American Consul wrote in a letter, "that horses on the street stop and snort, and some of them drop in their harness and die from suffocation. Many of the people are obliged to wear wet handkerchiefs to protect them from the strong fumes of sulphur."

And all the while, far in the distance, Pelée rumbled angrily and threw out clouds of smoke and ashes.

A public excursion to the summit had been planned. But now the prospective hikers were not so sure. Pelée was clearly no longer calm and peaceful. The aspect of the land everywhere had sharply changed. Therefore, said the announcement in the newspaper, "l'excursion qui avait été organisée pour demain matin n'aura pas lieu, le cratère étant absolument inaccessible." And so instead of hiking, the people waited—and watched.

On the afternoon of May 5 a flood of boiling mud sped down the mountainside at a speed of sixty miles an hour, engulfing the Usine Guerin, a large sugar factory, and the homes that surrounded it, killing thirty persons. All that remained was a chimney standing out of the mud.

Distinctly now, Pelée was on the rampage. The blue Caribbean sky had become hazy and darkened. The ceaseless fall of ashes thickened.

On the seventh of May, Pelée roared louder. Lightning flashed in the black clouds above the mountain, and thunder echoed across the heavens, mingling with the hollow bellowing of the crater. Across the sea in front of the city drifted a massive flotsam poured in by the streams from Pelée—a chaotic assortment of logs and pumice and other debris of burning forest and mountain.

The ocean rose and ebbed in great swells. Torrential rains fell from the turbulent, heated sky. Villages were swept away by cascading torrents along the rising streams. Black ash filled the air, each particle rubbing another to set up an electrical charge—the whole yielding great irregular flashes of lightning. Thunder added to the chaos.

As the days grew darker, the people of St. Pierre began to panic. Stores were closed and shuttered. "The exodus from St. Pierre is steadily increasing," said *Les Colonies*. "From morning to evening and through the whole night one sees only hurrying people, carrying packages, trunks, and children. . . . The steamers of the Compagnie are no longer empty."

Bravely, the paper tried to bring its readers back. It published an interview with Professor Landes, of the Lycée, and concluded that "the Montagne Pelée presents no more danger to the inhabitants of Saint Pierre than does Vesuvius to those of Naples."

"We confess," the editor announced, "that we cannot understand this panic. Where could one be better than at Saint Pierre? Do those who invade Fort-de-France believe that they will be better off there than here should the earth begin to quake? This is a foolish error against which the populace should be warned.

"We hope that the opinion expressed by M. Landes . . . will reassure the most timid."

As it happened, the paper need not have worried because, surprisingly, the nearly thirty thousand population of St. Pierre did not decrease, but *increased* instead. For one thing, many of the people who left found no security elsewhere on the island, and soon returned. For another, a number of persons from outlying districts migrated into St. Pierre for protection in case Pelée really blew her stack. They felt safer in the city.

Meanwhile, frightful detonations shook the island. Pelée now was discharging an enormous column of dense, black smoke, saturating the air with ashes and cinders. Odors of sulphur permeated the shadowed town, and now these were mixed with the smoke of forests burning along the outskirts of town and on the slopes of the mountain. Cane and coconut bent under the weight of the ashes. Branches broke.

Whole trees were stripped. And not knowing what to expect, the people waited.

Word came that Soufrière Volcano, on St. Vincent Island, ninety miles away, had exploded violently. There were reports of great destruction, but no one knew how much.

Everyone had troubles enough in St. Pierre. Monsieur Parel, the vicar-general of Martinique, happened at the time to be officiating in the absence of the bishop of the diocese, and for the bishop's benefit had been keeping a chronicle of events. On May 7 he entered the following: "Since four o'clock in the morning, when I was awakened in my room at the Séminaire-Collège by loud detonations, I have been watching the most extraordinary pyrotechnic display:—at one moment a fiery crescent gliding over the surface of the crater, at the next long, perpendicular gashes of flame piercing the column of smoke, and then a fringe of fire, encircling the dense clouds rolling above the furnace of the crater. Two glowing craters from which fire issued, as if from blast furnaces, were visible during half an hour, the one on the right a little above the other.

"I distinguished clearly four kinds of noises; first, the claps of thunder, which followed the lightning at intervals of twenty seconds; then the mighty muffled detonations of the volcano, like the roaring of many cannon fired simultaneously; third, the continuous rumbling of the crater, which the inhabitants designated the 'roaring of the lion'; and then last, as though furnishing the bass for this gloomy music, the deep noise of the swelling waters, of all the torrents which take their source upon the mountain, generated by an overflow such as had never yet been seen. This immense rising of thirty streams at once, without one drop of water having fallen on the seacoast, gives some idea of the cataracts which must pour down upon the summit from the storm-clouds gathered around the crater."

Les Colonies published an article of general information on volcanoes, and the people had only to look up for a vivid illustration—the real thing. Eighteen ships lay in the harbor, their decks gray with ashes. If burning cinders fell on their wooden decks . . .

Monsieur Arnoux, a member of the Astronomical Society of France, had gone to the heights above the city and there gained an excellent view of the mountain. "Enormous rocks," he wrote, "were being projected from the crater to a considerable elevation, so high, indeed, as to occupy a quarter of a minute in their flight, and describing an arc that passed considerably beyond the Morne Lacroix, the culminating point of the *massif*. About eight o'clock of the same evening we recognized for the first time, playing about the crater, fixed fires that burned with a brilliant white flame."

The newspaper had stated that, its offices being closed on Thursday, the next issue would appear on Friday.

But, said Angelo Heilprin, President of the Geographical Society of Philadelphia, who visited the scene shortly afterwards, "Saint Pierre knew no further Friday, and even of the Thursday it had but a few short hours. It knew not on this day the fate that awaited it on the morrow, and it clung to the hope that a good end would still come. The city went to sleep hoping but fearing, fearing and not knowing; and it was the last sleep, except that of eternal death, which the city had."

Dawn came to St. Pierre on the morning of Thursday, May 8, 1902, as a kind of half light spilled down from a seething sky. It was the Day of the Ascension, and the devout gathered by the hundreds in the cathedral and the cathedral square. From Pelée still came the thunder and the detonations and the mushrooming black clouds, and it seemed indeed that the end of the world was near.

For St. Pierre it was.

"The big hand of the clock of the Hôpital Militaire," Heilprin wrote, "had just reached the minute mark of seven-fifty when a great brown cloud was seen to issue from the side of the volcano, followed almost immediately by a cloud of vapory blackness, which separated from it, and took a course downward to the sea. Deafening detonations from the interior preceded this appearance, and a lofty white pennant was seen to rise from the summit of the volcano. With wild fury the black cloud rolled down the mountain slope, pressing closely the contours of the valley. . . . In two minutes or less it had reached the doomed city, a flash of blinding intensity parted its coils, and Saint Pierre was ablaze."

Over the wire from St. Pierre to Fort-de-France flashed the single word "allez"; it meant "go ahead," a request to finish a message traveling in the opposite direction. And then there was silence. It was the last communication from St. Pierre.

Monsieur Arnoux, on Mont Parnasse, watched in stunned surprise. "I

noted a small cloud pass out," he said, "followed two seconds afterwards by a considerable cloud, whose flight to the Pointe du Carbet
occupied less than three seconds . . . thus showing that it developed
almost as rapidly in height as in length. Innumerable electric scintilla-
tions played through the chaos of vapors, at the same time that the ears
were deafened by a frightful fracas.

". . . As the monster seemed to near us, my people, panic-stricken,
ran to a neighboring hill that dominated the house, begging me to do
the same. At this moment a terrible aspirating wind arose, tearing the
leaves from the trees and breaking the small branches, at the same time
offering strong resistance to us in our flight. Hardly had we arrived at
the summit of the hillock when the sun was suddenly veiled, and in its
place came an almost complete blackness. Then only did we receive a
fall of stones, the largest of which were about two centimetres of average diameter. . . . This phenomenon lasted for two or three minutes,
and was followed by a shower of stones and of mud-rain. . . ."

Captain Freeman, on the *Roddam*, afloat in the bay, witnessed the
spectacle and, above the roaring of the volcano, heard the terrifying
cries of agony and despair from the thousands who were perishing in
St. Pierre. Against the flames of the city he saw a few people running
wildly about the beach, but it was only a temporary view, for the fire
and overwhelming cloud caught them in their tracks and he saw no
more.

The Captain saw ships struck and capsized by the wave of fire. One
after another, and in the twinkling of an eye, they burst into flames
and sank. He saw the approaching cloud strike and blow the masts and
smokestacks off the *Roraima*. As he watched helplessly, thousands of
casks of rum stored in St. Pierre exploded and flowed like a burning
river down the streets and out onto the surface of the sea. The fiery
wave moved rapidly, surrounding the ships and setting them afire.

In two or three minutes all was over in St. Pierre.

The vicar-general, having gone to Fort-de-France the previous night,
gained passage on a ship that was to go collect the wounded, and got
his first view of St. Pierre that day from the sea. "We round the last
promontory which separates us from what was once the magnificent
panorama of St. Pierre. A little farther out blazes a great American
packet, which arrived on the scene just in time to be overwhelmed in

the catastrophe. Nearer the shore two other ships are in flames. The coast is strewn with wreckage, with the keels of the overturned boats, all that remains of the twenty or thirty ships which lay at anchor here the day before. All along the quays, for a distance of two hundred metres, piles of lumber are burning. . . .

"But Saint Pierre, in the morning throbbing with life, thronged with people, is no more. Its ruins stretch before us, wrapped in their shroud of smoke and ashes, gloomy and silent, a city of the dead. Our eyes seek out the inhabitants fleeing distracted, or returning to look for the dead. Nothing to be seen. No living soul appears in this desert of desolation encompassed by appalling silence."

And if no living soul were in view, who was to be rescued? Thirty thousand people were dead.

Despite a torrential rain, St. Pierre remained aflame for several days. Then it smouldered, its ruins coated with a paste of white ash. And a comparative quiet came to the island.

How much of the city remained, or could even be recognized? Searchers knew the Place Bertin by what remained of its fountain and by the prostrate trees overthrown in parallel lines toward the south. Rue Victor Hugo and Rue Bouillé, with their shops and residences, were heaps of concrete and boulders.

Not a roof remained anywhere. It was as if the people of St. Pierre had never built a roof.

Bits of mosaic appeared, scattered in the ash. Giant palms remained only as charred stumps. A corner remained of the cathedral, a wall of the hospital. Iron girders had been looped and twisted as if they were ropes. Rubbish lay everywhere, and beyond it the forest had gone, and the fields, and the suburbs, and some of the distant villages.

Rescuers poked through the ruins. In a bathroom they found six bodies so badly burned as to be hardly recognizable as bodies. Another place, there were eight clustered together. One woman lay with her hand thrown out as if to grasp something in the last throes of anguish. Nearby was an infant. Then another woman, crouching.

The digging began, and a large percentage of bodies were recovered without a scrap of clothing. Yet many clothed forms were also found, and the clothes seemed not to have been disturbed at all. In many instances, the bodies lay turned with the head facing the ground, with the hand clapped over the mouth and nose. Had a deadly vapor caught and suffocated them instantly? Had a burning gas almost immediately stopped their breathing? Some showed signs of momentary struggle. Most, however, showed no evidence that they had stirred at all after the fiery blast closed in.

Over and over in the minds of those who dug and those who hoped turned one persistent question: in such a massive and instantaneous holocaust, could anyone have survived?

Deep in the dungeon of the city jail had been a man named Auguste Ciparis. His cell possessed no windows and all that he could see of the outer world was light that sifted through a grated aperture in the upper part of the door.

On the morning of May 8 he waited as usual for breakfast to be brought in by his jailer when suddenly the dim illumination that came through the grating faded and the cell was plunged into near blackness. Immediately, hot air, laden with ash, flowed fiercely through the grating.

His flesh began to burn. His breathing failed. Weakly he called for help but got no answer. He leaped from wall to wall of his cell, lurching in agony, but there was no escaping the deadly heat. The scorching endured for only a moment, but in that time he almost ceased to breathe . . . permanently.

"Save me! Save me!" he shouted, but was answered only by his own coughs and groans of anguish.

Slowly, a half-light returned to his cell. There had been no smoke, no noise of any kind, no odor to suggest a burning gas, no fumes of sulphur. He had been clad in hat, shirt, and trousers, which were not burned. But beneath the shirt his back had been seared, and now he could smell the odor of burned flesh.

In his agony he had no idea that others had been burned above him—and worse than burned. No sound came to his ears. The jailkeeper did not arrive with breakfast that morning.

For three days he went without food. There was some water in his cell, apparently unaffected. It kept him alive. On Sunday, he heard voices and renewed his calls for help. Soon the dungeon was broken open and Ciparis was brought, half dead, to the free air above.

There was a report of one other survivor, a shoemaker named Léon Compère-Léandre, who came within an ace of being completely overwhelmed. He managed to gain some protection in a house but still was badly burned and unconscious.

The tornadic blast had done an effective task. It had scorched the lungs and burned the flesh of thirty thousand people, and sealed the lips of all but two.

By now, the news from Soufrière Volcano, on St. Vincent Island, had come in: a destructive cloud had blown from the volcano, killed two thousand people, and destroyed the countryside.

A few days later Pelée proved that she had not finished. Another cloud exploded and roared along the same path, toppling St. Pierre's remaining walls into utter ruin. "The consequences of this new disaster are incalculable," said Monsieur Parel. At Fort-de-France, and elsewhere on the island, panic erupted. "Since yesterday, all the families who were beginning to regain their confidence are plunged into the deepest despondency. They are embarking by thousands for St. Lucia, for Guadeloupe, Trinidad, France and for America!

"It is no longer the exodus of the north to the south, but of all Martinique to foreign lands. Such, Monseigneur," he added, closing his chronicle, "is the life we lead . . . I shall be the last to leave Martinique."

Again and again Pelée belched mud and steam and incandescent clouds. New paroxysmal eruptions burst forth on May 26, June 6, July 9, and August 30.

By this time Angelo Heilprin had come to Martinique (as had a host of others to write up the events for home consumption) and being the scientist that he was, nothing would do but that he get to the summit.

Courageously, he and his associates crawled up the mountain, immersed in clouds of steam and mist and rain and falling cinders. They could see little or nothing, but the sound, he said, was as if all the furnaces of the globe had been united into a single one.

Volcanic bombs—chunks of hardened lava—flew past, unseen, and thudded into the desolate earth around them. They heard explosions in the air, and the ominous crunching of rocks striking the ground.

"We moved up slowly, hardly more than a few paces at a time, but with hope given to us in the occasional rifting of the clouds. Time and time again the summit crest appeared beneath the rolling vapors, and it really seemed as if the cone, of which we were in search, would suddenly come to view. When we had reached three thousand eight hundred feet the fusillade of bombs became overpoweringly strong, and we were obliged to retreat. We were in battle. The clouds had become lighter, and we could at times see the bombs and boulders coursing through the air in parabolic curves and straight lines, driven and shot out as if from a giant catapult. They whistled past us on both sides, and our position became decidedly uncomfortable; many of the fragments took almost direct paths, and must have been shot into their courses as a result of explosions taking place above the summit of the volcano. They flew by us at close range. Descending perhaps one hundred feet lower on the slope, we took shelter under a somewhat rolling knob and waited for a possible cessation of the fusillade."

But the clouds did not clear until later, when they had gone part way down the mountain, and then "revealed the volcano in all its majestic fury. For the first time since we reached its slopes were we permitted to see its steam-column—that furious, swirling mass ahead of us, towering miles above the summit, and sweeping up in curls and festoons of white, yellow and almost black. It boiled with ash. The majestic cauliflower clouds rose on all sides, joining with the central column, and it was evident that the entire crater was working, bottom as well as summit, and with a vigor that would be useless to attempt to describe. Higher and higher they mount, until the whole is lost in the great leaden umbrella which seemed to overspread the whole earth. I estimated the diameter of the column as it left the crest of the mountain to be not less than fifteen hundred feet, and its rate of ascent from one and a half to two miles a minute, and considerably greater at the initial moment of every new eruption."

Not since the Lisbon Earthquake had a major disaster so attracted public attention. Within two months a flurry of books rolled off the presses, describing not only the sensational aspects of the disaster but of volcanoes in general—and a few earthquakes and tidal waves for good measure. Almost without exception they had fiery titles: *The Complete Story of the Martinique Horror, The Volcano's Deadly Work, Martinique Flood of Fire and Burning Rain, The World on Fire, In the Shadow of Death,* and one writer was so excited that, imprinted in bold capitals on the title page, were these words: NO SUCH FRIGHTFUL CALAMITY, UNEQUALLED FOR THE SUDDENNESS OF THE BLOW, THE NUMBER OF VICTIMS, THE COMPLETENESS

OF THE DESOLATION HAS EVER COME UPON THE CIVI-
LIZED WORLD WITH SUCH OVERWHELMING AND HAR-
ROWING FORCE. There was at least one love story, *The Prophet
of Martinique, Embracing a Vivid Account of the Historic Destruction
by Mont Pelée.* And, the inevitable allusion to Vesuvius: *Martinique,
the Second Pompeii.*

But all this was quite understandable, and perhaps the sensationalism
was even forgivable. St. Pierre had been annihilated in as dramatic a
blast of nature's fury as could possibly be imagined. For months thereafter Pelée continued vomiting incandescent, superheated steam clouds,
roaring and bellowing as if it would never stop. Then, suddenly, a
spine of rock, sharp-tipped like an obelisk, began rising from the summit crater. Somewhere within the seething caldron volcanic forces
were pushing up what was perhaps the old volcanic cap that had kept
Pelée stoppered for centuries.

Under the pressure of heat and steam, the rock of the tower was
weak and shot through with zones of fracture. As it rose, it also fell,
sometimes in chunks, sometimes decapitating itself. Yet up it came, one
hundred feet, two hundred, three, four, five . . . Smoke and steam rose
from it, and on some days the spine was lifted as much as thirty feet.

Heilprin, on an anniversary visit to the island, stood enthralled before
it. " 'Look!' I shouted to my companion, and my words failed me for
the magnificence of the view that presented itself. The spectacle was
one of overwhelming grandeur, and we stood for some moments awed
and silent in the shadow of this most impressive of mountain forms.
Nature's monument dedicated to the 30,000 dead who lay in the silent
city below, it rose up a huge monolith, 830 feet above the newly constructed summit of the volcano . . . a unique and incomparable type in
our planet's wonderland. . . . In its condition of vapor clouds blowing
out from its base and from the cone that supported it, with blue sulphur smoke curling its way along with these, it presented a spectacle
of almost overwhelming grandeur and one of terrorizing effect which
could hardly be matched elsewhere. None of the grand scenes of nature which I had before seen . . . impressed me to the extent that did
the view of Pelée's tower, from the crater-rim. . . ."

The spine of Mont Pelée reached a maximum height of 1,145 feet,
and in July and August of 1903 began disintegrating, eventually to dis-
appear in new and severe eruptions which lasted the rest of the year.

After 1905, Pelée quieted, and only some small fumaroles hinted at the fury below. It was not the first time, nor would it be the last, that great steam and ash clouds burst from a "sleeping" volcano. Parallel instances occurred in the crater of Tarumai, on Hokkaido Island, Japan, in 1909, at Lassen Peak, California, in 1915, and at Santa Maria in Guatemala in 1922.

A few people drifted back to St. Pierre and slowly the city began to rise from the ashes. Twenty years later it had a thousand inhabitants, and even a volcanological museum amid the ruins of the city. But the quiet was too good to last.

In 1929 Pelée exploded again, followed by a strange and ominous month of calm, and then three years of eruption in which hundreds of steam clouds (now called by their French name of *nuées ardentes*, glowing clouds) blew out of the mountain and swept downhill as well as into the sky. To embattled residents of Martinique it must have seemed that their island was now destined forever to be rocked like a boat on the stormy sea, and to be pelted by cinders and devastated by volcanic clouds till time closed down the fires within the earth. They must also have felt that surely by now they had had their share of death and destruction, and they may well have longed for something a little less spectacular and a little more refined in the way of volcanoes.

Today the town of St. Pierre has risen again, to a population of more than five thousand. There is a customhouse, a museum, and a geological research laboratory, and the city is a mecca for travelers interested in science who know what happened there. And perhaps again someday the sky will darken and the ground will rumble and the people will look up in resignation. "La cratère," someone will say, "est en éruption."

As for the rest of the world, the standard impression of volcanoes is likely to be something utterly unlike Pelée. It is apt to be a mental image of a magnificent, symmetrical peak spouting fountains of crimson and orange lava. Such, in truth, is the exception rather than the rule. There are a few, such as Vesuvius, Fujiyama, and Mayon of the Philippines, whose symmetry and picturesque setting place them among the most magnificent views on earth. To describe them would require the eloquence of a Jeremiah.

But volcanoes come in all shapes and sizes, and the only requisite to make a mountain a volcano is some kind of eruptive apparatus. Sometimes the lava must rise a long way to the top of the stack. Cotopaxi, in Ecuador, for example, is the world's highest active volcano, its summit rising 19,600 feet above sea level. The Hawaiian volcanoes reach to 13,825 feet above sea level—a total of thirty thousand feet from the ocean floor.

What actually issues from the inner recesses of the earth is difficult to ascertain. We have a fair idea, and can retrieve the results of eruptions after they have cooled. Yet the stuff that arrives at the throat of the volcano at the instant of eruption is hard to collect uncontaminated.

Whatever it is made of, an eruption is an impressive sight. Mark Twain, in *Roughing It*, describes this sight at Kilauea: "Here and there were gleaming holes a hundred feet in diameter, broken in the dark crust, and in them the melted lava—the color a dazzling white just tinged with yellow—was boiling furiously; and from these holes branched numberless bright torrents in many directions, like the spokes of a wheel, and kept a tolerably straight course for a while and then swept round in huge rainbow curves, or made a long succession of sharp worm-fence angles, which looked precisely like the fiercest jagged lightning. These streams made other streams and they mingled with and crossed and re-crossed each other in every conceivable direction, like skate tracks on a popular skating-ground. Sometimes streams twenty or thirty feet wide flowed from the holes to some distance without dividing—and through the opera-glasses we could see that they ran down small, steep hills and were genuine cataracts of fire, white at their source, but soon cooling and turning to the richest red, grained with alternate lines of black and gold. Every now and then masses of the dark crust broke away and flowed slowly down these streams like rafts down a river. Occasionally, the molten lava flowing under the superincumbent crust broke through—split a dazzling streak, from five hundred to a thousand feet long, like a sudden flash of lightning; and then acre after acre of the cold lava parted into fragments, turned up edgewise like cakes of ice when a great river breaks up, plunged downward and were swallowed in the crimson cauldron. . . .

"Through the glasses the little fountains scattered about looked very beautiful. They boiled, and coughed, and spluttered, and discharged sprays of stringy red fire—of about the consistency of mush for instance—from ten to fifteen feet into the air, along with a shower of brilliant white sparks—a quaint and unnatural mingling of gouts of blood and snowflakes!' "

But the lava itself is more than molten rock. It is also gases, chiefly steam. The procedure by which water vapors get mixed up in matter so hot is not precisely known. Part of the water may somehow have been trapped there since the days the earth was made; perhaps part of it is water seeping down through the earth's crust; perhaps some of it is a melting of rocks with water in their chemical make-up. In any case, the water is there, and because of its being superheated into steam, it provides the explosive power most volcanoes need to erupt. And often the steam comes pouring out on a grand scale. Mexico's Parícutin, for example, is estimated to have discharged as much as sixteen thousand tons of steam a day at its height, along with a hundred thousand tons of lava.

Parícutin first burst out of a sheepherder's pasture on the nineteenth of February, 1943, as wisps of smoke in thin white columns. By late afternoon flames leaped out of the ground. Clouds of dense smoke shot skyward. Explosions could be heard as often as seventeen a minute. Within five days the new volcano built its cone to a height of three hundred feet.

The cone went on a-building, reaching seven hundred feet in two weeks. Lava flows issued from the base and by night the cone looked as if a giant fireworks display had been ignited. Incandescent bombs sailed into the air. At the end of a year, Parícutin was 1,410 feet high. It finally reached 2,120 feet and became dormant or extinct in 1952.

This was but one of thousands of cinder cones that have been built, some as recent as Arizona's Sunset Crater, which erupted around A.D. 1066 and buried the homes of prehistoric Indians.

Because we are most startled by the making of a whole new mountain, we may forget that much of a volcano's ejecta goes up in steam. As to gases, we can get a clue from those given off for weeks after the lava begins to cool and harden. These include carbon dioxide, hydrogen, hydrochloric and hydrofluoric acids, and sometimes hydrogen sulphide and sulphur dioxide. Some volcanoes give off chlorides, leading to the suggestion that sea water somehow penetrates to the deep-seated pools of lava and mixes with them.

Lava may erupt straight up through the vent and out of the crater, or may breach the sides of the cone and pour out through fissures.

When this happened in 1935 on the flank of Mauna Loa, the lava flowed downhill toward the town of Hilo. Air Force bombers roared over the flow and bombed it, diverting it, slowing it, and giving it time to cool and harden, thus saving the threatened city.

Besides liquids, volcanoes eject solids, which may be a conglomeration of many things—pieces of rock torn from the conduit, bits of hardened lava that once blocked the vent, or any debris that has fallen into the opening. Blocks weighing thirty tons were once flung from Stromboli to a distance of two miles.

Or the ejecta of volcanoes can be so completely pulverized that the dust remains floating in the atmosphere for years, as happened at Krakatoa.

Krakatoa was an island in the Sunda Strait, a neck of tropical sea that separates Sumatra from Java and ties the Indian Ocean to the China Sea, a place which the British Royal Society likes to call "the greatest focus of volcanic activity upon the globe." Of Java's forty-nine volcanoes (some rising to twelve thousand feet above sea level), fully half have erupted within historic times.

Yet surprisingly, Krakatoa had been so timid through the centuries that it had gone virtually unnoticed. It was the largest of several islands that formed the crater rim of a submerged volcano. Evidently in bygone millennia the mountain had been bigger, and somehow had blown apart at the seams, leaving its jagged crater roughly twenty-five miles across at sea level. Afterwards a few other cones had been built up within this crater.

As early as 1880, earthquakes began shaking the straits, and in 1883 "booming sounds like the firing of artillery" reached Batavia and Buitenzorg, towns situated nearly a hundred miles away. For hours, doors and windows rattled in these towns and in neighboring villages. Aboard a mail-steamer passing through the strait, the compass-needles were wildly agitated.

Steam rose from Krakatoa. Ashes fell. More explosions shattered the peace of the strait. Then fire and pumice burst from the summit, and a dust column, around which flashes of lightning played, rose seven miles into the tropic sky. By night, molten, white-hot lava gave an eerie touch to the scene.

Presently, rocks of all sorts were being hurled to great heights along with the pumice. Not only was the vegetation of Krakatoa eradicated, but leaves of trees on adjacent islands were stripped away.

For more than three months this pattern of earthquakes and explosions and eruptions continued. New craters opened. Explosions increased in intensity and the dust cloud rose higher. A ship's captain passing by estimated that the cloud rose seventeen miles into the atmosphere.

The final stage began on the afternoon of August 26, 1883. Land and sea were rocked by one deafening detonation after another, some so loud that they could be heard at Bandong, 150 miles away. People in villages a hundred miles away could not sleep; to them the noise resembled artillery fire at close range. Windows rattled. Pictures shook. Chandeliers swayed.

So intense was the pandemonium in the strait that approaching ships shortened sail and stopped. A rain of pumice, still warm, fell on the decks. Passengers looking up saw that the cloud above Krakatoa was now dense and black, fiercely illuminated by flashes of lightning created in the seething dust. One sea captain described the cloud as like an immense pine tree, with stem and branches of volcanic lightning.

Ashes blew through the air around the ships, and the people on board breathed the acrid fumes of sulphur. As they watched the fabulous sight off the ship's bow they saw curving chains of fire and white balls of flame—incandescent lava fragments flying into the air and spilling down the slopes of the island.

All night the explosions continued, and cinders fell everywhere. One moment the sky was intensely black, and next a blaze of fire. Few people could sleep, for there was an almost continuous roar. Steam exploded in the volcano's vent, uncovering a caldron of molten lava and illuminating the base of the rising dust and smoke cloud. To add to the weirdness of the scene, St. Elmo's fire danced around the ships in the strait. Mud and rain fell on the masts and rigging and decks. Lightning jabbed into the sea and ships.

The island exploded finally on the morning of August 27 in a series of detonations mightier than any that had ever been heard by man. To a depth of a thousand feet the volcano was abruptly eviscerated. In a gigantic, culminating cataclysm, two-thirds of the island of Krakatoa was blown to smithereens.

Debris sailed out over hundreds of thousands of square miles of water, and dust flew so high into the air that it ultimately circled the globe, reddening sunsets as far away as England.

The colossal eruption generated giant tidal waves that swept up on all the land around the strait, stranding vessels, devastating towns and villages and lighthouses, and destroying over thirty-six thousand lives. On the southern end of Sumatra, one wave rose over seventy feet and carried a gunboat two miles inland where it was left thirty feet above sea level. In Katimbong the wave rose eighty feet, and on the shallow shore of Merak, along the Java coast, the waves reached the extraordinary height of 135 feet.

Air pressure from the explosions blew out windows and shattered walls at Batavia and Buitenzorg, a hundred miles away. As history's loudest bang, the noise was heard three thousand miles to the west, on the island of Rodrigues, in the Indian Ocean. It was also heard in Ceylon (2,058 miles), Bangkok and the Philippines (1,400 miles), and South Australia (2,250 miles). Sound waves traveled completely around the earth four times, as verified by barograph records at a number of locations, chiefly near Panama, half a world away. Though later sound waves were inaudible, they left an indelible record on sensitive instruments.

Other volcanoes have thrown out more of their insides (Papandayang, Java, 1772; Iceland, 1783; Tambora, Sumbawa, 1815), but none exceeded the violent paroxysms by which Krakatoa finally tore itself apart.

Today Krakatoa's crater is largely submarine, but it rumbles ominously from time to time and sends out billowing white balls of smoke and steam. The old crater is not dead yet.

Nor is the fascinating question of why Krakatoa disintegrated with such stupendous commotion. One conjecture is that when the vent opened, great quantities of sea water poured in, generating steam and power, as when a bucket of cold water is thrown into a furnace. But even more serious would be the cooling of lava in the upper part of the conduit. This may have formed a temporary cap, clogging the vent and sealing off the power below. The volcano rumbled on, of course, and when sufficient pressure had built up within, the cap and the whole island exploded.

If nothing else, Krakatoa demonstrated what some people already knew: that a volcanic eruption is one of the greatest natural spectacles on the face of the earth. A lava fountain has the innate fascination of a waterfall, or a campfire, or the breaking surf at the edge of the sea. The incandescent molten lava breaks out of its vent in a powerful yellow gush and rises hundreds of feet into the air. Immediately the colors begin to change, from orange, to deep orange, to red, to maroon, and finally—before cascading to the rim of the crater—to black. It is a sight that can be watched for hours, night and day.

Heat waves jiggle the scene before the observer's compelled attention. Above the roar can be heard the explosion of gases, the rush of lava, the fall of hardened rock. And when the eruption ceases, thundering slides of molten lava pour back into the vent.

On Hawaii great forests of ohia trees have been inundated with black lava, and their limbs seared and stripped. Highways are covered. Lookout points are blasted. Whole villages are covered with cinders, and buried beneath black dunes or crumbled and burned by the relentless advance of a lava flow.

Lava ordinarily comes sluggishly out of a volcano, but when it is thin and syrupy, and the slope is steep enough, it can flow at more than ten miles an hour, which means that you would have to step into a run to keep out of the way.

Many volcanoes, like Mauna Loa and Kilauea, are only mildly eruptive. (The islands of Hawaii are actually protruding segments of an enormous basaltic lava mass on which rest five giant volcanoes.) Mauna Loa is the world's largest volcano, and delivers the most lava of all. Kilauea, on the east slope of Mauna Loa, lies twenty-two miles from the top and ten thousand feet lower. Within Kilauea's summit is a fire pit some nine miles in circumference with cliffs 450 feet high. Here the rising lava boils and seethes and fountains, perpetually stirred by gases that break its surface. This "Everlasting House of Fire" stays relatively gentle over the years, but can, as in 1924, rumble and explode and send out giant cauliflower clouds of debris.

From all this one would wonder why Hawaiian volcanoes are classified as mild. Yet mild they are, and the spectacle when they erupt seems more pronounced because of the rarity of the event.

On the other hand, violence is no rarity at Stromboli, in the Mediterranean. This volcano lies in the Lipari or Aeolian Islands, north of Sicily, and has been active for as long as men have known it, erupting in moderate explosions every ten or fifteen minutes. Since the dawn of history, Stromboli has flung chunks of lava and blobs of magma high into the air, producing luminous clouds that give the mountain its name: lighthouse of the Mediterranean.

Most other volcanoes are less active, but in some cases a rare eruption can be just as destructive as Krakatoa. Bandai San in Japan once blew away half of a two-thousand-foot-high cone in two hours. And Tambora, on the island of Sumbawa, east of Java, once threw up thirty cubic miles of rock, a volume equal to a hundred cones the size of Vesuvius.

The eruptions at Crater Lake, Oregon, which occurred about ten thousand years ago when the volcano then standing rose to a height of about twelve thousand feet, must have been closely parallel to the Pelean type of eruption, for evidence shows that steam clouds blew out of the side of this so-called Mount Mazama and traveled a distance of thirty-four miles. The roof of the mountain either collapsed inward or blew away, and in the resultant crater—or caldera, to be precise— Crater Lake rests today, six miles in diameter.

Although Vesuvius, perhaps the world's best-known volcano, usually overlooks the Bay of Naples with quiet elegance, the quiet is not constant, and in fact Vesuvius was not always there. The site was once a volcano known as Mount Somma. The ancient Romans paid little attention to Somma, for as far as they knew it had never erupted. Then in A.D. 79, Somma made up for its centuries of inactivity, and Vesuvius was born. Much of the side toward the sea was blasted away or engulfed, destroying the towns of Herculaneum and Pompeii.

One of the eyewitnesses was Pliny the Younger, then eighteen, who described what he saw in a letter to Tacitus:

"A cloud . . . was ascending, the appearance of which I cannot give you a more exact description of than by likening it to that of a pine tree, for it shot up to a great height in the form of a very tall trunk, which spread itself out at the top into a sort of branches; occasioned, I imagine, either by a sudden gust of air that impelled it, the force of which decreased as it advanced upwards, or the cloud itself being pressed back again by its own weight, expanded in the manner I have mentioned; it appeared sometimes bright and sometimes dark and spotted, according as it was either more or less impregnated with earth and cinders. . . ."

He tells how his famous uncle, called to rescue people from towns along the seagirt edge of the volcano, set forth in his galleys directly to the disaster scene. "He was now so close to the mountain," the younger Pliny went on, "that the cinders, which grew thicker and hotter the nearer he approached, fell into the ships, together with pumice stones, and black pieces of burning rock: they were in danger too not only of being a-ground by the sudden retreat of the sea, but also from the vast fragments which rolled down from the mountain, and obstructed all the shore."

Night came, and "broad flames shone out in several places from Mount Vesuvius, which the darkness of the night contributed to render still brighter and clearer."

For sheer drama, this eruption would be long remembered. The blowing of its top left Mount Somma little more than a wide basin. That was the last to be heard of Mount Somma, but not of its offspring —an upstart volcano named Vesuvius, which was to build itself to a height of four thousand feet.

Vesuvius since 1631 has been fairly active, and in 1906 exploded with a spectacular show of pyrotechnics. For four days, floods of brilliant lava oozed from fissures along the flanks of the volcano. Earthquakes, one after another for hours, shook the countryside as if it were a rug being whipped. Then eruptions blew great quantities of red-hot lava thousands of feet into the Neapolitan sky, appearing by night as an enormous glowing column. Gas exploded under such pressure that it rose in clouds to a height of eight miles, a colossal jet that spouted for an entire day.

The eruption lasted eighteen days. When it ended, the crater of Vesuvius was 2,200 feet wide at the top and two thousand feet deep. Thus reamed out so thoroughly, Vesuvius did not begin to fill with lava again for seven years. Then it filled up and in 1926 spilled over. For three years there was comparative quiet. Then earthquakes rumbled ominously again and hydrochloric acid spouted from the gas vents. The crater became a lake of incandescent lava which soon poured out, and slag was hurled more than four miles, destroying villages. Then Vesuvius quieted again or, perhaps more correctly, merely simmered down.

In a sense, volcanoes are the safety valves of the earth. They have existed in all probability since the earth was formed, and were once undoubtedly much more widespread and rampant than now. Very likely most of today's volcanoes are surface manifestations of boiling and seething chambers of molten matter beneath the crust of the earth.

Occasionally this molten matter breaks through to the surface and gives birth to new volcanoes. Monte Nuovo, near Naples, was born in 1538. Izalco, in Salvador, began in 1770. In the Philippines, the volcano of Camiguin started from a fissure in a level plain in 1871 and remained active four years, reaching a height of 1,800 feet. Jorullo rose from a plantation west of Mexico City in 1759. Vulcan broke out of a harbor on the coast of New Britain, in the South Pacific, in 1937.

How many active volcanoes are there in the world? The best guess is about five hundred. Several thousand more are now extinct, and others unknown, dead or alive, lie at the bottom of the sea.

The active volcanoes occur in definite geographic patterns. One such pattern encircles the Pacific Ocean from South America up to the Aleutian Islands of Alaska, and then in an almost continuous belt linking the Kurile Islands of Japan with the Philippines, Celebes, New Guinea, the Solomons, New Caledonia, and New Zealand. Around the Indian Ocean stretches another "circle of fire": Timor, Flores, Sumbawa, Lombok, Bali, Java, Sumatra—even on to east Africa and Madagascar. The Mediterranean also is bordered by volcanoes, from Mount Ararat, near the Caspian Sea, to Mount Etna—the largest and most destructive in Europe.

In certain instances, great quantities of lava have welled out of the ground and congealed into vast layers, forming volcanic plateaus rather than cones. The Columbia Plateau is an example, but the largest is the Deccan Plateau in India, which is a lava field that originally covered five hundred thousand square miles to a maximum depth of ten thousand feet.

Since nobody knows where this great quantity of molten matter comes from, any guess is as valid as another. Much depends on viewpoint. If the earth is now cooling from a once molten state, then the lava may merely be rock that has not yet cooled. Or if the inner heat of the earth is due to increasing radioactivity, that means that the earth may some day become molten, which would account for a growing abundance of melted rock.

Some molten matter hardens into basalt, some into rhyolite, some deep within the earth to become granite. Some lava flies out into the air and cools in strands that gather along a roadside or in rock crevices like piles of loose hair. Some lava is so light and porous that it floats on water. Some is smooth and billowy, like congealed taffy. Some is jagged and rough, like that which the Spanish conquistadores came upon in their explorations of Mexico and what is now the western United States; they called it "malpais"—bad country.

Geysers and hot springs provide constant evidence of the earth's inner heat. So do steam vents, and the sterling example of volcanic action leading to steam activity was the eruption of June 6, 1912, at Mount Katmai, Alaska, which produced the famed Valley of Ten Thousand Smokes. No one is sure how much the land changed, because there were no detailed maps prior to the explosion. The eruption was heard 750 miles away at Juneau and far northward across the Alaska Range. Day turned into night because of the volcanic dust. Ten inches fell on Kodiak, a hundred miles away. Twelve miles away the dust deposits were three feet thick.

"Had this occurred at New York," says one geologist, "the city would have been buried under many feet of ash. Philadelphia would have been covered with a foot of ash and would have been in inky darkness for sixty hours. Ash would have been distributed over the landscape as far as Buffalo and Washington. The sounds of the explosions would have been heard at Atlanta and St. Louis, and the fumes would have been noticed in Denver and Miami."

More than seven cubic miles of rock and pumice spewed into the air. Not only did a crater three miles in diameter and 3,700 feet deep remain, but also a basin filled with volcanic rocks through which hot steam and gases filtered up and spiraled into the cold Alaska sky. Thus, the Valley of Ten Thousand Smokes.

Wherever such cataclysmic events as volcanic eruptions have shattered the serenity of the countryside, legends were bound to spring up. The Hawaiian story of "Pe-le and Hi-i-aka" is a dramatic account of Pe-le the fire goddess and her sisters. The original published account of this legend contained two hundred pages, including 170 *me-le* or dramatic chants.

The Spaniards called any lofty mountain *volcán*, though it may never have given any signs of combustion. Humboldt, in his *Essai Politique*, says that Chimborazo was called *volcán de nieve*, "snow volcano."

William H. Prescott refers to volcanoes at length in his *History of the Conquest of Mexico*, because the great cone of Popocatepetl was then in a state of frequent activity. It raged with uncommon fury, Prescott says, while the Spaniards were at Tlascala. The Indians shrank from approaching it, but the violence and mystery tempted the Spanish cavaliers, who wanted to climb it. Cortés encouraged this as a sign to the Indians of the daring of the conquerors.

A captain named Diego Ordaz did lead a party of nine Spaniards up, but the fiery turmoil at the summit was so great that they had to turn back. Nevertheless, it was achievement enough for Ordaz to be allowed a commemorative burning mountain on his escutcheon.

Cortés also tried to extract from volcanoes enough sulphur to help in the making of gunpowder, and one of his parties actually did so by lowering a soldier four hundred feet into a burning crater. It was an admirable enterprise, to be sure, but Cortés had to admit that it would be much more convenient to import his powder from Spain.

The business of gathering sulphur from volcanoes was met with more success at Lassen Peak in California where early pioneers vigorously mined the mineral.

One might suspect that there may be other useful aspects of volcanoes, and there are. The sudden blanketing of vegetation in ancient times has been a boon to present-day geologists and paleontologists trying to figure out what the members of this vegetal society looked like. Medium-warm lava molding itself around the base of a tree and excluding oxygen has preserved the imprint of the bark. Or when volcanic ash falls like snow, it brings down and preserves millions of insects, as in the case of the old Florissant lake beds of Colorado, which provide a comprehensive picture of what one segment of earth life was like in a bygone age.

But what of man's use of volcanoes for power? Obviously, even the thought of trying to control a Krakatoa explosion or a Pelean cloud is fantastic. But on a smaller scale man can and does utilize the power that lies beneath the earth. Iceland and New Zealand have long harnessed steam jets, geysers, and hot springs. A boring in Tuscany, where natural steam power has been in use for decades, once yielded a rate of 52,800 pounds per hour at atmospheric pressure. A deep boring yielded pressure at seventy-five pounds per square inch, which can be put directly to the work of driving turbines. A well was once drilled in California to tap a known steam reserve, and then another well was dug by the power derived from the first. In places like these, the steam may be deep-seated, and of almost inexhaustible quantity.

But whether for economic use or not, volcanoes have always played a dominant part in the lives of many people. The term *volcano* is derived from the island of Vulcano in the Tyrrhenian Sea above Cape Calava on the northernmost point of Sicily. In classical times, this was thought to be the entrance to the nether world, and the domain of Vulcan, the smith god, where were forged ornaments, arms, and equipment (including thunderbolts) for the gods.

Encyclopedias of the time contained numerous references to volcanoes, chiefly to Etna. "*Aetna,*" commented Bartholomaeus, "is an hill in the lande of Ile of *Cecile,* and out of that hill breaketh fire with brimstone, as it were in hell."

Agricola, the Saxon physician and chemist, compared the veins of the earth to the veins of an animal. Athanasius Kircher, a Thuringian Jesuit, in his *Mundus Subterraneus* of 1678, published a cross-sectional chart of the earth, with fire spitting in all directions. The drawing, he said, "portrays the compartments of heat or of fire, or what is the same thing, the fire cells, throughout all the bowels of the Geocosm." Kircher labeled a region of central fire, some "glory-holes of Nature," and fire-conducting channels which were "fissures of the earth through which the gusts of fire make their way."

The period between 1790 and 1820 has been styled the "heroic age" of the science of volcanology, for it was during this period that widely known and respected naturalists and geologists collected their facts and expounded their theories of volcanic action.

In the late eighteenth century Nicolas Desmarest, a French geologist, made some reasoned conclusions on the volcanic origin of basalt, and on the ages of volcanic flows. An Italian abbot by the name of Spallanzani discussed the role of gases in volcanic eruptions. Louis Prévost, an influential French geologist, investigated the eruption of an island between Sicily and Africa in July, 1831.

About the same time, George Scrope, an English geologist and member of Parliament, proposed that since the temperature of mines increased with depth the interior of the globe must be intensely hot. Hence: a source of volcanic energy.

From here and there around the globe came confirmation by celebrated geologists working in the field. Alexander von Humboldt was one. He reasoned that the crowding together of volcanoes afforded convincing proof that their action did not depend on slight causes located near the surface, but that they were instead phenomena of deep-seated origin. In South America he studied the elevated table-land of Quito, in Ecuador, which was surmounted by the high mountains of Pichincha, Cotopaxi, and Tungurahua. This, to Humboldt, was one sole volcanic hearth. "Even the earthquakes," he said, "which so fearfully devastate this portion of the globe, afford striking evidence of the existence of subterranean communications, not only between countries where there are no volcanoes—as has long been known—but likewise between volcanic apertures situated at a distance from each other. Thus the volcano of Pasto, east of the river Guaytara, continued during three months of the year 1797, to emit, uninterruptedly, a lofty column of smoke, until it suddenly ceased at the moment of the great earthquake of Riobamba (at a distance of 240 miles), and the mud eruption of the 'Moya,' in which from thirty to forty thousand Indians perished."

Darwin also made detailed studies of volcanic action. The American geologist James Dwight Dana did not believe that volcanoes were the "safety valves" of the earth through which all strain and stress were relieved. "We may strongly doubt," he said, "whether action so deep-seated as that of the earthquake must be, can often find relief in the narrow channels of a volcano, miles in length."

Dana called volcanoes indexes of danger instead, and opposed the idea that volcanic action depended on water gaining access to the "central fires of the globe." He worked out a number of conclusions relating to volcanic action, and with the classification of volcanic rocks (of which there are many) by the German geologist von Richthofen in 1868, the science of volcanology was on firm classical ground and the gateway to modern knowledge had been opened. With the subsequent establishment of volcanological observatories on Vesuvius and Etna, and in Hawaii and Java, the science was given new impetus.

Yet there would never come an end to the romance of volcanoes and volcanism in the literature, and Vulcan would be forever invoked to sound a mood or create a spectacle with his "glory holes of Nature."

It is spoken in Ezekiel: "And I will rain upon him . . . an overflowing rain, and great hailstones, fire, and brimstone."

Spenser, in *The Faerie Queene*, described an eruption thus:

> . . . burning *Aetna* from his boyling stew
> Doth belch out flames, and rockes in peeces broke,
> And ragged ribs of mountaines molten new,
> Enwrapt in coleblacke clouds and filthy smoke,
> That all the land with stench, and heaven with
> horror choke.

And in Jules Verne's *Twenty Thousand Leagues Under the Sea*, Captain Nemo speaks:

"Certainly; we are floating in a current of boiling water."

"It is possible!" I exclaimed.

"Look."

The panels opened, and I saw the sea entirely white all round. A sulphurous smoke was curling amid the waves, which boiled like water in a copper. I placed my hand on one of the panes of glass, but the heat was so great that I quickly took it off again.

"Where are we?" I asked.

"Near the island of Santorin, sir," replied the captain. . . . "I wished to give you a sight of the curious spectacle of a submarine eruption."

"I thought," said I, "that the formation of these new islands was ended."

"Nothing is ever ended in the volcanic parts of the sea," replied Captain Nemo; "and the globe is always being worked by subterranean fires. . . ."

16

METEORS

Show pity, Lord, O Lord, forgive;
Let a repenting rebel live.
. . . CHRISTIAN, *Lynchburg
and Its People*

THE OBJECT was small and irregular, brownish-black, and at most an inch in diameter. The old man turned it over and over in his hand, and a glint came to his dark, deep-set eyes. His worn cowhide jacket looked as though it had survived many a winter on the range.

"Yes," he said, smiling as he fondled the black object, "I think I have seen this before."

The museum director turned in astonishment. "You have?"

"Yes, sir."

"Are you sure?"

"Well, about as sure as a feller can be. 'Course, these sometimes looks pretty much alike."

"But you *have* seen it before?"

The old man scratched his head and thought for a moment. "If I recollect rightly, I know the feller who gave it to you."

"That was many years ago."

"I don't remember when. Have you got ary other one like it?"

"There were three of them," the director explained. "They were all about the same size, same color. And the same provenience—I mean they all came from about the same place."

"And where was that?"

"Horseshoe Mesa. At least that's what the card said."

"That's right. The camp was below Grandview Point."

"Then you *have* seen it."

"Yes, sir."

The museum director seated himself behind his desk, and invited the old-timer into a chair at the side. "Those three stones—or whatever they are—" he said, "have been in our collection for years. They were labeled as meteorites from Horseshoe Mesa. That's all. No date, no collector, no description, no donor, no information except 'Meteorite' and the locality."

"I 'spect that's not much to go on."

"It isn't. So the three stones just lay in the drawer gathering dust."

The old man's face broke into a wrinkled smile. His eyes sparkled. "Well, sir," he said, "I can tell you. I reckon I shouldn't, but I guess this little joke has gone on enough."

"Joke?"

"I don't right off recall the year, but it was when we were prospectin' down below Horseshoe Mesa. They was some tents set up on the mesa and the cook had one of them where he fixed vittles of an evenin' when the boys got back.

"One night towards the end of July . . . or it may have been August, I don't rightly recollect . . . they was one of them big meteor swarms in the sky, you know, when you look up and see stars shootin' ever which way."

"Yes, I know."

"Well, sir, that night the cook had just come out of the cook tent when he saw these fellers a-settin' on their haunches out there in the sagebrush, oglin' the sky for all they was worth. They'd point and shout and jabber to themselves that Judgment Day was nigh, and they like to work themselves into a frenzy believing the heavens was about to fall."

"What then?"

"The cook figured he'd play a trick on them fellers. So he turned around and went back to the stove and scooped up a shovelful of red-hot clinkers, and sneaked out to a tent behind them and listened for a minute. When the right time came when they was a sudden swarm of shootin' stars in the sky, he chucked the whole shovel of clinkers as high as he could.

"Well, sir, them coals come whizzin' down right in front of them fellers and landed with a plunk and a flare of sparks right in the sagebrush. You should have seen them fellers jump. One of the boys leaped over and grabbed a dead clinker and ran around holdin' it and yellin', 'A shootin' star fell! A shootin' star fell! Feel it! It's still warm!' And he saw the cook standin' there and he brung and showed him what he'd found."

The museum director leaned back in his chair and put his fingers carefully to his chin. "Well, I'll be damned," he said.

The old man got a faraway look in his eye again and said: "I guess the boys carried them pieces of cinder around for years, until . . ."

". . . until one day one of them brought the pieces to us," the director said, "and swore up and down they were meteorites because they'd fallen in front of him, and he'd picked them up while they were still hot, and furthermore he had witnesses to prove it!"

"I reckon you're right."

The old man rose to go. When he got as far as the door, he turned and looked at the small brownish-black specimens on the desk.

"I reckon you'll be throwing them out now," he said.

A smile appeared on the director's face. He rose and crossed over, taking the old man's hands and shaking them warmly. "Not on your life," he said. "With a story like that behind them, I wouldn't throw them out in a thousand years. We'll relabel them 'pseudo-Meteorites.' And I think I'll add a footnote: made, delivered, and discovered on Horseshoe Mesa, U.S.A."

The old man smiled and turned to go.

"Oh, one thing more," the director said.

"Yes?"

"I'm curious. Exactly how did you find out about all this?"

The old man's eyes twinkled again. "I was the cook," he said.

A star exists for every man, it is said, and the brightness varies with his fortunes. Bright star, happy life. Dim star, sad life. And when the man dies, the star falls.

Up there in the night sky another world, an eerie world, stretched into infinity, a world inhabited by strange animals, strange men, and strange gods. The stars themselves lay sprinkled in the firmament in odd designs, and for these designs there were names. This dark world was a nether world. It was a necropolis. It was a realm of legends. It was a shining but also shadowed and mysterious universe. What was it not?

"Bend not in adoration to the sun or the moon," implored the Koran, "but bend in adoration before God who created them both."

Yet the Mohammedan would see a shooting star and forget. "Look!" he would exclaim. "There goes Husain returning from a visit to Rida!"

To each in each country his star, and when it fell in western China the Lolos would dig a hole to receive it, lest some living person be struck and hurt. The Spartans, whose heavens augured good or ill, sent wise men to study the sky one night of every eighth year. Sight of a falling star meant that the king had sinned. Whereupon he was summarily deposed.

A fallen star, a fallen king. So went the destiny of nations according to meteors. Seneca, in his *Problems of Nature,* pointedly recalled that a meteorite "as big as the moon" fell in 168 B.C. at the Battle of Pydna in Greece, where Roman General Macedonicus Paulus was warring against Perseus.

Many such superstitious reflections—baleful and spiritual—surrounded the moon and the sun, and the spectacle of a shooting meteor. If you make a wish before a falling star disappears, that wish will come true. A corn, Pliny avowed, could be extracted easily if done at the moment the star fell. Estonians were apt to avert their eyes on New Year's night, for they believed that to see a star fall then was to expect death that year. If you counted as high as you could during the time a meteor fell, according to medieval belief, the number you reached was the number of years you could expect to be free of eye trouble.

"The starres of the firmament can not fall," said a Renaissance author. But John Donne had a different opinion: "He that sees a starre fall, runs apace, And findes a gellie in the place." And he added that a bride is like a fallen star—acquiescent jelly in her husband's embrace.

Today we have come a long way from such tales. We know that meteors are visitors from interplanetary space and recent evidence indicates that the larger ones must have come from the breaking up of a large body that had cooled slowly for a long time. This breaking up very likely was due to a collision, possibly with a small planet, or an asteroid, or even one of Jupiter's moons.

Most meteors, surprisingly, are very small—about the size of a grain of sand, and these seem to be remnants of comets rather than asteroids. On striking the earth's atmosphere they are heated to incandescence by friction, thereby ionizing the gaseous molecules of the atmosphere and lighting them up in a long trail. If a meteor is large enough to explode or split off into streamers, it becomes a fireball, or bolide (from the Greek *bolis*, missile). These may sometimes appear as large as the moon and give off fully as much light. One of the most spectacular was a group of about two hundred fireballs which blazed across Canada in 1913 at an altitude of about thirty-five miles. They made thundering noises and the sound even shook houses. But the meteors roared on— for at least 5,700 miles—and were last seen heading southeast over the Atlantic.

It takes a mighty speed to create this heavenly tracery. Based on years of systematic meteor photography at the Harvard Observatory and other locations, the height, length of trail, and speed of numerous meteors have been calculated. These speeds have been almost consistently computed at an average twenty-six miles per second. (A high-speed rifle bullet travels half a mile per second.) However, measured meteoric velocities must be combined with or subtracted from velocities of the earth along its orbit and around its axis. There is gravity to consider, also. And meteors have their own orbital velocity. Hence the precise computation of a meteor's speed is something for the advanced mathematician.

No matter. The friction is enough to disintegrate most meteors, and in the main the trails they leave behind are fragile, gone in an instant. But some trails may be composed of a luminous cloud of vaporized material that glows for half an hour.

The smallest meteors, called micrometeors, are measured in scant thousandths of an inch, and when slowed by the atmosphere fall as dust—honest-to-goodness stardust.

For evidence of the largest meteor of all time, look up to the moon, where there has been no atmosphere to impede the impact of these space missiles. The largest crater, Clavius, measures 146 miles across, and astronomers estimate that the cosmic projectile smashing into that spot weighed close to two hundred billion tons.

Happily for us, the rest are much smaller. An estimated four million meteors strike the earth's atmosphere every day, and no one knows how many get through to the earth's surface. Says one astronomer: "Although the total number of meteors striking our atmosphere each day and eventually settling to the earth's surface must run well into the billions, the total amount of material gained is very small, probably not more than a ton a day. Compared to the earth's mass . . . it is quite inconsequential. In a billion years it would amount to a layer over the entire earth's surface not much thicker than this page." More recent estimates give values as high as a thousand tons per day but this is still relatively inconsequential.

Meteors move around the sun either individually or in huge streams. The streams take apparently elliptical orbits and are usually associated with comets. As a rule, when the earth passes through a meteor stream the resultant swarm is not spectacular.

But it certainly can be, as in the middle of November, 1833. One of the many to record this famous swarm was Zenas Leonard, a Pennsylvania farm boy who became chronicler of Joseph Reddeford Walker's exploring party, first to travel west across the Sierra Nevada of California. On the night of November 12, 1833, as the party neared the mouth of the San Joaquin River, the men were thrown into great consternation. The air seemed to be literally filled with meteors falling toward earth, some of which appeared to explode in mid-air and others to be dashed to pieces on the ground. So frightened were the horses, Leonard said, "that it required the most active vigilance of the whole company to keep them together."

Elsewhere an estimated two hundred thousand meteors were observed over a period of six hours. Asbury Christian, including the event in his book *Lynchburg and Its People*, described what happened in Virginia:

"The first part of the night the air was very transparent and the stars were exceedingly brilliant. . . . At two o'clock the horizon suddenly became luminous with a burning meteoric shower. They came down like snow-flakes, and . . . disappeared. The shower continued until daybreak, and one in a well said that some were visible at eleven o'clock. It was a beautiful and awful sight. It looked like a snow-storm, with flakes of fire instead of snow. The whole town was excited. Some said the stars were falling and that Judgment Day was at hand. The negroes began to moan and pray, the abandoned women rushed to the Methodist church and wept and prayed until day, and many covered their heads to keep out the fearful sight. At the Franklin a few citizens were sitting at a card-table gambling, when one looked out and said, 'Doom's Day has come!' Immediately the table was overturned, and one that stammered called out to the others to pray. No one knew how, so he, trembling with fear and stammering, attempted to sing:

> Show pity, Lord, O Lord, forgive;
> Let a repenting rebel live.

None was able to take in the humorous situation at the time, but when the morning came it was greatly enjoyed."

This case points up the fact that a good time to observe a meteorite swarm is after midnight. As the earth plunges through space and turns on its axis, all localities between midnight and noon are on the "forward" side of the planet and hence running directly into meteors.

Christian drew a literary parallel between snowflakes and falling meteors, but in actuality there is an unusual correlation between rain showers and meteor showers. Dates of maximum rainfall, integrated all over the earth and averaged for many years, show that heavy rains appear one month after heavy meteor falls. Could it be that meteor dust seeds the clouds as man has tried to do?

From time to time one of these multimillion meteors that ram the earth daily is so big and so tough or both that it manages to penetrate the entire atmosphere before burning up. It crashes into the earth, shattering and scattering itself far and wide. With that it has become a meteorite, and there have been some notable ones. The Hoba West, which still lies where it fell near Grootfontein, South West Africa, weighs 110,000 pounds, the largest known. The largest in the United States fell near Willamette, Oregon, and weighed 30,800 pounds; it is on display at the Hayden Planetarium in New York City.

The meteors that fall are of two types: iron (chiefly a combination of nickel and iron) and stone (similar to earthly rocks). And sometimes they come pelting down in enormous numbers. A shower near Knyahinya, Czechoslovakia, in 1866, peppered a thousand meteorites into the soil, the largest weighing 645 pounds. Near Pultusk, Poland, in 1868, a remarkable shower of a hundred thousand stones shot into the earth. In the United States a fall of fourteen thousand occurred in 1912 near Holbrook, Arizona; most were small—about the size of buckshot—but each was covered with a characteristic black fused crust. Anyone caught in showers such as those assuredly must have felt that St. Matthew's prediction was coming true: "Immediately after the tribulation of those days shall the sun be darkened, and the moon shall not give her light, and the stars shall fall from heaven, and the powers of the heavens shall be shaken. . . ."

As objects of curiosity, meteorites have long attracted attention. Aleuts and Eskimos use them as amulets. In Japan they are considered fallen from the Milky Way and are given into the care of temple priests. Conversely, in some parts of China to find one is a bad omen.

Perhaps more astounding are the giant craters that have been gouged out of the earth's surface. The classic example—Arizona's Meteor Crater—is in the land of the Navajo Indians, who have a legend that one of their gods descended from the sky in clouds of fire and buried himself in the ground.

What actually fell? And when? There is no possible way of knowing. The estimate is of a mass weighing between one and ten million tons roaring out of the Arizona sky between five thousand and fifty thousand years ago. It caromed into the earth with stunning violence and dug a crater three-fourths of a mile wide and six hundred feet deep, throwing out perhaps as much as four hundred million tons of rock. The parent mass—an estimated hundred feet in diameter—plunged so deeply into the earth that only by electrical and magnetic surveys could its presence be detected. Much of it may have vaporized. Thousands of pounds of meteoric material have been picked up around the crater, some pieces weighing close to a thousand pounds.

There are other known meteor craters—but not many. The earth is pitted with thousands of circular solution pits, sometimes called sinkholes, of varying diameter, and it is not difficult for the wandering imagination to affix to these craters a meteoric origin. Also no one knows how many meteors have fallen into the sea or how many meteorite fragments now lie on the ocean floor.

Near Odessa, Texas, is a crater about five hundred feet in diameter and eighteen feet deep. Over a thousand small fragments have been found in the vicinity.

At Henbury, Australia, lie thirteen depressions within a radius of a quarter mile. They range in size from thirty to 250 feet in diameter and three to fifty feet deep. Hundreds of pieces of meteoric iron have been collected nearby.

The search for a legendary city of Wabar, in Arabia, ended in 1932 when the "walls" of the city turned out to be the rims of a series of craters, and the abundant "cinders" of the city "destroyed by fire from heaven" proved to be nearly pure silica-glass, a rare occurrence in Nature. This meant that tremendous heat fused the sands, much as lightning does when it strikes sand dunes and produces fulgurites. Not many iron fragments have been discovered, although one rusted piece weighed twenty-five pounds.

One of the largest meteorites seen to fall came down in Arkansas in 1930. The mass weighing 820 pounds, penetrated clayey soil and burrowed eight feet below the surface.

It is much less easy to say whether the wide, shallow, elliptical pits on the coastal plains of North and South Carolina and Georgia are or are not meteor craters. Known locally as bays, their axes trend almost uniformly northeast to southwest. They vary from a few hundred feet to nearly a mile long and are five to ten feet deep. If not meteoric, what then? One guess is that they have dissolved from the rock where natural drainage seeps underground, their orientation resulting from underlying rock structure.

Meteors have blasted out other depressions, such as the Wolf Creek crater of Australia, the Boxhole Crater of Austria, and those in Campo del Cielo, Argentina. Canada's Chubb Crater, in northern Quebec, is so big that seaplanes land and take off on the lake within it.

Beneath the surface of the earth geologists have found rock structures that seem to have resulted from meteoric impact. These "fossil" craters may be filled with sediment or be overlain by other rock formations, but there they are nonetheless, silent evidence of meteors that fell long before there were men to see them. Some geologists have suggested that such is the case with the Flynn Creek structure near Gainsboro, Tennessee, which lies in beds of Devonian time, some three hundred million years old. Other geologists swear that later encroaching seas would have eradicated all trace of the crater and its meteorite fragments, and that such craters are "cryptovolcanic" instead. *Crypto* means hidden or secret—and in that, at least, they are correct.

Probably the most earth-shaking impact known to man occurred at seven o'clock on the morning of June 30, 1908, when a fireball hurtled through the Siberian sky and planted itself with great violence into the taiga between the Yenisei and Lena rivers of Russia. Slamming into the earth with a crash that was heard for two thousand miles, the meteor, or more correctly cluster of meteors, created a shock wave that leveled all the trees on adjacent hills and blew them out in a radial pattern away from the point of impact.

A herd of reindeer was wiped out. A house was blown down and a farmer fifty miles away knocked unconscious.

The Tunguska meteor, as it was later known, rammed into one of the least hospitable regions on earth, and twenty years passed before any substantial details were gathered on it. True, it had landed with such a bang that shock waves traveled thousands of miles and jiggled barographs across England. But these jiggles had remained exasperatingly unexplained year after year.

Finally, when a Russian expedition started out after the information, plans had to be carefully formulated because there would be precious little time under even the best circumstances. The site lay just under the Arctic Circle, and the cold was intense. If they delayed too long, the thaw would swell the Tunguska and Angara rivers enough to make the country impassable, and great hordes of mosquitoes would rise up and cover the harried explorers in vicious, biting blankets.

In 1927 Professor Kulik of the Russian Academy of Sciences led an expedition into the frozen wilderness north of Irkutsk. Blizzards hampered them. Temperatures fell to forty degrees below zero.

They hired a Tungus guide with his family of four and his ten reindeer to take them to Wanawara, on the River Tunguska. The only trouble was that the guide happened to be highly independent; he refused to budge until ten in the morning, and only after consuming great quantities of tea. Then he would quit at four-thirty in the afternoon—to proceed with his tea-drinking.

The party went on, nonetheless, traveling from patch to patch of vegetation so that the reindeer could be fed. The trip must have seemed excruciatingly slow, for they could make at best only four or five miles a day.

When they arrived, the view was worth it. The devastation was appalling. Trees lay fanned out flat in every direction, radiating as if an unbelievably powerful explosion had gone off. The ground lay roundly blasted. Several craters existed, varying from thirty to one hundred fifty feet in diameter, and up to twelve feet deep. Every living thing must have been vaporized. Farther out, the trees lay uniformly and totally sprawled. Some trees, in fact, had been blown down at a distance of seventy-five miles.

What of the scattered and isolated people who lived in this hostile land? Had anyone heard the fall? Or seen it?

The stationmaster at Kansk, four hundred miles away, said: "Suddenly I felt what seemed to be a violent vibration of the air and heard a loud noise. I was terrified. The engine driver of train Number ninety-two was so scared that he stopped the train, fearing that it might be derailed, and when he reached us at the siding asked us to examine the train to see whether some of the goods might have exploded."

"After the flame disappeared," said a man at Wanawara, closer to the site, "there was an explosion which threw me off my feet a distance of seven feet or more. The glass and frames of the house broke and clods of earth were spit up from the square in front of my hut."

"The door of my stove flew to the far side of the room," said another man. "The windows shattered and blew in. Then there was a roar of thunder from the north."

So severe was the event, and so destructive to the forests, that Tungus natives became terrified and would not go near the site. To them, the event was a visitation from Agdy, god of fire. The place was cursed; the fireball had come to punish the wicked.

And so goes the story of one of the world's most devastating meteorite falls during the reign of man. But there is this footnote:

Russian scientists again investigated the site in 1959 and reported that it was considerably more radioactive than the surrounding land. This led to the suggestion that the blast might possibly have been the impact of an atomic-powered space ship (later considered fantastic) and stimulated a more formal inquiry which included a tabulation of records from other countries.

Dr. Vassily Fesenkov, chairman of the Committee on Meteorites of the Academy of Sciences of the U.S.S.R., reached the conclusion that the impact was not by meteor but by the head of a comet. In support of this view he cited recorded phenomena uncharacteristic of meteoric impact, chiefly magnetic disturbances, night glow, and absence of meteorite fragments.

Perhaps he is right. And perhaps we shall never know. One thing seems sure, however. If the meteor, or whatever it was, had struck four hours later, it would have landed in the city of St. Petersburg.

To emphasize the rare seems somewhat misleading; odds are that a man in his lifetime will never see a meteor strike the earth. But he will very likely see some other celestial phenomenon which will convince him that the sky can put on some spectacular shows.

Comets, for example, presumed by most scientists to be as harmless to us as the farthest stars, have shaken the world's population as have no other sky objects (including flying saucers). By nearly unanimous consent of authorities from the time of Theophrastus down to the Renaissance, comets were the harbingers of ill winds and tempests, and practically every other dire event imaginable, an invitation for prayers, chants, ritual dances, bell-ringing, fasting—and hand-wringing in general. For proof, we are told, only recall that comets preceded the deaths of Roman Emperor Macrinus, Attila the Hun, and Edward VII of England.

In Elizabethan England, comets were as feared as earthquakes. The difference was that a comet allowed time for doom-saying. Earthquakes could not be foretold or seen approaching, thus they could only be followed by explanatory tracts *ipso facto*. Yet the reasons comets portended such ill were quite logical. for all that. They represented a disorder of the heavens from which the earth would most surely suffer —drought, famine, war, pestilence, ruination of traditions. "Also," said one writer, "windes, earthquakes, dearth, landflouds, and great heate to follow." That covered about everything.

Except, well, what were comets after all? A "halo in the pure fuel of fire," as Aristotle had said? "A sort of reflection to the sun," as Hippocrates had ventured?

Since they are members of the solar system, comets are free-moving bodies controlled by the sun's gravitation. Every year five or six pass near enough to the earth to be seen or photographed by telescopic means; occasionally there may be more than a dozen in one year. Some are familiar, faithfully following astronomers' timetables. Others are new, passing the earth perhaps for the first time.

And some pass so close to the sun that tremendous tidal forces rip them asunder. The great comet of 1882, for example, was so bright that it could be seen in full daylight; astronomers watched it approach the sun as a single comet, pass perihelion, and reappear broken into four comets. Since their velocities of departure were slightly different, these four comets will next pass the sun at intervals of a century—between the years 2500 and 2900.

No one knows how comets come to be. If we could find out how the solar system originated, we might know. As a matter of fact, we don't even know for sure what comets are. One guess is that a comet is a loosely knit swarm of chunks of frozen gases in which may be embedded small stony or metallic particles. This swarm may be as big as a few hundred miles in diameter.

When a comet moves closer to the sun, some of this ice evaporates, releasing gases that form a cloud (coma) around the nucleus. The small particles (those less than 1/100,000 inch in diameter) stream away from the coma under the faint pressure of the sun's radiation. This forms the tail, and it matters not whether the comet approaches or recedes from the sun—the tail always points away into space. Particles heading toward the sun are turned back, which accounts for a shell of light around the head of the comet. This head may be up to 150,000 miles in diameter, but it is nearly all light and no bluster—as dense as our best vacuum.

Thus the tail of a comet would hardly disturb a fly, although to judge from some of the panic men have been thrown into at the coming of a comet you would think it capable of destroying the solar system. Men presumed that the atmosphere would be poisoned with deadly gases. "Comet pills" were sold in 1910 as protection against whatever might happen. Farmers went into cyclone cellars, others into mines. But the expected annihilation did not come, and the comet went away, and the people somehow returned to normality, as they always did.

There was a time when no one knew the difference between meteors and comets. That the tail of a comet always pointed away from the sun was not conclusively proved until 1531, by the German astronomer Peter Apian. The Danish astronomer Tycho Brahe then showed that a comet lay farther away than the moon, and one of his students, Johannes Kepler, did not even think of comets as belonging to the solar system.

These errors and others were detected and discussed by a group of early Fellows of the Royal Society: Robert Hooke, Christopher Wren, and Edmund Halley. Halley, with help from Newton, computed the parabolic orbits of two dozen comets. One in particular fascinated him, for he had noted records of its identical orbit in 1531, 1607, and 1682. Making every possible computation, he predicted that the comet would return some time in late 1758. Halley died before then, but true to his prediction, the comet returned—on Christmas Day of that year. And it has been "Halley's Comet" ever since. The earth passed through its tail in 1910 and will have a chance to do so again in 1986. The average period of revolution of the comet is about seventy-seven years, but orbital variations induced by the planets cause variations of as much as 2½ years either way.

It is tempting to continue this discussion into auroras, eclipses, magnetic storms, and cosmic rays, but we have already overstepped the limit of our subject, which is meteors. And it is still the "blasing starres" that most stir man's imagination.

What we know of meteors is really comparatively recent. Halley and others speculated on them in the eighteenth century, but the first positive evidence that meteors themselves were not caused by weather phenomena arose from an investigation of meteorites. The German philosopher Chladni gave, in 1794, some reasons for believing that certain known stones were of celestial and not terrestrial origin, but he was not widely believed. Yet interest had been aroused, and the idea was a fascinating one anyway. Evidence was collected, and when a shower of stones fell at L'Aigle, in Normandy, in 1803, the French Academy sent a young physicist named Jean Biot to investigate. After his report was issued, there was no further doubt, and old records dating back to 654 B.C. were substantiated. With the fabulous 1833 shower over the United States, the science of meteor study came into its own.

No matter how deeply we probe into the subject of meteors and how many questions we solve, there will probably never come a time when the sight of a shooting star will fail to lift our eyes and our minds upward, as Plato would say, and carry our souls into the sky. However good, however ill, however portentous of great things to come, the meteor will forever remain, as it has since time unknown, a symbol of the awesome hidden size and mystery of the universe.

17

DISASTER AND HUMAN BEHAVIOR

The fear of death is the beginning
of discipline.

. . . *Chinese proverb*

B Y NOW the little boy lost in the Florida hurricane is but
a memory. So are the loved ones of the anguished Netherlands farmer
—who perhaps does not so often walk alone in the fields any more.

The campers under Montana's Madison Canyon slide, still at their
campsites, will there be permanently memorialized rather than ex-
humed, for by the grace of God any of us might have been at the
same place to take the full force of Nature on the rampage. Or we
might have been on Martinique the day St. Pierre died.

In examining the elements of the ancients—fire, water, earth, and air
—we have judged the battle of man against wild nature and found, perhaps to our surprise, that men have not always surrendered to these
overpowering forces. "Neither snow, nor rain, nor heat, nor gloom of
night," boasts the Post Office motto, "stays these couriers from the
swift completion of their appointed rounds."

Can it possibly be that the elements have a kind of fascination that
is not macabre after all? Ever since there have been disasters and men,
men have flocked to the scenes of catastrophe as soon as they could

get there. And, of course, as if there weren't enough chaos already, the influx of hordes of people creates new trouble.

Charles E. Fritz and J. H. Mathewson, in a paper prepared for the National Academy of Sciences, call this phenomenon "convergence"— the informal, spontaneous movement of people, messages, and supplies toward the disaster area. Usually we think of catastrophe as a signal for everyone to scatter in all directions. Not so, say Fritz and Mathewson, pointing out that a large number of disaster *victims* are generally passive, cooperative, and subject to control. They rarely constitute a problem. But wait till the news gets around!

Within an hour after a tornado struck White County, Arkansas, in 1952, hundreds of automobiles began moving along Highway 67 into the towns that had been struck, and the traffic flow kept up for a week. Said a disaster report: "On Sunday, two days after the tornado, an estimated 1,700 cars an hour took to the highway leading into the Judsonia-Bald Knob area and, according to one of the top Patrol officials, by 10:00 a.m. Sunday morning cars were lined bumper to bumper for ten miles on either side of Judsonia. Eighty percent of the total personnel of the State Patrol was used in an attempt to unsnarl the massive traffic jam."

After a Waco, Texas, tornado in 1953 local officials figured that most of Texas was arriving. Cars jammed bumper to bumper for blocks. Aircraft of all sorts buzzed over, creating a sky traffic jam. The chief of police estimated that at one time ten thousand persons were crowding near the intersection of Fifth and Austin streets—the point of greatest life loss.

In report after report, the pattern is the same. Even before roadblocks can be set up, highways are clogged with sightseers flooding into the disaster area. In one case, all roads to the scene were jammed within ten minutes—despite a heavy downpour of rain. This interferes with trained fire fighters or rescue squads who may even have to get out and walk to the site. So desperate sometimes are the outsiders (including relatives of possible injured or dead) that they abandon their cars and run pell mell into the impact area.

Many people—probably most of those coming—genuinely want to help. This is commendable, to be sure. But hospitals are often completely blocked by outsiders and their automobiles, in addition to the victims. Some newcomers want to volunteer blood. Some want to work. Some want to search for friends or relatives. These are all valid desires, but the purpose is self-defeated.

There is also a communications convergence in addition to the convergence of people. Telephone lines are promptly overloaded, and since this frequently involves long-distance calls, vital channels to the outside are no longer available to reach rescue agencies. It became so bad after the Waco tornado that over twenty-two thousand long-distance calls (coming and going) were handled within the first twenty-four hours after disaster struck. There were an additional fifteen thousand telegraphic messages.

A third type of convergence involves the abundance of supplies that comes pouring in to aid the stricken victims. Fritz and Mathewson, in their report, point out that this spontaneous outpouring of unsolicited aid is of great value in material and psychological recuperation; but there are often negative consequences undreamed of by either the donors or the recipients.

Usually more material arrives than is needed or can be handled. This ties up personnel and facilities that could be put to better use, and adds to the congestion, which is already acute.

If a small town is devastated, as in the Arkansas tornado, there may not be a building left to house the incoming supplies. When finally they are warehoused under some sort of temporary shelter, the problem of sorting arises. Much of what is sent, believe it or not, is worthless: rags, a tuxedo, high-button shoes, derby hats. Work clothes? Hardly any. Some of the incoming clothing may be condemned for health reasons and then someone has to haul it out promptly and burn it.

In the Arkansas disaster, van after van of supplies came pouring in and quickly filled an auditorium, ceiling high, then an auto parts building, then another building that covered half a city block. Then a church. Then a fire station. Then a gymnasium. Then a warehouse. Then tents. And so it went, on and on.

In Waco, appeals brought such a staggering response that workers were practically crowded out of building space. Modern radio and television being what they are, widespread appeals reach a vast audience. After a Michigan tornado, when appeals for flashlights were broadcast over the radio, five hundred persons immediately grabbed their flashlights and jumped into their automobiles to drive to the scene.

Why do people converge?

Sometimes we are inclined to lump them all together as sightseers. But Fritz and Mathewson have made much more shrewd observations and have discovered that there are other reasons for converging.

Some of the people are *returnees*, as Fritz and Mathewson call them. They have been temporarily evacuated from their homes during or after the disaster, and when the danger has moderated, they want to get back as soon as possible. They are concerned about friends and neighbors, and about property. Man, after all, is a colonial species, and when the colony is shaken he feels a basic impulse to put it back together. But the difficulty is to identify legitimate returnees. How easily can a man prove to the authorities (they may be strangers) that he owns a particular home—when the home is demolished?

There are the *anxious*, who have some personal connection with the impact area. In today's far-flung fraternity, practically everybody has friends and relatives scattered far and wide. This means that the disaster-concerned population is scattered throughout the nation, and even the world.

Then come the *helpers*. Although they may sometimes get in each other's way, by and large they are beneficial—and for a reason we might not expect. Studies have shown that an overwhelming majority of victims of a disaster prefer at first not to accept the proffered assistance of various official welfare agencies. Rather, they want help from people they know or from sympathetic strangers. They also want to double up in the homes of relatives or friends because, as one investigator put it, they want to be not just cared *for* but cared *about*. This coming and going worsens what is called the internal convergence. It occurs speedily on the heels of the disaster, which is a critical time, and at or very close to the scene of the disaster.

Some people converge who are simply *curious*. Fortunately, the immediate circle of curiosity-seekers is generally no wider than neighboring communities—of perhaps an hour or two driving time away. The circle expands on the Sunday following, and with it grows the control problem.

Fritz and Mathewson have found evidence to suggest that most curiosity convergence in disasters does not arise from neurotic impulses or from "ghoulish glee." It may seem so to impatient victims of the disaster, and to rescue teams whose work in digging out may be hampered by strangers pressing in and watching. Why don't people mind their own business? Examples of such resentment crop up in nearly every disaster report.

However, curiosity by its very nature is excited by unusual circumstances. Even the victims of a disaster, once their own safety is assured, become intensely curious about the goings-on. Evidence drawn not only from natural disasters but from the psychological effects of British bombings during World War II, suggest a need on the part of the viewer to assimilate happenings that lie outside his frame of reference and that may affect his future safety. In other words, it is an adaptive, future-oriented response to disaster.

If this sounds like so much nonsense, then perhaps we are seeing things in the so-called "victim perspective." However, this positive function of curiosity—strange as it may seem—has been arrived at independently by various researchers. Irving L. Janis, in *Air War and Emotional Stress* (1951), says, "Numerous observers mention that there was considerable relief among the British when they discovered what the raids were really like. They had expected the attacks to be far more devastating than they actually turned out to be. The satisfaction of curiosity about the destruction produced by a raid is probably one of the ways in which grossly exaggerated expectations and fantasies were brought into line with reality."

Therefore, if the motivation, or even a part of the motivation, of the curious is a need to observe for their own future safety, then it seems desirable not to restrain them but to channel them.

In the final category of convergers are the *exploiters*, who seek private gain from public misfortune. The idea seems so abhorrent that we are likely to magnify it out of proportion and retain a picture of widespread looting and stealing. True, the National Guard sometimes appears on the scene to guard and protect. Such protection is a matter of public responsibility. But is there really much thievery?

Fritz and Mathewson don't think so. Some looting does occur. But what constitutes looting? "Borrowing" to save a life? Taking food to stave off hunger? These are gray areas of legality. Reports indicate that significant looting and major theft are virtually nonexistent in modern disasters. Petty thievery and pilfering, though unmeasurable, may be more widely indulged in. Profiteers and souvenir hunters also take some toll, but who will ever measure how much?

The final question always returns: can anything be done about this disorganized chaos? The answer is yes, definitely so. But as with Civil Defense, the effort is not easily accepted by the public.

By all means a preliminary disaster plan should be developed in the community. After a tornado or flood or hurricane strikes is no time to start figuring out what to do.

There is an immediate and critical need for accurate information, especially by news-dispensing media. One broadcaster states that in eighteen years of gathering and giving the news he has never seen an accurate first report from a disaster area; all initial reports have been exaggerated or garbled.

This leads to the recommendation for establishment of a central clearinghouse for information, set to go at all times. Certain persons could be designated as information specialists. Ham radio operators could be enlisted and organized. These people could inventory the stricken area, thus providing accurate information and guidance, and partially satisfy the curiosity of would-be convergers. This might reduce the size of the converging masses.

When these masses do come, they could be shunted to nearby centers of information or taken on conducted tours of the impact area as was done successfully after a San Angelo, Texas, tornado; two hours a day were set aside for a trip through the guarded area, and during these two hours an estimated 2,400 cars toured the area. The technique has been used elsewhere.

Convergence is inevitable. If you can't lick 'em, join 'em!

We have seen how modern communications media can help in times of disaster. They can also cause trouble. If radio and television outlets could refrain, for only a few minutes, from shrieking the alarm, convergence would be delayed. Granted that this is alien to the very concept of news reporting, still the delay could save a great many lives.

After a 1956 plane crash near West Palm Beach, Florida, Police Chief R. W. Milburn vowed he would seek some way of delaying the reporting of disastrous plane crashes by radio and television stations. Fast reporting of the crash, which killed three men, caused thousands of persons to rush to the scene, creating a traffic jam that blocked ambulances and fire trucks.

The same year, there was a fire in the Arundel Park Auditorium, south of Baltimore. Of a thousand people attending a dance and oyster roast, the fire killed ten and injured two hundred. "News flashes on the fire," said the *Baltimore Evening Sun*, "brought a crowd of several thousand curiosity-seekers who jammed Belle Grove Road and slowed the ambulances fighting their way out. . . . Fire equipment arriving to take part in the battle to control the flames had to move slowly through the crowd."

Ever since the days of Empedocles, man has fought the four elements —fire, water, earth, and air—or joined them, i.e., worshiped them and invoked their powers for the common good.

Now times are changing. While early man quailed and endured the forces of Nature, modern man is setting the battleground for an all-out assault. He has already won on many fronts: he forecasts storms and floods and seismic waves, and even earthquakes and volcanoes; he pins down landslides and forestalls avalanches of snow; he settles dusty plains, channels lava flows, and pushes marauding waves back out to sea. Where he doesn't succeed he probes harder and deeper.

Considering the mastery we already have over the elements, it is a tribute to man's ingenuity that he has been able to battle so well what seemed so formidable. It is not enough, however. We are still far from adequate control of these forces. We can't stop hurricanes. We can't harness tornadoes. We can't abolish hail or lightning.

At least not yet. Time is on our side, for no matter how the elements may rage—over land, over sea, overhead—or how often they may overwhelm mankind, they will never conquer the indomitable human spirit. That spirit will go right on tracking secrets that will help us to understand and to control and to benefit forever from Nature on the rampage.

BIBLIOGRAPHY

GENERAL

Adams, Frank D., *The Birth and Development of the Geological Sciences*, Dover Publs., New York, 1954.

Air Ministry, Meteorological Office, *The Metereological Glossary*, Chemical Publishing Co., Brooklyn, 1940.

Allen, John Stuart, *Atoms, Rocks and Galaxies*, Harper and Bros., New York, 1942.

Allen, Shirley W., *Conserving Natural Resources*, McGraw-Hill Book Co., New York, 1959.

Aubert de la Rue, Edgar, and others, *The Tropics*, Alfred A. Knopf, New York, 1957.

Ball, Robert S., *The Earth's Beginning*, D. Appleton & Co., New York, 1902.

Barcus, Frank, *Freshwater Fury*, Wayne State University Press, Detroit, 1960.

Billings, Marland P., *Structural Geology*, Prentice-Hall, Inc., New York, 1954.

Blair, T. A., *Weather Elements*, Prentice-Hall, Inc., New York, 1953.

Blumenstock, David I., *The Ocean of Air*, Rutgers Univ. Press, New Brunswick, N.J., 1959.

Botley, C. M., *The Air and Its Mysteries*, G. Bell and Sons, Ltd., London, 1938.

Brooks, C. E. P., *Climate Through the Ages*, McGraw-Hill Book Co., New York, 1949.

——, *Climate in Everyday Life*, Philosophical Library, New York, 1951.

Byers, Horace R., *General Meteorology*, McGraw-Hill Book Co., New York, 1959.

Civil Aeronautics Administration, *Pilots' Weather Handbook*, CAA Technical Manual No. 104, Washington, 1955.

Clayton, H. H., *World Weather*, The Macmillan Co., New York, 1923.

Cleland, Herdman F., *Geology, Physical and Historical*, American Book Company, New York, 1929.

Conrad, Joseph, *The Mirror of the Sea*, J. M. Dent and Sons, Ltd., London, 1933.

Daly, Reginald A., *Our Mobile Earth*, Charles Scribner's Sons, New York, 1926.

Davis, John H., Jr., *The Natural Features of Southern Florida*, Fla. Geol. Bull. 25, Tallahassee, 1943.

Douglas, Marjory Stoneman, *The Everglades: River of Grass*, Rinehart and Co., New York, 1947.

Donaldson, Bess A., *The Wild Rue*, Luzac and Co., London, 1938.

Dunbar, Carl O., *Historical Geology*, John Wiley & Sons, New York, 1949.

Fenneman, Nevin M., *Physiography of Western United States*, McGraw-Hill Book Co., New York, 1931.

——, *Physiography of Eastern United States*, McGraw-Hill Book Co., New York, 1938.

Flint, Richard F., *Glacial Geology and the Pleistocene Epoch*, John Wiley and Sons, New York, 1947.

Fritz, Charles E., and Mathewson, J. H., *Convergence Behavior in Disasters*, Publ. 476, National Research Council, National Academy of Sciences, Washington, 1957.

Garbell, M. A., *Tropical and Equatorial Meteorology*, Pitman Publ. Co., New York, 1947.

Gardner, Martin, *Fads and Fallacies in the Name of Science*, Dover Publs., New York, 1957.

Gilbert, Grove K., *An Introduction to Physical Geography*, D. Appleton and Co., New York, 1904.

Hawks, Ellison, *The Book of Natural Wonders*, Tudor Publishing Co., New York, 1937.

Heninger, S. K., Jr., *A Handbook of Renaissance Meteorology*, Duke University Press, Durham, N.C., 1960.

Houghton, Henry G. (Ed.), *Atmospheric Explorations*, John Wiley and Sons, New York, 1958.

Huberty, Martin R., and Flock, Warren L. (Eds.), *Natural Resources*, McGraw-Hill Book Co., New York, 1959.

Humphreys, W. J., *Weather Proverbs and Paradoxes*, Williams and Wilkins Co., Baltimore, 1934.

Huntington, Ellsworth, *Civilization and Climate*, Yale University Press, New Haven, Conn., 1915.

Inwards, Richard, *Weather Lore*, Rider and Co., London, 1950.

Kimble, George H. T., *Our American Weather*, McGraw-Hill Book Co., New York, 1955.

Koeppe, Clarence E., and De Long, George C., *Weather and Climate*, McGraw-Hill Book Co., New York, 1958.

Krick, Irving P., and Fleming, Roscoe, *Sun, Sea and Sky*, J. B. Lippincott Co., Philadelphia, 1954.

BIBLIOGRAPHY

Lahee, Frederick H., *Field Geology*, McGraw-Hill Book Co., New York, 1941.

Lane, Frank W., *The Elements of Rage*, Country Life Ltd., London, 1948.

Lansing, Alfred, *Endurance, Shackleton's Incredible Voyage*, McGraw-Hill Book Co., New York, 1959.

Leach, Maria (Ed.), *Dictionary of Folklore, Mythology, and Legend*, Funk and Wagnalls Co., New York, 1949.

Leet, L. D., *Causes of Catastrophe*, McGraw-Hill Book Co., New York, 1948.

———, and Judson, Sheldon, *Physical Geology*, Prentice-Hall, Inc., New York, 1954.

Lobeck, Armin K., *Geomorphology*, McGraw-Hill Book Co., New York, 1939.

Longstreth, Morris, *Understanding the Weather*, The Macmillan Co., New York, 1953.

Longwell, Chester R., and others, *Physical Geology*, John Wiley & Sons, New York, 1948.

Mather, Kirtley F., and Mason, Shirley L., *A Source Book in Geology*, McGraw-Hill Book Co., New York, 1939.

Miller, Denning, *Wind, Storm and Rain*, Coward-McCann, Inc., New York, 1952.

Monnett, V. E., and Brown, H. E., *The Principles of Physical Geology*, Ginn and Co., Boston, 1950.

Nesbitt, Paul H., and others, *The Survival Book*, D. Van Nostrand, Princeton, N.J., 1959.

Nevin, Charles Merrick, *Principles of Structural Geology*, John Wiley & Sons, New York, 1949.

Press, Frank, "Volcanoes, Ice and Destructive Waves," *Engineering and Science*, November, 1956.

Rawcliffe, D. H., *Illusions and Delusions of the Supernatural and the Occult*, Dover Publs., New York, 1959.

Robinson, Donald, *The Face of Disaster*, Doubleday and Co., Garden City, N.Y., 1959.

Seamon, L. H., and Bartlett, G. S., *Climatological Extremes*, Office of Climatology, U.S. Weather Bureau, Washington.

Shapley, Harlow (Ed.), *Climatic Change*, Harvard Univ. Press, Cambridge, Mass., 1953.

Shaw, Napier, *The Drama of the Weather*, Cambridge University Press, Cambridge, England, 1940.

Snow, Edward R., *Great Gales and Dire Disasters*, Dodd, Mead and Co., New York, 1952.

Spectorsky, A. C. (Ed.), *The Book of the Sky*, Appleton-Century-Crofts, Inc., New York, 1956.

———, *The Book of the Earth*, Appleton-Century-Crofts, Inc., New York, 1957.

——, *The Book of the Mountains,* Appleton-Century-Crofts, Inc., New York, 1955.

Stejneger, Leonhard, *Georg Wilhelm Steller,* Harvard Univ. Press, Cambridge, Mass., 1936.

Stewart, George R., *Storm,* Random House, New York, 1941.

Stick, David, *The Outer Banks of North Carolina,* Univ. of North Carolina Press, Chapel Hill, 1958.

Tannehill, Ivan R., *Weather Around the World,* Princeton Univ. Press, Princeton, N.J., 1943.

Thornbury, W. D., *Principles of Geomorphology,* John Wiley & Sons, New York, 1954.

United States Bureau of American Ethnology, *Annual Reports,* Smithsonian Institution, Washington.

United States Department of Agriculture Yearbook, *Climate and Man,* Washington, 1941.

——, *Water,* Washington, 1955.

United States Department of Commerce, *U. S. Coast Pilots,* Coast and Geodetic Survey, Washington, current editions.

Von Engeln, O. D., *Geomorphology,* The Macmillan Co., New York, 1942.

Wenstrom, William H., *Weather and the Ocean of Air,* Houghton-Mifflin Co., Boston, 1942.

Woodbury, Angus M., *Principles of General Ecology,* The Blakiston Co., New York, 1954.

WINDS

Aubert de la Rue, Edgar, *Man and the Winds,* Hutchinson & Co., London, 1955.

Ferrel, William, *A Popular Treatise on the Winds,* John Wiley and Sons, New York, 1904.

Kline, Chester A., "Windstorm Insurance," thesis, Univ. of Pennsylvania, Philadelphia, 1931.

Kloeffler, R. G., and Sitz, E. L., *Electric Energy from the Winds,* Kansas State College Bull. Vol. XXX, No. 9, 1946.

Kuettner, J., and Jenkins, C. F., *Flight Aspects of the Mountain Wave,* Atmospheric Analysis Laboratory, Air Force Research Center, Cambridge, Mass., 1953.

Namias, Jerome, "The Jet Stream," *Scientific American,* October, 1952.

Putnam, Palmer C., *Power from the Wind,* D. Van Nostrand Co., New York, 1948.

Riehl, H., and others, "The Jet Stream," *Meteorological Monographs* of the American Meteorological Society, Vol. 2, No. 7, 1954.

Thomas, Percy H., *Electric Power from the Wind,* Federal Power Commission, Washington, 1945.

BIBLIOGRAPHY

——, *Aerodynamics of the Wind Turbine*, Federal Power Commission, Washington, 1949.
Wexler, Harry, "The Circulation of the Atmosphere," *Scientific American*, September, 1955.

HURRICANES

Brooks, Charles F., "Hurricanes into New England, Meteorology of the Storm of September 21, 1938," *Geographical Review*, Vol. 29, 1939.
Conrad, Joseph, *Typhoon*, Hanover House, Garden City, New York, 1953.
Douglas, Marjory Stoneman, *Hurricane*, Rinehart and Co., New York, 1958.
Dunn, Gordon E., and Miller, Banner I., *Atlantic Hurricanes*, Louisiana State University Press, 1960.
Florida State Board of Conservation, *Information on Beach Protection in Florida*, Research Paper No. 8, Division of Water Survey and Research, Tallahassee, 1952.
Nordhoff, Charles, and Hall, James, *The Hurricane*, Little, Brown and Co., Boston, 1935.
Piddington, Henry, *Conversations About Hurricanes: for the Use of Plain Sailors*, Smith, Elder and Co., London, 1852.
Redfield, William C., "Observations on the Hurricanes and Storms of the West Indies and the Coast of the United States," *American Journal of Science and Arts*, Vol. XXV, No. 1, 1834.
Simpson, R. L., and Gentry, R. C., *Hurricanes*, National Hurricane Research Project, U. S. Weather Bureau, Washington, 1957.
Stick, David, *Graveyard of the Atlantic*, Univ. of North Carolina Press, Chapel Hill, 1952.
Tannehill, Ivan R., *Hurricanes*, Princeton Univ. Press, Princeton, N.J., 1952.
——, *The Hurricane Hunters*, Dodd, Mead and Co., New York, 1956.
United States Weather Bureau, *Hurricane Rains and Floods of August 1955, Carolinas to New England*, Technical Paper No. 26, Washington, 1956.

TORNADOES

Flora, Snowden D., *Tornadoes of the United States*, Univ. of Oklahoma Press, Norman, 1953.
Perry, Stewart E., and others, *The Child and His Family in Disaster:* A Study of the 1953 Vicksburg Tornado, Publ. No. 394, National Research Council, National Academy of Sciences, Washington, 1956.
United States Weather Bureau, Climatological Services Division, *Tornado Occurrences in the United States*, Technical Paper No. 20, Washington, 1952.

DESERTS

Benson, Lyman, and Darrow, Robert A., *A Manual of Southwestern Desert Trees and Shrubs*, Univ. of Ariz. Biol. Science Bull. No. 6, Tucson, 1944.

Corle, Edwin, *Desert Country*, Duell, Sloan and Pearce, New York, 1941.

Gautier, Emile, *Sahara: The Great Desert*, Columbia Univ. Press, New York, 1935.

Glueck, Nelson, *Rivers in the Desert*, Farrar, Straus and Cudahy, New York, 1959.

Howard, Richard A., *Sun, Sand and Survival*, Air Univ. ADTIC Publ. D-102, Maxwell Air Force Base, Ala., 1953.

Lowdermilk, Walter C., "The Reclamation of a Man-Made Desert," *Scientific American*, March, 1960.

Montet, Pierre, *Everyday Life in Egypt*, Edward Arnold, Ltd., London, 1958.

Pond, Alonzo W., *Afoot in the Desert*, Air Univ. ADTIC Publ. D-100, Maxwell Air Force Base, Ala., 1956.

Rigby, Douglas, *Desert Happy*, J. B. Lippincott Co., Philadelphia, 1957.

DUST

Bradley, John H., *Autobiography of Earth*, Coward-McCann, Inc., New York, 1935.

Chase, Stuart, *Rich Land, Poor Land*, Whittlesey House, McGraw-Hill Book Co., New York, 1936.

Finnell, H. H., "The Dust Storms of 1954," *Scientific American*, July, 1954.

Hulbert, Archer B., *Soil: Its Influence on the History of the United States*, Yale Univ. Press, New Haven, Conn., 1930.

Johnson, Vance, *Heaven's Tableland, The Dust Bowl Story*, Farrar, Straus and Co., New York, 1947.

Lawrence, Byrem, *A Concise Description of the Geological Formations and Mineral Localities of the Western States*, S. N. Dickinson, Boston, 1843.

Lord, Russell, *To Hold This Soil*, U. S. Dept. of Agriculture Misc. Publ. No. 321, Washington, 1938.

———, *Behold Our Land*, Houghton Mifflin Co., Boston, 1938.

Malin, James C., "Dust Storms, 1850-1900," *Kansas Historical Quarterly*, May-Nov., 1946.

Oliver, F. W., "Dust Storms in Egypt," *Geographical Journal*, Vol. CVI, 1945.

Sears, Paul B., *Deserts on the March*, Univ. of Okla. Press, Norman, 1947.

———, *This Is Our World*, Univ. of Okla. Press, Norman, 1937.

BIBLIOGRAPHY

Tannehill, Ivan R., *Drought, Its Causes and Effects*, Princeton Univ. Press, Princeton, N.J., 1947.

United States Department of Agriculture, *Soil*, Yearbook of Agriculture, Washington, 1957.

——, *Land*, Yearbook of Agriculture, Washington, 1958.

Webb, Walter Prescott, *The Great Plains*, Ginn and Co., Boston, 1931.

RAIN

Bromfield, Louis, *The Rains Came*, Grosset and Dunlap, New York, 1937.

Chatterjee, Shiba Prasad, *Le Plateau de Meghalaya*, Les Presses Modernes, Paris, 1936.

Foster, Edgar E., *Rainfall and Runoff*, The Macmillan Co., New York, 1948.

Gurdon, P. R. T., *The Khasis*, David Nutt, London, 1907.

Rafy, K. U., *Folk-Tales of the Khasis*, Macmillan and Co., London, 1920.

Richards, Paul W., *The Tropical Rain Forest*, Cambridge Univ. Press, London, 1952.

United States Weather Bureau, "The World's Heaviest Rains," *Special Report*, Washington, 1955.

HAIL

Atlas of American Agriculture, Advance Sheet 5, Pt. II, *Hail Records*, 1895-1914, 1922.

Flora, Snowden D., *Hailstorms of the United States*, Univ. of Oklahoma Press, Norman, 1956.

Illinois State Horticultural Society *News-Letter*: "April Hailstorm in Union County," May, 1946.

Literary Digest, "Hail at Its Worst," July 16, 1932.

Lyons, T. D., "Dakota Hail Storm," *Commonweal*, July 31, 1942.

United States Department of Agriculture, *Losses Caused by Hail, 1909-1918*, Bull. 1043, Washington, 1922.

——, *Hail Damage in Dry Farming*, Bureau of Plant Industry Bull. 188, Washington, 1910.

——, *Hail Injury to Fruit Growing, Great Plains Area*, Farmers' Bull. 727, Washington, 1916.

LIGHTNING

Crane, Verner W., *Benjamin Franklin and a Rising People*, Little, Brown and Co., Boston, 1954.

Eberhard, Wolfram, *Chinese Festivals*, Henry Schuman, Inc., New York, 1952.

Evans, E. A., and McEachron, K. B., "The Thunderstorm," the General Electric *Review*, 1936.

McEachron, K. B., *Playing With Lightning*, Random House, New York, 1940.

Parton, James, *The Life and Times of Benjamin Franklin*, Houghton-Mifflin Co., Boston, 1882.

Priestley, Joseph, *The History and Present State of Electricity*, J. Dodsley, London, 1767.

Schonland, B. F. J., *The Flight of Thunderbolts*, Clarendon Press, Oxford, 1950.

———, *Atmospheric Electricity*, John Wiley and Sons, New York, 1953.

United States Dept. of Commerce, National Bureau of Standards, *Code for Protection Against Lightning*, Handbook H40, Washington (current edition).

Van Doren, Carl, *Benjamin Franklin*, Viking Press, New York, 1938.

Viemeister, Peter E., *The Lightning Book*, Doubleday & Co., Inc., Garden City, N.Y., 1961.

Vonnegut, Bernard, *Possible Mechanism for the Formation of Thunderstorm Electricity*, Geophysical Research Papers No. 42, Air Force Cambridge Research Center, Mass.

SNOW

Atwater, M. M., "Snow Avalanches," *Scientific American*, January, 1954.

Browne, Belmore, *Conquest of Mount McKinley*, G. P. Putnam's Sons, New York, 1913.

Seligman, Gerald, *Snow Structure and Ski Fields*, The Macmillan Co., New York, 1936.

Shackleton, Ernest, *South*, Wm. Heinemann, London, 1919.

United States Department of Agriculture, *Snow Avalanches*, U. S. Forest Service, Washington, 1961.

———, *Snow-Survey Safety Guide*, Soil Conservation Service, Washington, 1958.

United States Weather Bureau, "Some Extremes of Snowfall," *Special Report*, Washington, 1955.

Wechsberg, Joseph, *Avalanche!*, Alfred A. Knopf, New York, 1958.

FLOODS

Barrows, H. K., *Floods, Their Hydrology and Control*, McGraw-Hill Book Co., New York, 1948.

Brooks, Charles F., and Thiessen, Alfred H., "The Meteorology of Great Floods in the Eastern United States," *Geographical Review*, April, 1937.

BIBLIOGRAPHY

Hoyt, William G., and Langbein, Walter B., *Floods*, Princeton Univ. Press, Princeton, N.J., 1955.

Jacks, G. V., and Whyte, R. O., *Vanishing Lands*, Doubleday, Doran and Co., New York, 1939.

Krutch, Joseph W., *The Desert Year*, William Sloane Associates, New York, 1952.

Ludwig, Emil, *The Nile*, Garden City Publ. Co., Garden City, N.Y., 1947.

Netherlands Booksellers and Publishers Association, *The Battle of the Floods: Holland in February, 1953*, Amsterdam.

O'Connor, Richard, *Johnstown, the Day the Dam Broke*, J. B. Lippincott Co., Philadelphia, 1957.

Powell, John Wesley, *Exploration of the Colorado River of the West*, Smithsonian Institution, Washington, 1875.

Shuler, E. W., "A Rise Down the Canyon," *Scientific Monthly*, August, 1930.

United States Geological Survey, *Floods of April-June 1952 in Utah and Nevada*, Water Supply Paper 1260-E, Washington, 1957.

United States Senate, *Water Resources Activities in the United States: Floods and Flood Control*, Committee Print No. 15, Washington, 1960.

WAVES

Bigelow, Henry B., and Edmondson, W. T., *Wind Waves at Sea, Breakers, and Surf*, H. O. Pub. No. 602, U. S. Navy, Washington, 1947.

Carson, Rachel, *The Sea Around Us*, Oxford Univ. Press, New York, 1951.

——, *Under the Sea-Wind*, Oxford Univ. Press, New York, 1952.

Cornish, Vaughan, *Ocean Waves and Kindred Geophysical Phenomena*, Cambridge Univ. Press, London, 1934.

Florida State Board of Conservation, *Information on Beach Protection in Florida*, Water Survey and Research Paper No. 8, Division of Water Survey and Research, Tallahassee, 1952.

Golder, Frank A., *Bering's Voyages, Vol. 2, Steller's Journal*, American Geographical Society, New York, 1925.

Johnson, Douglas Wilson, *Shore Processes and Shoreline Development*, John Wiley and Sons, New York, 1919.

London, Jack, *The Cruise of the Snark*, The Macmillan Co., New York, 1911.

Miller, Don J., *Giant Waves in Lituya Bay, Alaska*, U. S. Geol. Survey Professional Paper 354-C, Washington, 1960.

Minikin, Robert C., *Winds, Waves, and Maritime Structures*, Charles Griffin and Co., London, 1950.

Proudman, J., *Dynamical Oceanography*, John Wiley and Sons, New York, 1953.

Shepard, Francis P., *The Earth Beneath the Sea*, Johns Hopkins, Baltimore, 1959.

——, and others, *The Tsunami of April 1, 1946*, Univ. of Calif. Press, Berkeley, 1950.

Slocum, Joshua, *Sailing Alone Around the World*, The Century Co., New York, 1900.

Spectorsky, A. C., *The Book of the Sea*, Grosset and Dunlap, New York, 1954.

Sverdrup, H. U., and others, *The Oceans*, Prentice-Hall, New York, 1942.

Williams, Jay P., *Alaskan Adventure*, The Stackpole Co., Harrisburg, Pa., 1952.

EARTHQUAKES

Bronson, William, *The Earth Shook, The Sky Burned*, Doubleday and Co., Garden City, N.Y., 1959.

Bureau of Social Affairs, *The Great Earthquake of 1923 in Japan*, Home Office, Japan, 1926.

Davison, Charles, *Great Earthquakes*, Thomas Murby and Co., London, 1936.

Eiby, G. A., *About Earthquakes*, Harper & Bros., New York, 1957.

Frazer, J. G., *Pausanias's Description of Greece*, Macmillan and Co., London, 1897.

Heck, N. H., *Earthquakes*, Princeton Univ. Press, Princeton, N.J., 1936.

Imamura, Akitune, *Theoretical and Applied Seismology*, Maruzen Co., Tokyo, 1937.

Jones, Horace L., *The Geography of Strabo*, G. P. Putnam's Sons, New York, 1927.

Jordan, David S. (Ed.), *The California Earthquake of 1906*, A. M. Robertson, San Francisco, 1907.

Kendrick, T. D., *The Lisbon Earthquake*, Methuen and Co., Ltd., London, 1955.

Macelwane, J. B., *When the Earth Quakes*, Bruce Publ. Co., Milwaukee, 1947.

Mallet, Robert, *Great Neapolitan Earthquake of 1857*, Chapman and Hall, London, 1862.

Richter, Charles F., *Elementary Seismology*, W. H. Freeman Co., San Francisco, 1958.

LANDSLIDES

Alden, William C., *Landslide and Flood at Gros Ventre, Wyoming*, Am. Inst. of Min. & Met. Engrs., Tech. Publ. 140, New York, 1928.

Canadian Department of Mines Memoir No. 27. Report of the Commission, *Turtle Mountain, Frank, Alberta*, Ottawa, 1912.

BIBLIOGRAPHY

Close, Upton, "Where the Mountains Walked," *National Geographic Magazine*, May, 1922.

Eckel, Edwin B. (Ed.), *Landslides and Engineering Practice*, Highway Research Board Special Report 29, National Academy of Sciences, National Research Council, Publication 544, Washington, 1958.

Hennes, Robert G., *Analysis and Control of Landslides*, University of Washington Engineering Experiment Station Bull. 91, 1936.

Highway Research Board Bull. 49, *Analysis of Landslides*, National Research Council, Publ. 220, Washington, 1952.

Jones, F. O., *Landslide Conditions Along Lake Roosevelt, Washington*, U. S. Geological Survey open file, Washington.

Knox, G., "Landslides in South Wales Valleys," *Proceedings* of the South Wales Inst. of Engrs., 1927.

McConnell, B. G., *Great Landslide at Frank, Alta.*, Canadian Department of the Interior, Ottawa, 1904.

Sharpe, C. F., *Landslides and Related Phenomena*, Columbia University Press, New York, 1938.

VOLCANOES

Bonney, Thomas G., *Volcanoes, Their Structure and Significance*, G. P. Putnam's Sons, New York, 1899.

Cahalane, Victor H., *A Biological Survey of Katmai National Monument*, Smithsonian Institution Publication 4376, Washington, 1959.

Coleman, Satis N., *Volcanoes New and Old*, John Day Co., New York.

Darwin, Charles, *Geological Observations*, D. Appleton and Co., New York, 1896.

——, *Journal of Researches*, D. Appleton and Co., New York, 1896.

Correspondence Relating to the Volcanic Eruptions in St. Vincent and Martinique in May, 1902, Parliament, London, 1902.

Fenton, C. L., and Fenton, M. A., *Mountains*, Doubleday, Doran and Co., New York, 1942.

Heilprin, Angelo, *Mont Pelée and the Tragedy of Martinique*, J. B. Lippincott Co., Philadelphia, 1903.

——, *The Tower of Pelée*, J. B. Lippincott Co., Philadelphia, 1904.

Perret, Frank A., *The Eruption of Mt. Pelée*, 1929-1932, Carnegie Inst. Publ. No. 458, Washington, 1935.

Prescott, William H., *History of the Conquest of Mexico*, Modern Library, New York, n.d.

The Royal Society, *The Eruption of Krakatoa, and Subsequent Phenomena*, Report of the Krakatoa Committee, Harrison and Sons, London, 1888.

Tyrrell, George W., *Volcanoes*, Henry Holt and Co., New York, 1931.

METEORS

Baldwin, Ralph B., *The Face of the Moon*, Univ. of Chicago Press, Chicago, 1949.

Bok, Bart J., *The Astronomer's Universe*, Cambridge Univ. Press, London, 1958.

Christian, W. Asbury, *Lynchburg and Its People*, J. P. Bell Co., Lynchburg, Va., 1900.

Crowther, J. G., "More About the Great Siberian Meteorite," *Scientific American*, May, 1931.

Dreyer, J. L. E., *A History of Astronomy from Thales to Kepler*, Dover Publs., New York, 1953.

Ellison, M. A., *The Sun and Its Influence*, Routledge and Kegan Paul, Ltd., London, 1955.

Ewers, John C. (Ed.), *Adventures of Zenas Leonard, Fur Trader*, Univ. of Okla. Press, Norman, 1959.

Gamow, George, *The Moon*, Abelard-Schuman, New York, 1959.

Houghton, Henry G., *Atmospheric Explorations*, John Wiley and Sons, New York, 1958.

Kahn, Fritz, *Design of the Universe*, Crown Publ., Inc., New York, 1954.

Kiepenheuer, Karl, *The Sun*, Univ. of Mich. Press, Ann Arbor, 1959.

Krogdahl, Wasley S., *The Astronomical Universe*, The Macmillan Co., New York, 1952.

Lyttleton, Raymond A., *The Comets and Their Origin*, Cambridge Univ. Press, Cambridge, 1953.

Macpherson, Hector, *Modern Astronomy*, Oxford Univ. Press, London, 1928.

Massey, H. S. W., and Boyd, R. L. F., *The Upper Atmosphere*, Philosophical Library, New York, 1958.

Mehlin, Theodore G., *Astronomy*, John Wiley and Sons, New York, 1959.

Porter, John G., *Comets and Meteor Streams*, John Wiley and Sons, New York, 1952.

Shapley, Harlow, and Howarth, Helen, *A Source Book in Astronomy*, McGraw-Hill Book Co., New York, 1929.

Spencer, L. J., "Meteorite Craters as Topographical Features on the Earth's Surface," *Geographical Journal*, Royal Geographical Society, London, March, 1933.

Stetson, H. T., *Sunspots and Their Effects*, McGraw-Hill Book Co., New York, 1937.

Stormer, Carl, *The Polar Aurora*, Oxford Univ. Press, London, 1955.

Struve, Otto, and others, *Elementary Astronomy*, Oxford Univ. Press, New York, 1959.

Urey, Harold C., *The Plants, Their Origin and Development*, Yale Univ. Press, New Haven, Conn., 1952.

Watson, Fletcher, *Between the Planets*, J. and A. Churchill, 1947.

BIBLIOGRAPHY

Newspapers

Austin, Texas, *American-Statesman*
Chicago *Tribune*
Cleveland *Plain Dealer*
Jacksonville, Florida, *Times-Union*
Kobe, Japan, *Chronicle*
Los Angeles *Examiner*
Miami *Herald*
Montreal *Gazette*
New York *Times*
Phoenix, *Arizona Republic*
Pittsburgh *Press*
St. Louis *Post Dispatch*
San Francisco *Chronicle*
San Francisco *Examiner*
Washington *Post*

Periodicals

American Geophysical Union *Transactions*
American Journal of Science
American Philosophical Society *Memoirs*
American Water Works Association *Journal*
Climatological Data
Commonweal
Engineering and Science
Flying
General Electric *Review*
Geographical Journal
Geographical Review
Geological Society of America *Bulletin*
Illinois State Horticultural Society *Newsletter*
Kansas Historical Quarterly
Kansas State College *Bulletin*
Literary Digest
Living Age
Meteorological Monographs
Monthly Weather Review

National Geographic Magazine
Natural History
Saturday Review
Science
Science News Letter
Scientific American
Scientific Monthly
Smithsonian Institution *Annual Reports*
South Wales Institute of Engineers *Proceedings*
Time
Today's Health
United States Beach Erosion Board *Bulletin*
——, *Memoranda*
United States Weather Bureau *Special Reports*
Weatherwise

INDEX

INDEX